INTRODUCTION TO
Physical
Inorganic Chemistry

INTRODUCTION TO

Inorganic

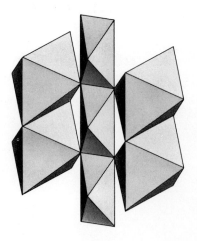

Physical Chemistry

KENNETH B. HARVEY
AND
GERALD B. PORTER

Department of Chemistry
University of British Columbia
Vancouver, British Columbia

 ADDISON-WESLEY PUBLISHING COMPANY, INC.
READING, MASSACHUSETTS · PALO ALTO · LONDON

This book is in the

ADDISON-WESLEY SERIES IN CHEMISTRY

Francis T. Bonner

Consulting Editor

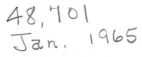

Copyright © 1963

ADDISON-WESLEY PUBLISHING COMPANY, INC.

Printed in the United States of America

Library of Congress Catalog Card No. 63-13609

Preface

The rapid advancement of modern science makes a constant reappraisal of teaching methods an inevitable necessity. Nowhere is this truer than in the field of inorganic chemistry, where prolific research is producing an accumulation of data which is staggering in both volume and diversity. One result has been the raising of doubts in the minds of scientists as to the advisability or even the practicability of the teaching of descriptive inorganic chemistry in its classic form. A ramification of this line of thought, in progressive institutions, is the decreasing emphasis on qualitative inorganic analysis. Fortunately, the problem itself provides the solution, for the theoretical aspect of science has progressed with the experimental, so that it is no longer necessary to treat introductory inorganic chemistry from a phenomenological point of view. On the contrary, advances in the theories of structure and reaction mechanism make it possible to correlate the bulk of chemical phenomena with fundamental atomic and molecular properties.

Therefore, our objective in this book is to emphasize the principles underlying chemical behavior rather than the phenomena themselves. On the other hand, we try to make the approach an experimental one by including sufficient data so that the student himself can make an objective evaluation of the explanation he has been given. Indeed, to foster the student's ability to make such judgments must always be one of the principal aims of the teaching of science.

Because this book attempts to describe the chemical behavior of 103 elements in different states of aggregation, its scope is pretentiously broad. There is certainly more material than can be accommodated in the average one-year course of study. (We, personally, cover little of the material in Chapters 6 and 10. Depending on the level at which the course is given and the prerequisites for it, a different choice of chapters may be preferable.) At the same time, the book has some omissions, a few of which might appear serious. For example, there is no systematic treatment of the descriptive chemistry of the elements and their compounds. However, a surprising amount of this material actually is covered in the text, although from a different point of view. Any such deficiency may, we feel, be adequately compensated for by an accompanying laboratory course. A more serious, but unavoidable, omission is that there is no detailed mathematical treatment of many subjects. But since this course is intended to follow the first university course in general chemistry, more mathematics, at this level, would serve only to confound the majority of students. On the other hand, it is to the credit of mathematics teachers that the mathematical capabilities of students at this level are rapidly improving, so that in a few years such a conclusion may no longer be valid.

Detailed acknowledgment of all our sources of material is virtually impossible. Let us simply say that we have made extensive use of existing literature in the field, which is inevitable in writing an introductory textbook. We must also acknowledge a debt of gratitude to our colleagues at the University of British Columbia, for innumerable helpful discussions. Many will no doubt be sur-surprised at how efficiently their brains have been picked. We are grateful, too, for the helpful suggestions of reviewers, including our students, who used the preliminary edition. Finally, we must express our appreciation for the assistance we have received from our wives and from the staff at Addison-Wesley in the preparation of the manuscript.

Vancouver, British Columbia   K.B.H.

November 1962   G.B.P.

Contents

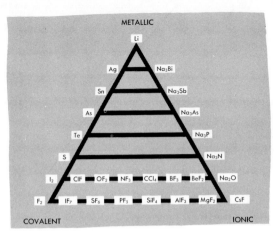

CHAPTER ONE

Introduction

The study of the chemistry of 103 elements is a major undertaking, and an intelligent approach to the vast amount of information to be assimilated requires that we do more than catalog this data; we must seek the principles underlying the phenomena being studied. If successful, we will then have a theoretical and/or empirical background which will allow us to correlate known chemical behavior with fundamental quantities and enable us to predict the behavior in unfamiliar situations. At the same time, it is necessary that the reader become conversant with the language and methods of chemistry and learn to recognize the physical and chemical parameters relevant to the problem at hand.

1–1. THEORY AND EXPERIMENT

Learning should, in fact, proceed through the same objective evaluation of experimental facts that is common to a well-executed research program. The correlation between theory and experiment must be examined critically to bring out the shortcomings and limitations of the relationship. Inherent in such an examination is an awareness of the approximations and assumptions involved in the development of the theory. A student who leaves the study of a subject querying the validity of the explanation he has been given, or concerned about how the theory might be improved to eliminate a shortcoming, can usually be satisfied that he has gained the necessary familiarity with the material.

The manner in which a principle is discovered or a theory evolves from experimental data is rarely a straightforward one in practice. Some knowledge of the theoretical background of a phenomenon is necessary for the intelligent planning of an experiment so that the results will be relevant to the problem. The data obtained may then suggest an explanation or provide an empirical relationship which, in turn, leads to further experimentation.

1

Experiments are rarely carried out without some idea of what may happen, but there is always the delightful possibility that something exciting will be discovered accidentally. Much the same element enters into the selection of results for inclusion in a textbook. One hopes for the benefit of the student, and the reputation of the authors, that such a selection is as objective as possible. Unfortunately, this aspect is out of the hands of the student. The evaluation of the results is not, however, and it is one of the major aims of this book to develop in the student the habit of scientific criticism.

1–2. PHYSICAL INORGANIC CHEMISTRY

For the purposes of introduction, a convenient primary breakdown of the phenomena to be studied can be made in terms of structure and the process of reaction. The reader will quickly realize that such a division is not definitive. Certain chapters, such as those on atomic and molecular structure and crystal chemistry, are largely devoted to problems of structure, and others, such as that on thermochemistry, rest more or less on the dividing line. The partition is nevertheless a meaningful and very useful one.

(a) Structure

The description of the structure of a chemical species, from an experimental point of view, has several facets. One must, first of all, establish the stoichiometry of the compound. If, for example, we are concerned with boron chloride, this would mean determining that there are three chlorine atoms and one boron atom combined to give a formula BCl_3. As a second step, we would be likely to investigate the symmetry of the molecule or the spatial configuration of the nuclei. If this were done, with one or more of the methods described in Section 5–1(b), we should find that the four nuclei are coplanar, with the chlorine nuclei situated symmetrically about the boron nucleus. In the more sophisticated terminology of Chapter 5, the molecule would be described as trigonal planar.

Carrying the process one step further, we would use the same methods of investigation to make the description quantitative and to establish that the separation of the nuclei is 1.76 A and that the $\angle ClBCl$ is 120°. Finally, to complete the description, it is necessary to make some statement regarding the energetics of the molecule. This is most conveniently done by stating that the energy released in the formation of one mole of gaseous BCl_3 from atomic boron and chlorine is 317.7 kcal, i.e.,

$$B(g) + 3Cl(g) = BCl_3(g) + 317.7 \text{ kcal.}$$

It is apparent from our description in terms of the position of the atoms or nuclei that the atoms retain at least some of their individuality when combined in a molecule. It is logical, therefore, to introduce the concept of the chemical bond between atoms as the medium through which combination occurs. The

TABLE 1-1

PHYSICAL PROPERTIES ASSOCIATED WITH THE FOUR BOND TYPES

Property	Ionic	Covalent	Metallic	van der Waals
Mechanical	Strong, giving hard crystals	Strong, giving hard crystals	Strength varies, malleability common	Weak, giving soft crystals
Thermal	Fairly high mp; low coefficient of expansion	High mp; low coefficient of expansion	Variable mp; coefficient of expansion large	Low mp; large coefficient of expansion
Electrical	Solids are moderate insulators; ion conductors in melt and solution	Insulators in both solid and melt	Good conductors through electron transport	Insulators
Optical	Absorption is same as that of individual ions	High refractive index in solid; absorption differs in three phases	Liquid and solid both opaque	Absorption is similar in three phases
Example	NaCl	Diamond	Copper	Inert gases

acceptance of this concept was, in fact, probably one of the greatest advances in the study of molecular structure. Much of the effort of present-day scientific research, both theoretical and experimental, is directed toward an elucidation of the forces responsible for the chemical bond.

From an experimental point of view, it is convenient to view the chemical bond in the light of four idealized types: ionic, covalent, metallic, and van der Waals. The physical properties associated with crystals in which the individual bond types predominate are summarized in Table 1-1. Such a classification is extremely useful, and is firmly entrenched in modern terminology, but it must be realized that, in practice, relatively few bonds approach these idealized types. Most bonds are of an intermediate type as shown in the triangle diagram, due to Ketelaar, in Fig. 1-1. It should also be recognized that the classification is largely an empirical one and results, to some extent, from a limited comprehension of the forces involved.

In spite of this limitation we can still make deductions regarding the general nature of the forces involved. Consider, for example, the forces acting between two atoms X and Y, which are capable of forming a diatomic molecule XY. For bond formation to be possible, it is clear that there must be present attractive

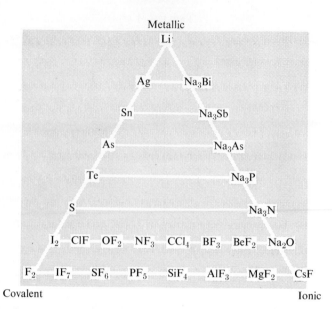

FIG. 1–1. Triangle diagram illustrating the transitions between ionic, covalent, and metallic bonding. (Reproduced from *Chemical Constitution*, by J. A. A. Ketelaar, Elsevier Publishing Company, Amsterdam.)

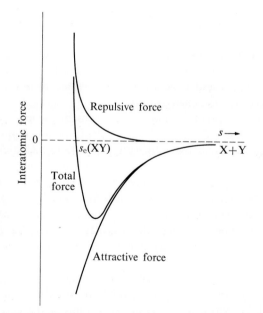

FIG. 1–2. Forces acting between atoms X and Y in the process of bond formation.

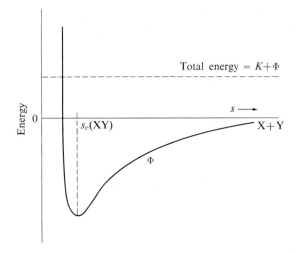

FIG. 1–3. Variation of potential energy Φ with internuclear separation s in the formation of the diatomic molecule XY.

forces that depend inversely on the separation of the atoms. At the same time,
since the nuclei do not coalesce, there must be repulsive forces, also inversely
dependent on the atomic separation. Furthermore, if a stable configuration is to
result, the repulsive forces must act over a shorter distance and exhibit a much
higher functional dependence on the separation s. In other words, the repulsive
forces will be very small for larger values of s but will increase very rapidly in the
region of the equilibrium internuclear distance s_e as s decreases. At s_e, the attractive and repulsive forces are equal so that the net force is zero. This relationship
is shown clearly in Fig. 1–2.

The energetics of bond formation may be pictured in the same way. A rigorous
treatment would require the application of quantum mechanics but, apart from
quantization of the energy, the situation would be much the same as depicted
classically in Fig. 1–3. For large values of s, the potential energy of interaction Φ
will be negligible so that the total energy E will be kinetic energy K, and given by
the expression

$$E = K + \Phi = \tfrac{1}{2}m_X v_X^2 + \tfrac{1}{2}m_Y v_Y^2.$$

For smaller values of s, Φ will no longer be negligible but will decrease and pass
through a minimum for $s = s_e$. Past this point it increases rapidly as the repulsive
forces take over. In the absence of an additional phenomenon, the total energy E
will remain constant so that as s decreases, K must increase and pass through a
maximum at s_e. For smaller values of s, K decreases and becomes zero when
$\Phi = E$. It will be clear that, if a bond is to be formed, the total energy must be
reduced during the process of interaction. If this does not occur, the atoms will
simply move apart again, retaining their initial kinetic energy.

There are many ways in which energy may be removed or dissipated, however. It might, for example, be emitted in the form of radiation (chemiluminescence) or transferred through collision to other atoms or molecules or to the wall of the containing vessel. If this occurs, the atoms will be contained within the potential well and a bond will be formed.

Valid as they are, these deductions concerning the properties of interatomic forces still leave unanswered the question as to their origin. A substantial portion of this book will be devoted to answering this question in a manner which will allow us to predict, to a certain extent, chemical behavior in terms of fundamental properties.

(b) The process of reaction

In considering the reactive process between chemical species, several factors must be taken into account. First, there is the question of whether a reaction will occur at all and, if so, to what extent it will go to completion. Second, we shall be concerned with the speed, or the rate, at which the reaction occurs. Finally, and perhaps most important, we will wish to know the mechanism through which the reaction proceeds.

As our discussion of bond formation has indicated, the question of whether or not a reaction will occur is largely one of energetics. If the energy of the products is less than that of the reactants, then, under normal conditions, a reaction may reasonably be expected to take place. The complete answer is more complex, however, and requires consideration of entropy as well as energy changes. The principles involved are well understood, and thermodynamics enables us to establish the desired relationship between the pertinent parameters and the equilibrium constant, which is the quantitative expression of the extent of reaction.

The mechanism and rate of a reaction are intimately associated and are obviously related to the process of bond formation. Most chemical reactions are far more complex than the atom combination of Section 1–2(a), however, and the term "mechanism" is usually applied to the role played by individual chemical species. This role is often far from simple, as is well illustrated by the photochemically induced reaction of hydrogen and chlorine to form hydrogen chloride:

$$H_2 + Cl_2 \rightarrow 2HCl.$$

The first step in the reaction is the dissociation of Cl_2 through the absorption of a photon or light quantum of energy $h\nu'$ according to the equation

$$Cl_2 + h\nu' \rightarrow 2Cl. \tag{1-1}$$

This is in turn followed by the reactions

$$Cl + H_2 \rightarrow HCl + H, \tag{1-2}$$

and

$$H + Cl_2 \rightarrow HCl + Cl, \tag{1-3}$$

to produce not only the end product HCl but a chlorine atom. The reaction is

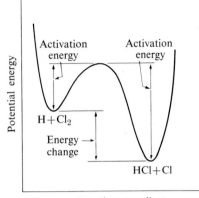

FIG. 1–4. Schematic illustration of the variation in potential energy during the formation of HCl from H + Cl_2. Because the energy of the products is lower than that of the reactants, the activation energy for the reverse reaction is considerably higher than that in the forward direction.

thus self-sustaining and is termed a chain reaction, since a single chlorine atom may be responsible for the formation of many (10^6) HCl molecules.

The determination of the mechanism of a reaction usually proceeds through a study of its kinetics. This involves measurement of the dependence of the rate of reaction on the concentration of the various species involved, the temperature, the pressure, and perhaps other factors. The net result, if the investigation is successful, is a description of the overall reaction in terms of a series of elementary reactions, such as those of Eqs. (1–1), (1–2), and (1–3), and an expression for the overall rate in terms of the rates of the elementary reactions. Often, as in the present example, the elementary reactions involve intermediate species which are not initially present.

The elementary reactions usually exhibit a fairly simple dependence on the concentration of the reactants, and it is these reactions which receive theoretical attention in attempts to explain the reaction rate on a molecular basis. A simple reaction may, in fact, be treated by an extension of the ideas used in the discussion of bond formation. For the reaction of Eq. (1–3) between hydrogen atoms and chlorine molecules, the situation would be as depicted in Fig. 1–4. The potential energy curve now exhibits two minima, or potential wells, and may be roughly described as a combination of the curves for the Cl_2 and HCl systems, except that the abscissa is now a generalized reaction coordinate and not an internuclear separation. We can see that although the formation of HCl results in a favorable energy change, the system H + Cl_2 must first acquire sufficient energy to pass over the hump between the two minima. The difference in energy of the products and reactants is equal to the difference in the activation energies for the forward and reverse directions.

Clearly, the magnitude of the activation energy is an important factor in determining the rate of reaction and, together with other parameters of a statistical nature, it is the basis of most reaction rate theories. Perhaps more important, however, are the processes by which energy is transferred to and from the species concerned, also its conversion to electronic energy from other forms, and vice versa. Such processes are currently the subject of rather intense research activity.

1-3. REFERENCE LITERATURE

It would be unusual indeed if a single presentation of a subject served to meet the requirements of all students. Furthermore, it is always advantageous to approach a subject from more than one point of view. Thus the student will find a fairly extensive bibliography at the end of each chapter. References listed under group A treat the material of the chapter at more or less the same level as the present text and serve the purpose outlined above. References in group B are more advanced and include, in some cases, what may be considered the definitive work on the subject.

BIBLIOGRAPHY

A

PAULING, L., *General Chemistry*. San Francisco: Freeman, 1958.
SIENKO, M. J., and R. A. PLANE, *Chemistry*. New York: McGraw-Hill, 1961.
WILSON, E. B., *An Introduction to Scientific Research*. New York: McGraw-Hill, 1952.

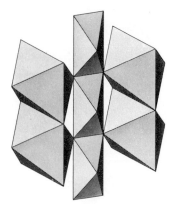

CHAPTER TWO

Ionic Crystals

From the overall picture of chemical bonding presented in Chapter 1, we shall turn now to a detailed study of the characteristics of substances which can be considered aggregates of ions. The task at hand is to examine the physical and structural properties of some typical ionic crystals, since these properties provide an insight into the nature of the prevailing forces. We shall see that a remarkably simple theory can be developed to interpret the properties of this class of substances. Although the theory must be made more sophisticated to treat saltlike compounds in general, it is quite satisfactory for the alkali halides and many other salts.

2–1. THE NATURE OF THE CRYSTALLINE STATE

In examining the external appearance, or *habit*, of a crystal, we are immediately impressed by the series of naturally occurring plane faces which usually appear to have some kind of regularity of arrangement. Well-formed crystals of alum or rock salt which exhibit these features are not difficult to grow in the laboratory or at home. (See the book by A. Holden and P. Singer, which is listed in the bibliography.) Many commonly occurring minerals have a distinctive habit which is readily recognizable, and a visitor to a mineralogical museum cannot fail to appreciate some of the beautiful, naturally occurring crystals of quartz and pyrites which have been discovered. Some examples of these are shown in Fig. 2–1.

Although all crystals display a regularity in the disposition of their faces, this regularity is sometimes obscured by the presence of faces of several different shapes. Crystals of sodium chloride, although usually found as cubes, often grow with their corners modified by triangular faces [Fig. 2–2(b)]. Furthermore, if a small amount of urea is dissolved in the solution from which the crystal is grown, these

FIG. 2–1. Photographs of some well-formed naturally occurring crystals: (a) rock salt, (b) fluorite, (c) quartz, (d) pyrites. (Thanks are due to Dr. R. M. Thompson of the geology department, University of British Columbia, for the loan of these crystals.)

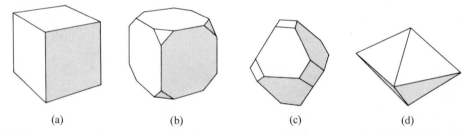

      (a)   (b)   (c)   (d)

FIG. 2–2. Sketches of typical NaCl crystals. Pure cubic and octahedral forms are shown in (a) and (d), respectively. Both forms are exhibited simultaneously in (b) and (c).

small triangular faces develop in preference to the cubic faces, as seen in Fig. 2–2(c). In the extreme case, the cubic faces are absent, and the crystal assumes an octahedral habit, as shown in Fig. 2–2(d). Sodium chloride crystals are said, then, to occur in two *forms*, octahedral and cubic. Intermediate crystals, as shown in Fig. 2–2(b) and (c), with both types of faces exhibit both forms. (Note that the word "form" has special significance in crystallography, and should not be used when referring only generally to crystal shape.)

    Crystals in general may exhibit one or more of a large number of possible forms including the cube, octahedron, tetrahedron, rhombohedron, and other polyhedra. When several forms are present, their identity may be obscured by the complexity of the habit. Such crystals are best studied by observing the angular relationship of the faces (goniometry). Another advantage of this method is that it is independent of the distortion resulting from preferred growth on particular faces.

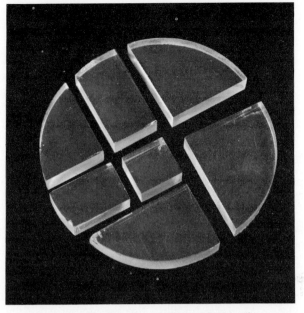

FIG. 2–3. Cleavage in a sodium chloride disc.

The external regularities exhibited by crystals naturally lead us to expect a similar regularity in the internal arrangement. The phenomenon of *cleavage*, i.e., the property of splitting cleanly along certain planes, lends further emphasis to this premise. A crystal of sodium chloride, for example, can be cleaved very easily along planes parallel to the cube faces, in such a way that a regular cube can readily be obtained from a distorted crystal. Any attempt to cleave such a crystal along an arbitrary plane will shatter it. If a crystal of rock salt is dropped, it will tend to fracture along these cleavage planes to produce small cubes or orthogonal prisms (Fig. 2–3).

Results such as these led Hauy, in 1784, to propose that crystals are made up of submicroscopic fundamental units of a shape appropriate to the symmetry of the macroscopic crystal. In the case of sodium chloride, these would be minute cubelets stacked together, as shown in Fig. 2–4. Hauy completely sidestepped the question of the constitution of the fundamental units, but Barlow and Pope, in 1906, suggested the packing together of spherical atoms of a characteristic size into a geometrical entity determined by the forces between neighboring atoms. Experimental evidence concerning the internal structure of crystals awaited the birth of the science of X-ray crystallography (Von Laue, 1912), and the first crystal structure analysis was reported by Bragg in 1913. This work, on sodium chloride, clearly revealed the atomic nature of the unit of pattern, and laid the foundation for present-day concepts of the crystalline state.

The geometrical aspects of the internal structure of crystals will be discussed more completely in Chapter 7 but, for convenience in describing crystals, it is

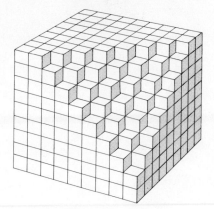

Fig. 2–4. Stacking of submicroscopic cubelets in sodium chloride to produce cubic and octahedral faces.

necessary that we introduce the concept of the *unit cell*. A unit cell is a repeating unit of the atomic pattern but, since its choice is to some extent arbitrary, we cannot formulate a general definition. For the present it is sufficient to say that we choose as the unit cell that which is the smallest repeating unit with the full symmetry of the crystal structure. As we shall see, a unit cell may be chosen which has less symmetry than the crystal structure [e.g., Fig. 2–5(a) and (b)], but for reasons to be put forth later (Chapter 7), the unit cell with full symmetry, in this case Fig. 2–5(a), is preferable.

2–2. CRYSTAL STRUCTURES OF SOME SIMPLE SALTS

Since Bragg first applied X-ray diffraction to the problem of crystal structure determination, vast numbers of crystals have been examined by this technique. In the case of the simpler structures, extreme precision is possible because of their simplicity. (The unit cell of sodium chloride, for example, is reported to contain sodium and chlorine ions at a separation of 2.81989 A at 18°C.) As an introduction to modern ideas of ionic bonding, we shall consider in detail four of these simpler structures.

(a) The sodium chloride structure

As we would expect from observing its external appearance, the unit cell of sodium chloride is cubic. This unit cell is represented in Fig. 2–5. To show the structure more clearly, the atoms, or more specifically the ions, are shown as small spheres. Insofar as an ion can have a definite size, the picture of a unit cell of sodium chloride shown in Fig. 2–6 is more realistic, but it hides most of the structure. There are 27 ions shown in the diagram of Fig. 2–5(a), but it is important to realize that there are, in fact, only eight ions (four ion pairs or molecules) in

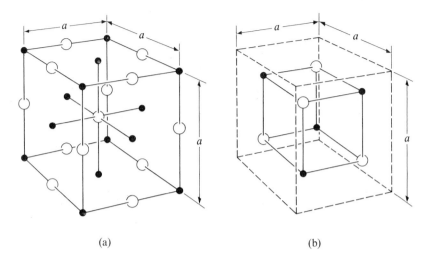

(a)   (b)

FIG. 2–5. Alternative unit cells of sodium chloride. Part (a) illustrates clearly the symmetry and coordination of the structure but exhibits more atoms than a true crystallographic cell such as that in part (b).

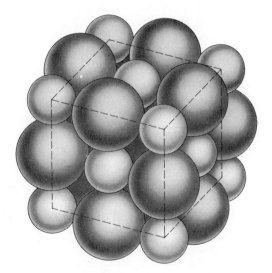

FIG. 2–6. Packing of sodium and chloride ions in the rock-salt structure.

a unit cell of sodium chloride. This can be clearly seen if we choose a different unit cell with no ions at the corners as shown in Fig. 2–5(b). Alternatively, referring again to Fig. 2–5(a), we may consider the ions at the corners to be shared by eight unit cells, those on the edges by four unit cells, etc. As mentioned above, the choice of unit cell is somewhat arbitrary, but it is customary to choose one with ions at the corners. Apart from symmetry considerations, the edges of the unit

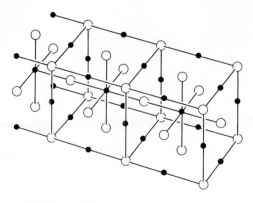

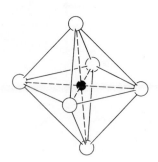

FIG. 2–7. Relationship of adjacent unit cells (outlined with heavy lines) in sodium chloride.

FIG. 2–8. Octahedral coordination in the rock-salt structure.

cell are used as reference axes, and such a choice gives rise to simpler coordinates. Figure 2–7 shows adjacent unit cells with anions at the corners.

When we consider only the pattern made by the cations, we note that they are located at the corners and centers of the faces of a unit cell. This special relationship gives rise to the name *face-centered cubic* for this type of structure. Of course, since the positions of the cations and anions are symmetrically equivalent, the anions also have the face-centered configuration.

In considering this or any other structure, it is important to observe the *coordination*, or, the relationship between an ion and its nearest neighbors. In the case of the sodium chloride structure, the nearest neighbors of a cation are six equidistant anions, and vice versa. This coordination is shown clearly in Fig. 2–8. Since the anions are at the corners of a regular octahedron with the cation at the center, we speak of *octahedral coordination* in which the coordination number is six. Thus, even though sodium and chloride ions (and many others which adopt this structure) are regarded as monovalent, each ion is surrounded by six other ions. We can represent bonds in this system by the dashed lines of Fig. 2–8. But, as we shall see shortly, all of the ions in a crystal interact with each other in principle, and it is incorrect to consider only neighboring ions as being bonded to each other.

The face-centered cubic structure is a common one and is assumed by nearly all of the alkali halides and most of the oxides, sulfides, selenides, and tellurides of the alkaline earth metals. Silver fluoride, chloride, and bromide also have the sodium chloride structure, but the iodide does not. In any event, these latter compounds do not fit in too well with simple theories of ionic bonding.

(b) The cesium chloride structure

The unit cell for cesium chloride is shown in Fig. 2–9. In this case, the cations are located only at the corners of the unit cell; hence the name *simple cubic* for

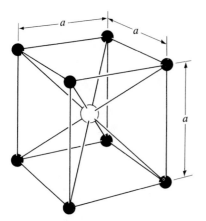

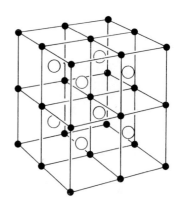

FIG. 2–9. Unit cell of cesium chloride, showing the cubic coordination.

FIG. 2–10. Stacking of eight unit cells in the cesium chloride structure.

the lattice. The centers of the unit cells are occupied by anions. By reasoning analogous to that used in the example of the sodium chloride structure, we find that there is but one ion pair per unit cell. The assembly of a number of these unit cells on the points of the cubic space lattice is shown in Fig. 2–10. Note that either the cations or the anions by themselves form a simple cubic arrangement, and that the positions occupied by the cations and anions are entirely equivalent symmetrically. Each cation is therefore surrounded by eight anions at equal distances (and vice versa), an arrangement referred to as *cubic coordination*.

The cesium chloride structure is normally exhibited by the cesium and thallium chlorides, bromides, and iodides, and by numerous other compounds and many alloys. It is interesting to observe that a number of the alkali halides may adopt either the sodium chloride or the cesium chloride structure, depending on the conditions during their formation. Thus cesium chloride forms a high-temperature modification with the sodium chloride structure above 445°C, while the iodide and bromide of cesium will adopt the sodium chloride structure if they are crystallized out of the vapor onto specially prepared surfaces. On the other hand, at high pressure the halides of both rubidium and potassium, with the exception of the fluorides, undergo transitions to the cesium chloride structure.

(c) The fluorite structure

Compounds of the AX_2 type exhibit a great deal more variety in their structural arrangements than do AX-type compounds. That most commonly met is the calcium fluoride (or fluorite) structure, also cubic, which is illustrated in Fig. 2–11. The cation and anion positions are not equivalent, and for this reason there are two common ways of representing the unit cell. The one in Fig. 2–11(a) shows the cations at the corners and face-centering positions of the cube, with the anions occupying the centers of each octant. The second, Fig. 2–11(b), has a simple cubic

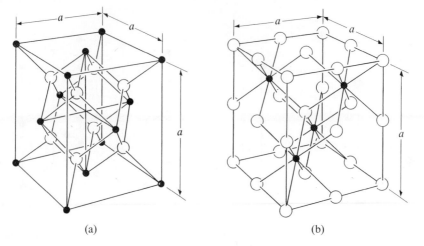

(a)   (b)

FIG. 2–11. Alternative unit cells of fluorite to show (a) the tetrahedral coordination of the anion, and (b) the cubic coordination of the cation.

lattice of anions with the cations at the centers of alternate cubes. The coordination of the anion is clearly shown in Fig. 2–11(a). We see that the four nearest neighbor cations are at the corners of a regular tetrahedron, so that there is tetrahedral coordination, and the coordination number is four. The cations, on the other hand, are surrounded by eight anions at the corners of a cube, as best seen in Fig. 2–11(b). The overall structure is thus said to have 8 : 4 coordination.

This arrangement is assumed by many difluorides other than calcium fluoride, including those of strontium and barium. The oxides, sulfides, selenides, and tellurides of lithium, sodium, and potassium crystallize in the closely related *antifluorite* structure, which is geometrically identical with the fluorite structure, but which has the cations and anions interchanged.

(d) The rutile structure

Only one other ionic structure will be mentioned at this point: the titanium dioxide, or rutile, structure. In contrast to the crystals so far described, the rutile crystal has a unit cell which is tetragonal rather than cubic. This unit cell is characterized by two dimensions: a, which is common to two of the sides, and c, the length of the remaining side, which is shorter than the others. The angles between the sides are 90°. The rutile unit cell is illustrated in Fig. 2–12, where we see that the six oxygen neighbors of the titanium ion are at the corners of an octahedron. Depending on the values of a and c, the octahedron may be slightly distorted. The three titanium ions surrounding each oxygen anion are coplanar with it, giving 6 : 3 coordination.

We see another aspect of the rutile structure if we focus our attention on the octahedra formed by each set of six anions surrounding a cation. There then appears the pattern shown in Fig. 2–13, in which the octahedra are joined in one

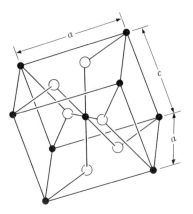

FIG. 2–12. Unit cell of rutile structure.

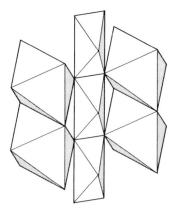

FIG. 2–13. Linking of octahedra in rutile. A cation is located at the center of each of the octahedra formed by the anions.

direction by shared edges to form strings. The strings are then joined together so that each anion is part of three octahedra, illustrating again the coordination number of three for the anion.

A number of other oxides, including those of tin and lead, exhibit the rutile structure. It is also common among the difluorides of the transition metals.

2–3. THE EXISTENCE OF IONS

The geometrical configurations of these crystal structures give no evidence as to whether they are ionic or not. A number of observations lead us to suspect the presence of ions in these and other crystalline solids, but the evidence is very indirect indeed. The presence of ions both in aqueous solutions of salts and in molten salts is substantiated by tests of conductivity and by numerous other experiments; hence it is natural to expect that these ions exist in the crystal itself. Deductions of this sort were, in fact, responsible for the postulate of the ionic bond. Perhaps the strongest indirect evidence for the existence of ions in the solid was the success achieved in calculating crystal energies by using a theory based on this premise. Even the techniques of X-ray crystallography could not provide an unambiguous answer to the question until improved methods of measurement made it possible to devise accurate *electron density maps*, which not only tell us the positions of the nuclei but also provide information as to the density of the electron charge around the nuclei. One such map, for sodium chloride, is illustrated in Fig. 2–14.

The figure shows the absolute electron density in a plane passing through the nuclei in one of the cubic faces of sodium chloride. Only part of the cell face is illustrated, since the rest of it is symmetrically related. The electron density on

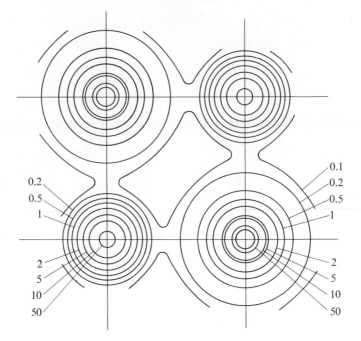

FIG. 2–14. Electron density map of part of the cubic face of sodium chloride. The electron density (electrons/A^3) is constant along each of the contour lines and increases rapidly toward the center of the ions.

each one of the closed lines is constant; as we move toward the nucleus, we see a rapid increase in electron density, indicated by the close spacing of the now circular lines. These lines are densest near the nucleus of the chloride ion, where a value of about 170 electrons/A^3 is reached; the corresponding value near the center of the sodium ion is only 70 electrons/A^3. Around the perimeter of the ions, the density drops to the comparatively small value of 0.2 electrons/A^3 and, in the unmarked regions, it is even less than this. It is possible, then, to define an approximate boundary for each ion and, by an integration procedure, to calculate the total number of electrons around each ion. In this way, it has been found that 10.05 electrons are in the region surrounding the sodium nucleus, while the corresponding value for chlorine is 17.70. These values when compared with 10.00 and 18.00 for sodium and chloride ions, respectively, indicate that within the limits of experimental error, complete electron transfer has taken place, and that ions are indeed present in the crystal structure.

It may occur to the reader, when considering the electron density map of Fig. 2–14, that the ions appear to be much like the spheres by which they are usually represented in crystal models. This idea was suggested long before the advent of these electron density maps and, in fact, was extended to include the concept of a fixed radius for each ion. Within its limitations, the postulate of the ionic radius has proved to be an extremely useful one, and it is well worth examining in detail.

TABLE 2–1

PHYSICAL PROPERTIES OF THE ALKALI HALIDES

	Structure type	a, angstroms	mp, °K	bp, °K	α, $10^{-6}/°K$	β, $10^{-12}\,cm^2/dyne$
LiF	F	4.02	1121	1949		1.43
LiCl	F	5.14	880	1626		3.17
LiBr	F	5.50	823	1535		3.90
LiI	F	6.00	742	1465		5.30
NaF	F	4.62	1268	1975	39	2.06
NaCl	F	5.62	1073	1705	40	3.97
NaBr	F	5.94	1020	1665	43	4.75
NaI	F	6.46	933	1575	48	6.21
KF	F	5.34	1131	1775		3.14
KCl	F	6.28	1044	1684		5.50
KBr	F	6.58	1007	1655		6.45
KI		7.06	954	1595		8.07
RbF	F	5.64	1068	1685		3.66
RbCl	F	6.58	995	1665		6.16
RbBr	F	6.88	965	1615		7.38
RbI	F	7.32	920	1575		9.00
CsF	F	6.02	976	1525		4.25
CsCl	cubic	7.12	918	1565		5.55
CsBr	cubic	7.54	909	1575		6.28
CsI	cubic	7.92	899	1558		7.83

α = coefficient of thermal expansion.
β = volume compressibility.

(a) Ionic radii

Detailed electron density maps, such as that of Fig. 2–14, provide a rather sophisticated way of presenting X-ray data, but are unnecessary if the internuclear distances are all that is required. Especially for simple ionic crystals, this information can be obtained readily and with great precision. Table 2–1 lists values for the lattice constant a and other properties of the alkali halides. Referring to Figs. 2–5 and 2–9, we readily see that the nearest neighbor separation or internuclear distance s_e is given by the expressions

$$s_e(NaCl) = \frac{a}{2}, \quad \text{and} \quad s_e(CsCl) = \frac{a}{2}\sqrt{3}.$$

An interesting relationship comes to light if we present the data in the form of Figs. 2–15 and 2–16, where the internuclear distance is plotted as a function of the

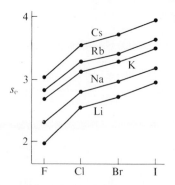

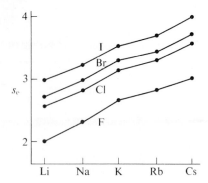

FIG. 2–15. Alkali halide internuclear dis-   FIG. 2–16. Alkali halide internuclear distances, in angstroms, plotted as a function   tances, in angstroms, plotted as a function
of anion type.   of cation type.

anion and cation, respectively. In Fig. 2–15, for example, the lines representing
the halides of the alkali metals are very nearly parallel. In other words, the difference between the internuclear distances for the halides of a given pair of alkali
metals is very nearly independent of the particular halogen in combination. A
similar relation is seen to hold for sets of halogens in Fig. 2–16. These regularities
are just what one would expect if the crystals are composed of spherical ions,
each of characteristic size, packed together in contact. This implies that we can
assign to each ion a characteristic radius such that the addition of two radii gives
the internuclear distance in the crystal. The quantity so defined is known as an
ionic radius. In terms of this concept, our physical model is no longer one of
nuclei at positions on a lattice framework, but rather one of close-packed charged
spheres. The packing of sodium and chloride ions in the sodium chloride structure
is illustrated in Fig. 2–6. In principle, the usefulness of this point of view should
extend beyond a simple empirical method for estimating internuclear distance,
since it implies that the structure of ionic crystals is determined by the geometry
of the packing of these spheres. In fact, limited success has been achieved by
utilizing the theory in this way, but fuller consideration will be given to this matter
later.

Table 2–2 lists in concise form both the internuclear distances and the differences
Δ between them. On the whole we see that the differences in any given row or
column are reasonably constant, but that there are deviations, some serious, so
that we cannot expect to achieve perfect additivity in a set of ionic radii even for
the alkali halides. A greater problem presents itself, however, if we are to define
a set of ionic radii, because the experimentally determined internuclear distances
can provide us only with differences and not with absolute radii. One ionic radius
must be fixed in some independent manner before the set of radii can be placed
on an absolute scale. A number of different procedures have been employed to
this end, based in the earlier cases on empirical relationships and more recently
on considerations of quantum theory.

TABLE 2–2

INTERNUCLEAR DISTANCES IN THE CRYSTALLINE ALKALI HALIDES
(in angstroms)

	Li	Δ	Na	Δ	K	Δ	Rb	Δ	Cs
F	2.01	0.30	2.31	0.36	2.67	0.15	2.82	0.19	3.01
Δ	0.56	—	0.50	—	0.47	—	0.47	—	0.55
Cl	2.57	0.24	2.81	0.33	3.14	0.15	3.29	0.27	3.56
Δ	0.18	—	0.16	—	0.15	—	0.15	—	0.16
Br	2.75	0.22	2.97	0.32	3.29	0.15	3.44	0.28	3.72
Δ	0.25	—	0.26	—	0.24	—	0.22	—	0.24
I	3.00	0.23	3.23	0.30	3.53	0.13	3.66	0.30	3.96

Landé, in 1920, derived a set of radii by assuming that anion-anion contact occurs in lithium iodide. From the differences in s_e we can deduce that the radii of the cations increase in the following order:

$$r(Li^+) < r(Na^+) < r(K^+) < r(Rb^+) < r(Cs^+).$$

For the anions it can be seen that:

$$r(F^-) < r(Cl^-) < r(Br^-) < r(I^-).$$

In the structure made up of the largest anion and the smallest cation, LiI, it is reasonable then to expect that the anions might be in contact with one another rather than with cations. Further weight is lent to this argument by an inspection of the differences in the internuclear distances in the fluorides and iodides:

$s_e(LiI) = 3.00 \text{ A}$ $s_e(KI) = 3.53 \text{ A}$ $s_e(RbI) = 3.66 \text{ A}$
$s_e(LiF) = 2.01$ $s_e(KF) = 2.67$ $s_e(RbF) = 2.82$

$\Delta = 0.99$ $\Delta = 0.86$ $\Delta = 0.84$

The anomalously large internuclear distance implied for lithium iodide is readily explained if this distance is determined by anion-anion rather than anion-cation contact. Figure 2–17 illustrates the phenomenon and indicates how the radius of the anion can be derived from the cation-anion distance. In the case of lithium iodide, one finds that

$$r(I^-) = s_e(LiI)/\sqrt{2} = 2.12 \text{ A}.$$

Other methods of dividing s_e were devised by Bragg, Wasastjerna, and Goldschmidt, but all procedures lead to what is essentially the same set of empirical radii. [See Table 2–3(a) and (b).]

TABLE 2–3(a)

IONIC RADII (in angstroms)

		Li^+ 0.68	Be^{2+} 0.30						
O^{2-} 1.45	F^- 1.33	Na^+ 0.98	Mg^{2+} 0.65	Al^{3+} 0.45					
S^{2-} 1.90	Cl^- 1.81	K^+ 1.33	Ca^{2+} 0.94	Ga^+ 1.13	Ga^{3+} 0.60	Ge^{2+} 0.93	Ge^{4+} 0.54		
Se^{2-} 2.02	Br^- 1.96	Rb^+ 1.48	Sr^{2+} 1.10	In^+ 1.32	In^{3+} 0.81	Sn^{2+} 1.12	Sn^{4+} 0.71		
Te^{2-} 2.22	I^- 2.19	Cs^+ 1.67	Ba^{2+} 1.29	Tl^+ 1.45	Tl^{3+} 0.91	Pb^{2+} 1.21	Pb^{4+} 0.81	Bi^{3+} 1.16	Bi^{5+} 0.74

TABLE 2–3(b)

	+	2+	3+	4+	5+	6+	7+
Sc			0.81				
Ti		0.90	0.76	0.60			
V		0.88	0.74	0.60	0.50		
Cr		0.84	0.69	0.56		0.45	
Mn		0.80	0.66	0.54			0.35
Fe		0.76	0.64				
Co		0.74	0.63				
Ni		0.72	0.62				
Cu	0.95	0.69					
Zn		0.70					
Ag	1.13						
Cd		0.92					
Au	1.30						
Hg	1.25	1.05					

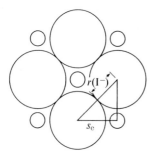

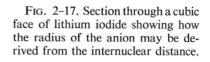

FIG. 2–17. Section through a cubic face of lithium iodide showing how the radius of the anion may be derived from the internuclear distance.

The semitheoretical procedure due to Pauling is based on the premise that the size of an ion is determined by the distribution of the outermost electrons. It will be shown in Chapter 3 that this distribution depends on the nuclear attraction and may be written empirically as a function of an effective nuclear charge Z_{eff}. This charge will be somewhat less than the true nuclear charge because of screening by inner electrons, and can be estimated empirically. On this basis, it is possible to write

$$r = C_n/Z_{\mathrm{eff}}, \tag{2–1}$$

with C_n being a constant determined by the total number of electrons in the inert gas configuration attained. If the relationship is applied to isoelectronic ions in combination (e.g., NaF), then in the expression for the ratio of the radii, C_n is the same for both ions and cancels, so that

$$\frac{r(\mathrm{Na^+})}{r(\mathrm{F^-})} = \frac{Z_{\mathrm{eff}}(\mathrm{F^-})}{Z_{\mathrm{eff}}(\mathrm{Na^+})}.$$

The effective nuclear charges for $\mathrm{Na^+}$ and $\mathrm{F^-}$ are 6.48 and 4.48, respectively (see Section 3–5), so that the internuclear distance in sodium fluoride (2.31 A) should be divided in the ratio

$$\frac{r(\mathrm{Na^+})}{r(\mathrm{F^-})} = \frac{4.48}{6.48},$$

providing values of 0.95 and 1.36 A for the radii of the sodium and fluoride ions, respectively.

Pauling applied the expression in ratio form to other pairs of isoelectronic ions in combination (KCl, RbBr, CsI) and, having deduced the radii, was able to determine the values of C_n for different inert gas configurations. The original expression of Eq. (2–1) was then used to calculate a set of univalent radii. These radii were described as univalent because the method of calculation took no account of the net ionic charge; hence a correction must be applied to the radii of multivalent ions before these radii can be used to estimate internuclear distances. The accuracy of the set of crystal radii thus obtained was further enhanced by the application of an expression to allow for the change in radius with coordination number.

Other methods of derivation and additional refinements have been suggested by Zachariasen and others, but the different methods yield very similar results. In any event, the ionic radius is an empirical concept and, since the additivity principle is obviously just an approximation, differences of a few hundredths of an angstrom are without significance.

(b) Theoretical significance of ionic radii

Although the semiempirical treatment of Pauling provides a basis for the concept of the ionic radius, it can hardly be considered a rigorous theoretical definition. Indeed, it is doubtful that modern theories of atomic structure would admit such a definition because of the asymptotic fall-off of the electron density at large distances from the nucleus. Figure 2–18 illustrates the radial electron density distribution in the spherically symmetrical monovalent fluoride ion, as derived theoretically by Hartree. These calculations apply to the case of the free ion, however, and it would be more pertinent to consider the coordinated ion in the crystal. Theoretically this poses a much more difficult problem, but fortunately it is in just this case that experimental data are available in the form of the detailed electron density maps provided by X-ray analysis. We observed in the sodium chloride electron density map (Fig. 2–14) that the contour levels of electron density around each ion are very nearly spherically symmetric, even at the point of "contact" of two neighboring ions. The boundary of either ion may then be defined by the minimum in electron density along a line joining the nuclei. It is interesting to compare the values of ionic radii defined in this manner with the accepted empirical values.

Figure 2–19 shows the variation in electron density along a line joining the nearest neighbor nuclei in lithium fluoride. Division of the internuclear distance according to accepted empirical radii is indicated by the vertical line; this division is significantly different from a division made according to the minimum in the

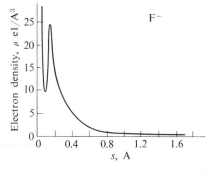

FIG. 2–18. Theoretical electron density in the fluoride ion as a function of the radial distance.

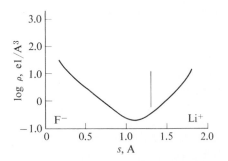

FIG. 2–19. Experimentally derived electron density along a line joining the lithium and fluoride nuclei in lithium fluoride. The vertical line at 1.3 A divides the internuclear distance according to the accepted ionic radii.

TABLE 2–4

IONIC RADII DERIVED FROM ELECTRON DENSITY MAPS
(in angstroms)

Structure	Cation	Anion
CaF_2	$r(Ca^{2+}) = 1.26$	$r(F^-) = 1.10$
LiF	$r(Li^+) = 0.92$	$r(F^-) = 1.09$
MgO	$r(Mg^{2+}) = 1.02$	$r(O^{2-}) = 1.09$
NaCl	$r(Na^+) = 1.18$	$r(Cl^-) = 1.64$

curve. Most important is the fact that the procedure based on the electron density maps attributes a considerably larger radius to the cation than do the other procedures. Thus, $r(Li^+)$ is 0.92 A according to the electron density map, compared with the accepted value of 0.68 A; and $r(F^-)$ is correspondingly smaller: 1.09 A instead of 1.33 A. Detailed X-ray analyses of this type have been carried out for only a few substances, but in all cases the cations have a larger radius than predicted empirically. Table 2–4 lists the ionic radii which have been obtained by division of the internuclear distance according to the electron density minimum method, and the structure from which the information was obtained.

There are several points of interest concerning these radii. First, the radii are in fairly good internal agreement with regard to additivity, e.g., $r(Na^+) + r(F^-) = 2.34$ A, and $r(Ca^{2+}) + r(O^{2-}) = 2.40$ A compared with the observed values of 2.31 A and 2.40 A, respectively. Second, the fluoride ion radii determined independently in CaF_2 (1.10 A) and LiF (1.09 A) are in good agreement, despite the different types of coordination in the two structures. Finally, if these values for the radii are accepted, then the proportionately larger cations eliminate all possibility of anion-anion contact. Obviously much more data are required before definitive conclusions can be drawn, and when these data become available, they should be of immense assistance to the proper understanding of ionic crystals. At the same time, the arguments presented here should serve to emphasize the empirical nature of the set of ionic radii given in Table 2–3, and to stress the fact that their chief value lies in their practical usefulness in the field of structural chemistry.

2–4. BONDING FORCES IN IONIC CRYSTALS

Information about the manner and degree of bonding in ionic crystals comes to us from many sources. That the forces involved are strong ones is indicated by the relatively high melting and boiling points exhibited by the alkali halides (Table 2–1) and by other ionic crystals. Further, when we plot some of the melting points as a function of the internuclear distance in the crystals (Fig. 2–20), a strong

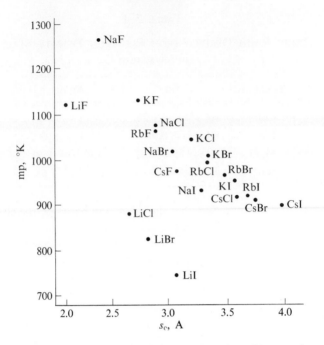

FIG. 2–20. Melting points of the alkali halides as a function of internuclear separation.

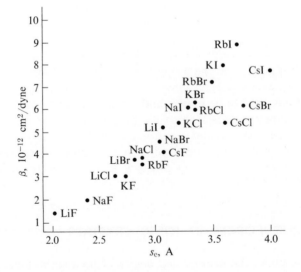

FIG. 2–21. Volume compressibilities of the alkali halides as a function of internuclear distance.

inverse relationship is noted. A completely analogous situation obtains with regard to the boiling points, indicating that the strength of the bonding decreases markedly with an increase in separation of the ions. A similar conclusion can be drawn from thermal expansion data (unfortunately meager), where it is observed that crystals with the largest lattice constant exhibit the greatest degree of expansion when heated.

Considerably more data are available on the compressibility of the alkali halides, as shown in Fig. 2–21. As might be expected, the resistance to compression decreases with increased internuclear distance and, significantly, decreases by nearly an order of magnitude over the range of ion separations considered. This change is larger than that observed for either the melting points or for thermal expansion. Since the forces opposing compression of the ionic crystal are those of repulsion between the ions, we can surmise that these repulsive forces have a much stronger dependence on the internuclear distance than do the attractive forces which resist thermal expansion.

Finally, we must investigate the effect of the net ionic charge of the ions on the physical properties of ionic crystals. That the effect is a profound one is well illustrated by comparing the melting points of some crystals composed of iso-electronic ions of different net charge, as in Table 2–5.

TABLE 2–5

	NaF	MgO
mp, °K	1268	3073
s_e, A	2.31	2.10

	KF	CaO
mp, °K	1131	2853
s_e, A	2.67	2.40

(a) Crystal energies of the alkali halides

As mentioned above, the bonding of close-packed ions to give a stable configuration implies an equilibrium in which attractive forces are balanced by repulsive forces. The expression for the total bonding energy will therefore include two terms, the attractive energy and the repulsive energy (Fig. 2–22), each of which will be dealt with separately. The former will be calculated by the application of classical electrostatics and the latter by the use of an empirical expression suggested by quantum mechanics.

According to the laws of electrostatics (Gauss' law) we may, with no loss of accuracy, treat a charged sphere as a point (with the same net charge) located at

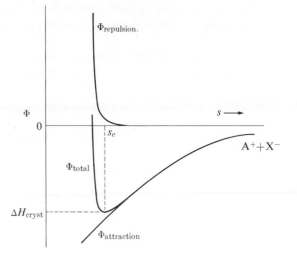

FIG. 2–22. Variation of interaction energy of oppositely charged ions according to their separation.

the center of the sphere. Thus our model for the calculation of the attractive energy will be a set of point charges at the positions of the nuclei in the crystal. Coulomb's law states that the force F between two point charges q_1 and q_2 a distance s apart (in vacuum) is given by

$$F = \frac{q_1 q_2}{s^2} . \tag{2–2}$$

If the charges are of the same sign, then F is positive and repulsion occurs, while oppositely charged particles give rise to a negative force and the particles are attracted to one another. The potential energy of interaction of the charged particles, or the work done in bringing them from a separation of infinity to a separation s, is given by the negative of the integral of Eq. (2–2) over these limits, i.e.,

$$\Phi = -\int_{\infty}^{s} \frac{q_1 q_2}{s^2} \, ds = \frac{q_1 q_2}{s} . \tag{2–3}$$

When q_1 and q_2 are of opposite sign the energy of interaction is negative, indicating a lowering of energy of the system in bringing the charges together. For our purposes Eq. (2–3) is more convenient in the form

$$\Phi = q_1 \mathcal{E}_2, \tag{2–4}$$

where $\mathcal{E}_2 = q_2/s$ is the electrostatic potential, due to q_2 at a distance s. More generally, if we wish to consider the interaction of q_1 with a number of point charges $q_2, q_3, \ldots, q_n$, then

$$\Phi = q_1 \mathcal{E}, \tag{2–5}$$

where $\varepsilon = q_2/s_2 + q_3/s_3 + \cdots + q_n/s_n$ is the total electrostatic potential at the site of q_1.

The application of Eq. (2–5) to the set of point charges making up the model of our crystal should now be clear. As an example, we shall suppose that we are dealing with an AX-type crystal with the sodium chloride structure. The ions have net charges given by z_+e and $-z_-e$, where e is the charge on the electron and z_+ and z_- are positive integers. Choosing a particular ion, say a positive one, we must first calculate the potential at the site of this ion due to all of the surrounding ions. Examining Fig. 2–7, we can see that this calculation may conveniently be performed by considering the ions in groups, as follows:

> 6 nearest neighbors at a distance s;
> 12 next nearest neighbors at a distance $s\sqrt{2}$;
> 8 anions at the corners of a cube at a distance $s\sqrt{3}$;
> 6 cations at the centers of adjacent unit cells at a distance $2s$; etc.

The total electrostatic potential at the site of a cation is then given by a series of the type

$$\varepsilon_{\text{cation}} = -\frac{6z_-e}{s} + \frac{12z_+e}{s\sqrt{2}} - \frac{8z_-e}{s\sqrt{3}} + \frac{6z_+e}{2s}\cdots, \qquad (2\text{–}6)$$

and the energy of interaction is found to be

$$\Phi_{\text{cation}} = z_+e\varepsilon_{\text{cation}} = -\frac{z_+z_-e^2}{s}\left(6 - \frac{12z_+}{z_-\sqrt{2}} + \frac{8}{\sqrt{3}} - \frac{6z_+}{2z_-}\cdots\right). \qquad (2\text{–}7)$$

The ratio of the charges on the ions, z_+/z_-, is a constant for a given type of structure ($z_+/z_- = 1$ for NaCl, for example), so that the series in parentheses is solely a function of the geometry of the crystal and will be the same for all crystals of the same structure type regardless of the values of z and s. It is termed the Madelung constant, and we shall denote it by the symbol $\mathfrak{M}$. The Coulomb interaction energy of a cation with all of the other ions of the crystal is then given by

$$\Phi_{\text{cation}} = -\frac{z_+z_-e^2\mathfrak{M}}{s}.$$

The same procedure may now be used to calculate the Coulomb interaction energy of an anion, Φ_{anion}, with all of the other ions of the crystal. The total attractive energy is then given by one-half the sum of the cationic and anionic energies, since simply adding the two would take each interaction into account twice. For structures of the sodium chloride type, $\Phi_{\text{anion}} = \Phi_{\text{cation}}$, and the total attractive energy is

$$\Phi_{\text{att}} = \tfrac{1}{2}(\Phi_{\text{cation}} + \Phi_{\text{anion}}) = -\frac{z_+z_-e^2\mathfrak{M}}{s}. \qquad (2\text{–}8)$$

The evaluation of the Madelung constant is by no means as straightforward as would appear from Eq. (2–7). Inspection of the expression for $\mathfrak{M}$ reveals that the series of terms of alternate signs converges very slowly, because the number of ions (numerator) increases at a rate comparable to the separation (denominator). Various procedures have been devised to overcome this difficulty. The simplest, due to Evjen, considers the ions in groups which are more or less neutral electrostatically, producing a series that is more quickly converging. In the more sophisticated methods, such as that of Ewald, a continuous semiempirical expression for the charge distribution is used and the Madelung constant is derived by an integrational procedure. A good outline of techniques for evaluating $\mathfrak{M}$ is given in the book by Kittel listed at the end of this chapter.

The repulsion energy which originates in the interpenetration of the electron clouds of the ions presents a problem, since it is not well defined theoretically. It is known, however, that it acts over a short distance and exhibits a rather high inverse dependence on s (Fig. 2–21). It is common, therefore, to represent the repulsion energy by an expression of the type B/s^n or $Be^{-s/\rho}$. The former was used in the original Born-Landé treatment, but the exponential expression has some basis in quantum mechanics and was employed in later calculations by Born and Mayer and others. Adding the exponential expression to Eq. (2–8), we find the total potential energy of interaction to be

$$\Phi_{\text{total}} = -\frac{z_+z_-e^2\mathfrak{M}}{s} + Be^{-s/\rho}. \tag{2–9}$$

The two unknown constants B and ρ in Eq. (2–9) may be eliminated by introducing the equilibrium internuclear separation s_e and the compressibility β as empirical quantities. Note first of all that the condition of equilibrium requires that the attractive and repulsive forces balance one another. In other words, the potential energy must exhibit a minimum for $s = s_e$ (Fig. 2–22). Mathematically expressed, this means that

$$\left(\frac{d\Phi}{ds}\right)_{s=s_e} = 0 = \frac{z_+z_-e^2\mathfrak{M}}{s_e^2} - \frac{Be^{-s_e/\rho}}{\rho},$$

and

$$B = \frac{\rho z_+z_-e^2\mathfrak{M}e^{s_e/\rho}}{s_e^2}. \tag{2–10}$$

Substituting Eq. (2–10) for B in Eq. (2–9) and multiplying by Avogadro's number N gives the crystal energy per mole, in the form known as the *Born-Mayer equation:*

$$\Delta H_{\text{cryst}} = \Phi_{\text{total}} = -\frac{z_+z_-e^2N\mathfrak{M}}{s_e}\left(1 - \frac{\rho}{s_e}\right). \tag{2–11}$$

The remaining unknown, ρ, may be expressed in terms of the volume compressibility β, but this calculation is usually carried out separately. Calculations show, in fact, that ρ varies little over the series of alkali halides, and we may, to a good approximation, use the average value of 0.311×10^{-8} cm for all calculations.

The derivation of ρ in terms of β, the volume compressibility, is a fairly straightforward application of differential calculus. We begin by relating β to Φ with the aid of thermodynamics and then use our previously derived expression for Φ [Eq. (2–11)] to obtain the desired relationship.

If a crystal is compressed by the application of a pressure P (at constant temperature), then the change in interaction energy $d\Phi$ is equal to the pressure-volume work done, i.e.,

$$d\Phi = -P\,dV.$$

From this equation, it follows that

$$\frac{d\Phi}{dV} = -P,$$

and

$$\frac{d^2\Phi}{dV^2} = -\frac{dP}{dV} = \frac{1}{V\beta}, \tag{2–12}$$

since, by definition,

$$\beta = -\frac{1}{V}\left(\frac{\partial V}{\partial P}\right)_T.$$

To relate Eq. (2–12) to (2–11), we must express $d^2\Phi/dV^2$ in terms of s. To do this, we make use of the fact that

$$\frac{d\Phi}{dV} = \frac{d\Phi}{ds}\frac{ds}{dV},$$

and

$$\frac{d^2\Phi}{dV^2} = \frac{d\Phi}{ds}\frac{d^2s}{dV^2} + \left(\frac{ds}{dV}\right)^2\frac{d^2\Phi}{ds^2}.$$

If equilibrium obtains, then $s = s_e$ and

$$\left(\frac{d\Phi}{ds}\right)_{s=s_e} = 0,$$

so that

$$\left(\frac{d^2\Phi}{dV^2}\right)_{s=s_e} = \left(\frac{ds}{dV}\right)^2\frac{d^2\Phi}{ds^2}. \tag{2–13}$$

The molar volume may be expressed as a function of s_e^3 of the type

$$V = CNs_e^3.$$

For NaCl type crystals, for example, $V = 8Ns_e^3/4$ (4 molecules per unit cell), and $C = 2$. For CsCl type crystals $V = 8Ns_e^3/3\sqrt{3}$ and $C = 8/3\sqrt{3}$. Differentiating, we find that

$$\frac{dV}{ds} = 3CNs_e^2,$$

and

$$\left(\frac{dV}{ds}\right)^2 = 9C^2N^2s_e^4. \tag{2–14}$$

Substituting Eq. (2–14) in (2–13), we obtain

$$\frac{d^2\Phi}{dV^2} = \frac{1}{V\beta} = \frac{1}{9C^2N^2s_e^4}\left(\frac{d^2\Phi}{ds^2}\right)_{s=s_e}. \tag{2-15}$$

It is a simple matter to complete the derivation, for we have already found that

$$\frac{d\Phi}{ds} = \frac{z_+z_-\mathfrak{M}}{s^2} - \frac{Be^{-s/\rho}}{\rho},$$

and differentiating a second time, we obtain

$$\frac{d^2\Phi}{ds^2} = -\frac{2z_+z_-e^2\mathfrak{M}}{s^3} + \frac{Be^{-s/\rho}}{\rho^2}.$$

Substituting for B, as given by Eq. (2–10), and multiplying by N to give molar quantities, we find that

$$\left(\frac{d^2\Phi}{ds^2}\right)_{s=s_e} = \frac{z_+z_-e^2\mathfrak{M}N}{s_e^3}\left(\frac{s_e}{\rho} - 2\right). \tag{2-16}$$

Now, Eq. (2–16) need only be combined with Eq. (2–15) to give, after cancellation and rearrangement,

$$\frac{s_e}{\rho} = \frac{9Cs_e^4}{z_+z_-e^2\mathfrak{M}\beta} + 2. \tag{2-17}$$

To illustrate the application of Eq. (2–11), we shall calculate the crystal energy of sodium chloride. The pertinent data in this case are:

$$z_+ = z_- = 1, \qquad e = 4.80 \times 10^{-10} \text{ esu},$$
$$s_e = 2.81 \times 10^{-8} \text{ cm}, \qquad N = 6.02 \times 10^{23},$$
$$\mathfrak{M} = 1.75, \qquad \rho = 0.311 \times 10^{-8} \text{ cm}.$$

Substituting in Eq. (2–11), we obtain

$$\Delta H_{\text{cryst}}(\text{NaCl}) = -\frac{4.80^2 \times 10^{-20} \times 6.02 \times 10^{23} \times 1.75}{2.81 \times 10^{-8}}\left(1 - \frac{0.311 \times 10^{-8}}{2.81 \times 10^{-8}}\right)$$

$$= -7.68 \times 10^{12} \text{ ergs/mole},$$

or -184 kcal/mole, which is in good agreement with the experimental value of -183.3 kcal/mole.

Direct experimental determination of the crystal energy is not possible, since it would require measurement of the heat of the reaction

$$\text{Na}^+(\text{g}) + \text{Cl}^-(\text{g}) \rightarrow \text{NaCl (crystal)}. \tag{2-18}$$

TABLE 2–6

CRYSTAL ENERGIES ($-\Delta H_{cryst}$) OF THE ALKALI HALIDES
(kcal/mole)

	Born cycle	Born-Mayer ($\rho = 0.311$ A)	Huggins	Direct measure-ment	Quantum mechan-ical
LiF	246.7	244	243.6		239
LiCl	202.3	199	200.2		187.7
LiBr	193.0	183	189.5		
LiI	180.0	168	176.1		
NaF	219.0	217	215.4		205.1
NaCl	186.2	184	183.5	181.3	183.2
NaBr	177.0	175	175.5	176	
NaI	165.7	162	164.3	166	
KF	194.3	192	192.5		166.9
KCl	169.3	167	167.9		
KBr	161.8	160	161.3	160	
KI	152.3	150	152.4	153	
RbF	185.4	183	183.0		
RbCl	162.3	160	162.0		
RbBr	155.9	153	156.1	151	
RbI	147.3	145	148.0	146	
CsF	173.6	173	175.7		
CsCl	155.5	150	153.1		
CsBr	149.3	144	149.6		
CsI	141.4	136	142.5	141.5	

The most direct procedure which is experimentally practicable involves measurements of the equilibrium

$$Na^+(g) + Cl^-(g) \rightleftharpoons NaCl(g),$$

combined with vapor pressure data for the solid, but the experimental difficulties are formidable. As a result, few crystal energies have been determined in this manner and then only with moderate accuracy.

The most commonly used method of calculation, devised by Born and Haber, is based on the application of Hess' law to readily available empirical thermochemical quantities. Details of the method will be given in Chapter 4.

The crystal energies of the alkali halides, as calculated by using the Born-Mayer equation and experimentally derived by the Born-Haber method, are listed in

Table 2–6. Considering the simplicity of the physical model used in the theoretical calculations, the agreement is indeed remarkable. There can be little doubt that our picture of these crystals as close-packed arrangements of ions is essentially correct. Even better agreement is achieved by the more refined treatments, such as that of Huggins. These take into account the van der Waals interaction between the ions, use a more complex function for the repulsive energy, and include a number of relatively minor corrections that we have omitted. A good discussion of these extended equations may be found in the book by Born and Huang, or the review of Waddington, listed at the end of the chapter.

In addition, a number of crystals have been the subject of quantum mechanical calculations by Löwdin, Yamashita, and others. Some of the crystal energies obtained in this way are also listed in Table 2–6. In contrast to the extensions of the Born-Mayer classical treatment, the quantum mechanical methods are purely theoretical and allow calculation of the lattice constant, compressibility, and other physical properties in addition to the crystal energy. A good account of the procedure, using the Heitler-London or valence-bond approach (Chapter 5), may be found in the book by Löwdin.

It is interesting to examine, even if only briefly, the many details which must be taken into account if an accurate calculation of the crystal energy is desired. First of all, Eq. (2–9), which we have used to calculate the potential energy of interaction, must be extended to include the van der Waals energy of interaction (5 to 10 kcal/mole). This may be done by adding to Eq. (2–9) a term of the form $-C/s^6$, where C is a function of the polarizabilities of the ions (Chapter 7). A further improvement may be effected by adding additional terms in the term for repulsive energy, primarily to take account of repulsions between other than nearest neighbors. It would be logical, for example, to add a term $-B'e^{(s\sqrt{2})/\rho}$ to represent the interaction with next nearest neighbors. Note, however, that both of the newly added terms exhibit a dependence on s much like the original repulsion term, so that their inclusion would be expected to modify the value obtained for ρ. This in fact is observed, and a value of $\rho \approx 0.34$ A is more commonly used in these refined treatments. Another way of looking at the situation is to say that, because of the similarity of the three terms in their dependence on s, and our empirical derivation of ρ, even the simple Born-Mayer treatment takes some account of the van der Waals forces and repulsion by other than nearest neighbors. In a sense, then, the good agreement shown in Table 2–6 is fortuitous.

Before comparing the improved calculated values with the experimental ones, it is important to realize exactly what physical quantity has been calculated. According to our model, we have calculated the potential energy of interaction of a static system of point charges. In equating this to the total energy, one assumes the kinetic energy to be zero, and even at 0°K this is not true, since the ions will be vibrating. Thus, to obtain the total energy at 0°K, we must add the zero-point energy (of the order of one kcal/mole) as determined by the frequency of vibration. If, furthermore, the theoretical value is to be compared with a thermochemical value, valid at 298°K (and this is the most common procedure), then a correction must be applied to account for the increase in thermal energy with increased temperature. This can be done if heat capacity data are available for the crystal over the range 0°K to 298°K (see Chapter 8), and adds one to two kcal/mole to the crystal energy. Finally, for the sake of rigor, it should be pointed out that our calculated crystal energy does not correspond to the enthalpy change ΔH for the reaction of Eq. (2–18), but rather to the change in internal energy ΔU. As we shall show in Chapter 4, the difference arises from the change in volume during the process, but the correction is very minor (about 0.05 kcal/mole) and is usually neglected.

(b) Crystal energies of other ionic compounds

Although the sodium chloride structure was used as the model for the derivation of Eq. (2–11), the manner of formulation makes the equation quite general. One needs only to insert the appropriate values for z_+ and z_-, the net charges on the ions, and use the Madelung constant suitable to the structure type. Surprisingly, it is found that the constant ρ is not particularly sensitive to the structure type, and to a good approximation the value $\rho = 0.311$ A may be used in all cases. Madelung constants have been calculated for all of the common structure types, and some are listed in Table 2–7. A word of caution is necessary if reference is made to other texts, since liberties are often taken with the original definition of the Madelung constant. In cases where the charges on the anion and cation are unequal in magnitude ($z_+ \neq z_-$), the quantity $z_+ z_- \mathfrak{M}$ is usually quoted for the Madelung constant. Thus 5.03878, twice the value given in Table 2–7, is usually quoted for the Madelung constant of calcium fluoride. Such a procedure leads to unnecessary confusion, particularly in the case of the rutile structure, and does not adhere to the proper definition of the Madelung constant, since the net charges are not functions of the structure type. The values of $\mathfrak{M}$ listed in Table 2–7 are independent of z_+ and z_- and may be used directly in Eq. (2–11).

To illustrate, we shall calculate the crystal energy of SnO_2, which has the rutile structure. The lattice constants are $a = 4.72$, $c = 3.16$; hence $c/a = 0.670$ and

TABLE 2–7

MADELUNG CONSTANTS

Structure type	$\mathfrak{M}$
NaCl	1.74756
CsCl	1.76267
CaF_2	2.51939
TiO_2^*	$2.408 - 2.055(0.721 - c/a)^2$
ZnS (zincblende)	1.63805
ZnS (wurtzite)	1.64132

* The Madelung constant for the rutile type structure is a function of the crystal parameters but may, to a good approximation, be represented by the function of c/a given above. For rutile itself, $c/a = 0.721$ and $\mathfrak{M} = 2.408$.

$\mathfrak{M} = 2.403$. The net ionic charges are $z_+ = 4$, $z_- = 2$, and $s_e = 2.10$. Substituting in Eq. (2–11) gives

$$\Delta H_{cryst}(SnO_2) = -\frac{4 \times 2 \times 4.80^2 \times 10^{-20} \times 2.403 \times 6.023 \times 10^{23}}{2.18 \times 10^{-8}}$$

$$\times \left(1 - \frac{0.311 \times 10^{-8}}{2.10 \times 10^{-8}}\right)$$

$$= -1.08 \times 10^{14} \text{ ergs/mole}$$

$$= -2590 \text{ kcal/mole}.$$

Considering the approximations involved, especially with regard to ρ, the 5% difference between the calculated value and the experimental crystal energy of -2718 kcal/mole is not unreasonable.

2–5. CRYSTAL ENERGIES AND PHYSICAL AND CHEMICAL PROPERTIES

A number of important physical and chemical properties of ionic salts are either influenced by or related to crystal energy. Since we have investigated the latter from theoretical and experimental points of view, it is instructive to examine the correlation of crystal energy with some of these properties. We shall begin with an examination of the melting and boiling points, and go on to the factors governing the structure type.

(a) Melting and boiling points of the alkali halides

In view of the relatively large crystal energies we have found, the high melting and boiling points and the large liquid range exhibited by the alkali halides are intuitively reasonable. On closer examination, however, we see that the phenomena of fusion and vaporization merit further study. Thus, comparing Figs. 2–23(a) and (b), which show the mp and bp of the alkali halides as functions of anions, with the similar plot of Fig. 2–24 for their experimental crystal energies, we observe a rather different behavior. The crystal energies exhibit a regular variation as the anion or cation is changed in accord with the change in internuclear separation. The mp and bp curves, on the other hand, show marked deviations from regularity, particularly for the lithium salts. Since one would intuitively expect a larger crystal energy to correlate with a higher temperature (i.e., a high thermal energy required to bring about fusion or vaporization), this result is surprising. The reasons for this behavior become clear, however, when the energy relationship of these processes is examined.

Treating fusion and vaporization together for convenience, we are concerned with the process of sublimation as represented, for NaCl for example, by the equation

$$\text{NaCl (crystal)} \rightarrow \text{NaCl(g)}, \qquad \Delta H_{sub}. \tag{2–19}$$

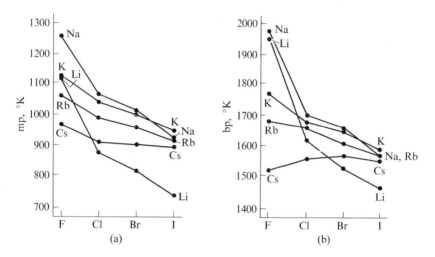

FIG. 2–23. Melting points (a) and boiling points (b) of the alkali halides as a function of ion type.

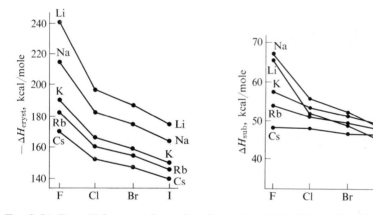

FIG. 2–24. Born-Haber crystal energies of the alkali halides as a function of ion type.

FIG. 2–25. Heats of sublimation of the alkali halides as a function of ion type.

The energy involved, ΔH_{sub}, is the heat of sublimation. This quantity for the alkali halides is shown in Fig. 2–25, plotted in the same manner as before. That the graph parallels those for the mp and bp of alkali halides is simply an illustration of the empirical Trouton's rule ($\Delta H_{vap}/T_{bp} = C$), and the similar relation, due to le Chatelier and Matignon, for sublimation. The relationship between the crystal energy and the heat of sublimation is shown by writing the process of Eq. (2–19) as the sum of the two processes

$$\text{NaCl (crystal)} \rightarrow \text{Na}^+(g) + \text{Cl}^-(g), \qquad -\Delta H_{cryst}, \qquad (2\text{–}20)$$

and

$$\text{Na}^+(g) + \text{Cl}^-(g) \rightarrow \text{NaCl}(g), \qquad -\Delta H_{diss,ion}. \qquad (2\text{–}21)$$

TABLE 2–8

DISSOCIATION ENERGIES AND INTERNUCLEAR DISTANCES IN DIATOMIC ALKALI HALIDE MOLECULES

Molecule	s_e, A	ΔH_{diss}, kcal	Molecule	s_e, A	ΔH_{diss}, kcal
LiF	1.55	181	RbF	2.27	131
LiCl	2.02	151	RbCl	2.79	111
LiBr	2.17	144	RbBr	2.94	107
LiI	2.39	136	RbI	3.18	100
NaF	1.84	152	CsF	2.35	125
NaCl	2.36	131	CsCl	2.91	107
NaBr	2.50	125	CsBr	3.07	103
NaI	2.71	118	CsI	3.32	95
KF	2.13	137			
KCl	2.67	116			
KBr	2.82	111			
KI	3.05	104			

The first of these will be recognized as the reverse of the hypothetical equation used to define the crystal energy, while the second represents the reverse of the dissociation of the gas phase molecule into gaseous ions. (The energy required to dissociate the molecule into ions is designated $\Delta H_{diss,ion}$ to distinguish it from the energy required for dissociation into atoms, ΔH_{diss}.) We have then

$$\Delta H_{sub} = -\Delta H_{cryst} - \Delta H_{diss,ion}. \qquad (2\text{--}22)$$

It is apparent now that the heat of sublimation (and mp and bp) is determined not only by the crystal energy but also by the dissociation energy of the diatomic molecule present in the gas phase. Furthermore, both ΔH_{sub} and ΔH_{cryst} are known experimental quantities, so that Eq. (2–22) may be used to obtain an experimental value for $\Delta H_{diss,ion}$. These have been calculated for the alkali halides and are listed in Table 2–8 and plotted in Fig. 2–26.

In seeking the reason for the irregular mp and bp of the alkali halides, it is necessary that we consider carefully the curves of Figs. 2–24, 2–25, and 2–26. The approximate parallelism of the curves for ΔH_{cryst} in this type of plot is due to the simple dependence of the crystal energy on s_e as exhibited in Eq. (2–11). For the diatomic molecule, a similar situation exists since, if the bonding is purely ionic, the energy of dissociation into ions may also be represented by Eq. (2–11), with $\mathfrak{M}$ equal to unity. In either case, deviations from regularity will result if there are significant contributions to the binding energy from forces other than ionic ones. Note, furthermore, that ΔH_{sub} is only one-third to one-quarter the

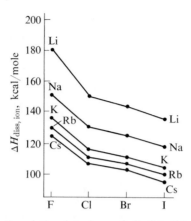

FIG. 2–26. Heats of dissociation into ions of alkali halide diatomic molecules.

magnitude of ΔH_{cryst} or $\Delta H_{diss,ion}$, so that relatively small deviations in either of the latter quantities may give rise to a significant irregularity in the heat of sublimation.

It is clear from Fig. 2–25 that the largest deviations from regularity appear when a small cation is bonded to a large anion, or vice versa, as in the lithium salts or cesium fluoride. It is in just these cases that a large contribution by the van der Waals forces would be expected, since the large ions will be readily polarized by the smaller ions, inducing a dipole moment (Fig. 2–27). The dipole will then interact with the charge on the polarizing anion (Chapter 7). Furthermore, it is reasonable to expect that the contributions will be largest in the gas phase, because the symmetry of coordination in the crystal will tend to reduce the magnitude of the induced dipole. On the other hand, quantitative confirmation of these ideas by use of the current theoretical approach is impossible, because of inaccuracy in the method of calculating the repulsion energy. The empirical procedure for deriving the repulsion constant ρ simply adjusts the parameter to make any reasonable equation give good results.

It may occur to the reader that an anomalously low heat of sublimation could also be explained by the presence of polymeric species (e.g., Li_2F_2, Li_3F_3, etc.) in the vapor phase. This is, in fact, known to be the case, but the equilibrium concentrations of the polymeric species can be measured and the heat of sublimation corrected accordingly. It will be noted that the heat of sublimation is defined in Eq. (2–19) in terms of monomer only, implying that the heats of sublimation used have been so corrected.

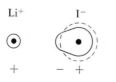

FIG. 2–27. Polarization of the iodide ion in diatomic lithium iodide. The small, positively charged lithium ion causes a displacement of the center of negative charge in the iodide ion, producing a dipole moment.

(b) Factors governing the coordination number

While all but three of the alkali halides assume the sodium chloride structure, some of them, as mentioned earlier, undergo a transition to the cesium chloride structure under appropriate conditions. We are led, then, to inquire what factors govern the choice of structure and, in particular, why only the chloride, bromide, and iodide of cesium normally adopt the simple cubic cesium chloride structure.

The stable structure under any conditions will be that which leads to the lowest energy of the system, i.e., the largest numerical value of the crystal energy. The Born-Mayer theory [Eq. (2–11)] predicts that the crystal energy is proportional to the Madelung constant and, on this basis alone, the cesium chloride structure should always be favored. However, the crystal energy is also determined by the internuclear distance. At small ionic radius ratios, because of anion-anion contact, the internuclear distance will be shorter in the sodium chloride modification than in the cesium chloride structure. Thus, if we consider a series of hypothetical ionic crystals in which the anion radius remains constant while the cation radius changes, the crystal energy should vary as shown in Fig. 2–28. When the radius ratio is about unity, the cesium chloride structure has a lower energy and is favored because of the larger Madelung constant. If the radius ratio is decreased to less than 0.73, further decrease in the internuclear distance is largely prevented, in the case of the cesium chloride structure, by anion-anion contact between the anions of constant radius. Hence, the crystal energy is lower in this region of radius ratios for the sodium chloride structure. Another change in structure type is to be expected when the radius ratio reaches 0.41, but there are valid reasons to question the purely geometric argument, since it is doubtful whether the predicted zincblende structure can be represented by ionic bonding only (Chapter 7). In summary, the above argument predicts that the sodium chloride structure will be assumed when the radius ratio is less than 0.73, and that the cesium chloride structure is favored when the radius ratio is greater than 0.73.

In view of the simplicity of the argument, it is not surprising that there are many exceptions to this rule (Table 2–9). In addition to the fact that there are inac-

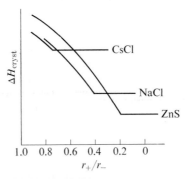

FIG. 2–28. Relative crystal energies of the NaCl, CsCl, and ZnS structures as a function of the radius ratio r_+/r_-, with the anion radius r_- held constant.

TABLE 2–9

RADIUS RATIOS FOR THE ALKALI HALIDES

	Li	Na	K	Rb	Cs
F	0.51	0.74	1.0	0.90	0.80
Cl	0.38	0.54	0.73	0.82	(0.92)
Br	0.35	0.50	0.68	0.75	(0.85)
I	0.31	0.45	0.61	0.67	(0.76)

curacies in the Born-Mayer equation, the dependence of ionic radius on coordination number has been ignored. Zachareisen showed theoretically that in the transition from sodium chloride to cesium chloride structures, a three percent increase in the internuclear distance is to be expected. This phenomenon has been verified in the transition of cesium chloride itself, at 445°C, to the sodium chloride structure. Applying this result to a comparison of the crystal energies of the two possible forms, we find that the situation is reversed and that the sodium chloride structure would be more stable than the cesium chloride one. Even this must be considered as only one of the many factors which can have a bearing on the crystal energy. Since the crystal energies are so similar, some second-order effect, such as polarization, could easily determine the structure adopted. This latter view is substantiated by the fact that, of the nine alkali halides for which the radius rule predicts the cesium chloride structure, only the three composed of the largest and most easily polarizable (deformable) ions actually assume this structure. The radius ratio rule might then be regarded as a necessary, but not sufficient, condition.

The change in structure from the sodium chloride to the cesium chloride type, when the crystal is subjected to high pressure, can be simply interpreted as follows. Compression of the crystal will result in a decrease in the internuclear distance, and, according to Fig. 2–22, an increased energy. Comparison of the densities of a crystal in the two forms (see Problem 2–10) reveals, as would be expected on the basis of its coordination number, that the cesium chloride form has a higher density and will therefore occupy a smaller volume than the sodium chloride one. Application of le Chatelier's principle then indicates that the cesium chloride form would be favored at very high pressure, a fact which has been observed for a number of the alkali halides.

BIBLIOGRAPHY

A

COULSON, C. A., *Valence*. New York: Oxford, 1961.

DAY, M. C., and J. SELBIN, *Theoretical Inorganic Chemistry*. New York: Reinhold, 1962.

GOULD, E. S., *Inorganic Reactions and Structure*. New York: Holt, 1962.

HESLOP, R. B., and P. L. ROBINSON, *Inorganic Chemistry*. Amsterdam: Elsevier, 1960.

HOLDEN, A., and P. SINGER, *Crystals and Crystal Growing*. New York: Doubleday and Co., Inc., Science Study Series, Anchor Books, 1960.

KETELAAR, J. A. A., *Chemical Constitution*. Amsterdam: Elsevier, 1960.

KITTEL, C., *Introduction to Solid State Physics*. New York: Wiley, 1953.

MOELWYN-HUGHES, E. A., *States of Matter*. London: Oliver and Boyd, 1961.

PAULING, L., *Nature of the Chemical Bond*. Ithaca, New York: Cornell, 1960.

VAN ARKEL, A. E., *Molecules and Crystals*. London: Butterworth, 1956.

B

BORN, M., and K. HUANG, *Dynamical Theory of Crystal Lattices*. New York: Oxford, 1954.

EVANS, R. C., *An Introduction to Crystal Chemistry*. New York: Cambridge, 1963.

LÖWDIN, P. O., *A Theoretical Investigation into Some Properties of Ionic Crystals*. Uppsala: Almquist, 1948.

SEITZ, F., *The Modern Theory of Solids*. New York: McGraw-Hill, 1940.

WADDINGTON, T. C., "Lattice Energies and Their Significance in Inorganic Chemistry," *Advances in Inorganic Chemistry and Radiochemistry*, Vol. 1. New York: Academic Press, 1959.

WELLS, A. F., *Structural Inorganic Chemistry*. New York: Oxford, 1961.

Tables of Interatomic Distances and Configuration in Molecules and Ions. London: The Chemical Society, 1958.

PROBLEMS

2–1. Summarize the evidence of a macroscopic nature which implies a regularity in the internal arrangement of atoms in crystals.

2–2. Deduce the number of nearest and next-nearest neighbors in sodium chloride and cesium chloride crystals. Derive expressions for the separation of nearest and next-nearest neighbors in terms of the lattice constant of these structure types.

2–3. An important preliminary step in a crystal structure analysis is the determination of the number of molecules per unit cell from the experimentally determined density of the crystal and from the unit cell dimensions yielded by measurements on X-ray diffraction photographs. Derive an expression for the density of a cubic crystal in terms of the molecular weight M and the number of molecules per unit cell n. Use these data to calculate the density of rock salt in gm/cm^3. Check your answer against the experimental value in a handbook, and explain why you would not expect the two to be identical.

2–4. The oxides Na_2O, K_2O, and Rb_2O all have the antifluorite structure, with lattice constants equal to 5.55 A, 6.44 A, and 6.74 A, respectively. Derive a general expression for the internuclear distance in this structure in terms of the lattice constant a, and use the expression to calculate s_e in the oxides listed. Consider the radii of the alkali metal ions (Table 2–3) to have been established by the arguments of Section 2–3(a), and deduce a value for the radius of the O^{2-} ion.

2–5. Listed below are the lattice constants (in angstroms) for the alkaline earth chalcogenides which exhibit the sodium chloride arrangement. Use this information and that of the preceding problem to derive a set of ionic radii for the divalent ions involved. Compare your radii with those of Table 2–3.

MgO	CaO	SrO	BaO
4.20	4.80	5.14	5.52
MgS	CaS	SrS	BaS
5.19	5.68	6.00	6.35
MgSe	CaSe	SrSe	BaSe
5.45	5.91	6.23	6.62
	CaTe	SrSe	BaSe
	6.35	6.64	6.99

2–6. Summarize the Born-Mayer approach to the calculation of the binding energy of ionic crystals. Describe the physical model employed and state clearly the approximations and assumptions involved. In what sense is this an empirical treatment?

2–7. Calculate the crystal energies for the series of alkaline earth oxides of Problem 2–5. Compare these binding energies with those for the alkali halides. (See also Problem 4–9.)

2–8. Estimate the crystal energies for the following compounds, using the radii of Table 2–3 to obtain the internuclear distances. (See also Problem 4–10.)

Compound	Structure type
TlBr	cesium chloride
MnO	sodium chloride
$SrCl_2$	fluorite
Li_2O	antifluorite
MnF_2	rutile, $c/a = 0.675$
MnO_2	rutile, $c/a = 0.651$

2–9. Calculate the radius ratios for the series of crystalline compounds in Problem 2–5, and state whether the observed structures are in agreement with the radius ratio rule.

2–10. Under appropriate conditions, the chloride, bromide, and iodide of rubidium assume the cesium chloride structure with the following lattice constants: 3.92 A, 4.06 A, and 4.31 A, respectively. Compare the internuclear distance and density for each compound in the two types of structure. Which structure would you expect to be preferred at high pressures?

2–11. According to the radius ratio rule, the cesium chloride structure is to be preferred, because of the larger Madelung constant, when the ratio is greater than 0.73. Show that this argument breaks down if, as indicated in Problem 2–10, the difference in coordination results in a 3% larger internuclear distance in the cesium chloride structure.

2–12. Use Eq. (2–17) to calculate ρ for all, or a representative sample of, the alkali halides (the fluorides, chlorides, bromides, and iodides of lithium and sodium, for example), and confirm that $\rho = 0.311$ A is a reasonable average value. Inspect the series of values of ρ for systematic variations. Would you expect better overall agreement between the calculated and experimental crystal energies if individual values of ρ were used in the calculation? Keeping in mind the limitations of the Born-Mayer approach, suggest an explanation for your observations.

2–13. If the bonding in the alkali halides were solely ionic, then, according to Eq. (2–11), the binding energy should be an approximately linear function of $1/s_e$. Plot ΔH_{cryst} and $\Delta H_{diss,ion}$ as functions of $1/s_e$, for the crystal and for the diatomic molecule, to confirm this relationship. Is there any indication in your graphs that the van der Waals forces contribute more significantly to the binding energy of the diatomic molecule than to the crystal energy? Explain.

2–14. A comparison of Tables 2–2 and 2–8 shows that the internuclear distances in the gas phase molecules are considerably smaller than those in the corresponding crystals. Explain why this should be so, when the binding energy is larger in the crystal.

2–15. In the earlier Born-Landé calculations of crystal energies, the repulsive energy is represented by a term of the type B/s^n. Expressing the repulsive energy in this way, derive an equation for the crystal energy, analogous to that of Eq. (2–11).

2–16. In the Born-Landé equation for crystal energy, derived in Problem 2–15, the parameter n is often assigned a value according to the inert gas configuration of the ions involved. These are: 5 for the He configuration, 7 for Ne, 9 for Ar, 10 for Kr, and 12 for Xe, or the arithmetic mean when the configurations are not the same. Calculate the crystal energies for some of the alkali halides, using the Born-Landé expression, and compare the values with those obtained using the Born-Mayer equation.

2–17. Derive an expression for the repulsion parameter n in terms of the compressibility, and confirm that the values assigned to n in Problem 2–15 are reasonable.

CHAPTER THREE

Atomic Structure

With the Rutherford atom as our model, we turn now to a detailed inquiry into the electronic structure of atoms and its correlation with a number of physical properties. Historically, the optical spectra of atoms have proved to be the richest source of information on atomic structure, and it is with this that we shall begin our inquiry.

Such spectra can be produced by exciting atoms in an electric arc or discharge; and even at the turn of the century, there existed a great wealth of experimental data on the nature of light emitted by atoms at high temperatures. Much of this information had been correlated with empirical equations of remarkable accuracy, but the classical theories of mechanics and electromagnetism could offer no explanation for the phenomenon. In fact, the very existence of a stable configuration composed of a positive nucleus and negative electrons defies the classical laws of electrodynamics. The interpretation of atomic spectra awaited (indeed, was instrumental in bringing about) the development of quantum mechanics at the hands of Schrödinger, Heisenberg, Dirac, and others. The application of quantum mechanics first to atomic and then to molecular structure has revolutionized the physical sciences and given birth to chemistry as we know it today.

In the early part of this chapter, we shall examine the basic postulates of quantum mechanics and the experimental results which lead to their formulation, while the latter part will be concerned with the application of quantum mechanics to the electronic structure of atoms. Chapter 5 will deal with the quantum mechanics of molecules and the chemical bond. Both treatments must necessarily be of a qualitative nature.

3-1. ATOMIC SPECTRA

Although it is readily apparent to the naked eye that the light emitted by a tungsten lamp is different in color from that emitted by a mercury or sodium lamp, it is not visually obvious that the light from these sources is fundamentally different. The difference in the nature of the radiation is revealed when the light is dispersed by passing it through a prism (refraction) or grating (diffraction) and the spectra are recorded on a photographic plate or other device. It is then found that the incandescent tungsten filament emits a *continuous spectrum* of color or wavelengths over the whole of the visible region, and that the vapor lamps yield *line spectra*, indicating that the light is being emitted at only a restricted number of wavelengths. The light from the sodium lamp is very nearly monochromatic (i.e., one color), since most of the intensity lies in the two closely spaced lines at 5896 A and 5890 A known as the sodium D lines. The spectrum of the mercury lamp is somewhat more complicated, but here also three principal components at 4358 A, 5460 A, and 5780 A stand out in the visible region.

Even the apparently continuous spectrum of solar radiation is found on close examination to be interspersed with sharp black lines. These are the Fraunhofer lines, which are the result of absorption at selected wavelengths by atoms in the sun's atmosphere. They provide a good example of an *absorption spectrum* as opposed to the *emission spectrum* of the sodium and mercury vapor lamps.

As we shall see shortly, it is the atomic line spectrum which is such a valuable source of information concerning the electronic structure of the atom. The continuum emitted by an incandescent source is primarily a function of temperature and is of little value in the study of atomic structure. Fortunately, all of the principles involved in correlating line spectra with atomic structure are readily introduced through a study of the simplest of atomic spectra, that of the hydrogen atom.

(a) The hydrogen atom spectrum

The hydrogen atom absorption is shown (in Fig. 3–1) to be a series of lines in the far ultraviolet region of the electromagnetic spectrum. This series was named the *Lyman series* in honor of its discoverer. The wavelengths of the lines in this series were found by Balmer to be accurately represented by the expression

$$\lambda = \frac{n^2}{n^2 - 1} G, \tag{3-1}$$

where G is a constant and n takes the values $n = 2, 3, 4, \ldots$. The wavelength λ is not the most convenient unit for theoretical purposes, and the *Balmer formula* is more commonly written in the form

$$\nu = R\left(1 - \frac{1}{n^2}\right), \tag{3-2}$$

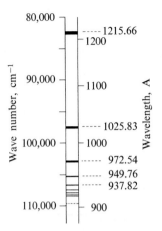

FIG. 3–1. Schematic diagram of the hydrogen atom absorption spectrum (Lyman series). The relative intensity of the lines is approximately indicated by their width, and the series limit is represented by a dashed line.

where R, the Rydberg constant, has the value 109,677.581 cm^{-1} and ν is the wave number in cm^{-1}. It is related to the wavelength and to the frequency ν' by the expressions

$$\nu = \frac{1}{\lambda} = \frac{\nu'}{c}, \tag{3-3}$$

where c is the velocity of light. Considering the simplicity of the Balmer formula [Eq. (3–2)], the one part in ten million agreement between observed and calculated wave numbers is indeed remarkable.

The Lyman series represents the total extent of the absorption by normal hydrogen atoms, but the emission spectrum, obtained when the atoms are excited in an electric discharge, is much richer. In addition to the Lyman series, one observes several other series of lines, including the Balmer series in the visible region and the Paschen, Brackett, and Pfund series in the infrared region. These series, some of which are shown in Fig. 3–2, are alike in that they can all be represented by a formula similar to that of Eq. (3–2). In fact, the whole of the hydrogen atom emission spectrum can be represented by the single formula

$$\nu = R\left(\frac{1}{n_2^2} - \frac{1}{n_1^2}\right), \tag{3-4}$$

where n_2 is constant for a given series (Lyman, $n_2 = 1$; Balmer, $n_2 = 2$; etc.), and n_1 takes the values $n_1 = n_2 + 1, n_2 + 2, n_2 + 3, \ldots$. As n_1 increases, the spacing of the lines in a series decreases, and ν approaches a limit given by

$$\nu_\infty = R/n_2^2. \tag{3-5}$$

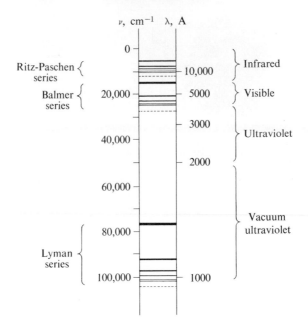

FIG. 3–2. Principal lines of the hydrogen atom emission spectrum.

Another way of expressing the results of Eq. (3–4) is to say that the wave number of any line of the hydrogen atom spectrum may be expressed as the difference between two *terms* of the type

$$T(n) = R/n^2, \tag{3-6}$$

with suitable restrictions on the value of n. That is,

$$\nu = T_2 - T_1. \tag{3-7}$$

Recognizing this, we find that the spectral lines can all be portrayed on a single diagram in which the terms are represented as horizontal lines proportionately positioned on a vertical scale of wave numbers. The values of the terms are calculated from Eq. (3–6) by letting n take the values 1, 2, 3, ... The principal lines of the atomic hydrogen spectrum are displayed in Fig. 3–3 on such a diagram. The advantage of this type of diagram lies in the emphasis that it places on the importance of the terms at the expense of the spectral lines themselves, an emphasis which will be amply justified.

(b) Spectra of other atoms

Although we have considered the spectrum of the hydrogen atom only, the principle holds quite generally that any line of an atomic spectrum can be represented as the difference of two terms. These can often be expressed in a simple

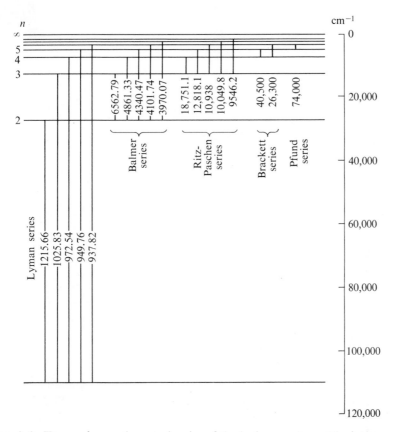

FIG. 3–3. Term values and spectral series of the hydrogen atom. The integer n on the left corresponds to the n of Eq. (3–6). Shown also are the wavelengths, in angstroms, of the principal lines.

form, such as the case of the hydrogenlike ions He^+, Li^{2+}, Be^{3+}, where the terms are given by

$$T(n) = \frac{RZ^2}{n^2} \tag{3–8}$$

and are, to a first approximation, simply those for hydrogen multiplied by the square of the atomic number Z. This means that the corresponding spectral series are identical to those of the hydrogen atom, but are shifted by a factor Z^2 to shorter wavelengths. This is seen in Table 3–1, which lists the first members of the Lyman series (Lyman α-line) for the hydrogenlike ions.

The spectra of the alkali metals both in absorption (vapors) and in emission are also similar to that of hydrogen, in that series of lines are observed. The spectra are complicated, however, by the partial overlapping of the series and, in addition,

TABLE 3–1

LYMAN α-LINES OF HYDROGENLIKE IONS

Ion	cm^{-1}	A
H	82,259.56	1215.664
He$^+$	329,188.7	303.777
Li^{2+}	740,779.8	134.993
Be^{3+}	1,317,118.1	75.924

the terms must now be represented by more complicated formulas of the type

$$T = \frac{R}{(m + p)^2},$$ (3–9)

where p is a constant for a given series. It does not serve our purpose to pursue the analysis of these spectra in further detail. It is sufficient to point out that, even in these more complicated cases, the formulas representing spectral lines can be interpreted as a difference of terms.

Actually, while the form of Eqs. (3–8) and (3–9) is correct, it is found that for exact agreement with experiment, the Rydberg constant R must be taken as a function of the mass of the nucleus. [See Section 3–4(a).]

3–2. ATOMIC STRUCTURE AND ATOMIC SPECTRA

Niels Bohr was the first to recognize that a radical departure from the concepts of classical physics was necessary to explain the Rutherford atom and correlate the knowledge of it with observed atomic spectra. In the classical case, the motion of an electron under the influence of the Coulomb force of attraction toward the nucleus may be compared with the orbital motion of the planets. The fundamental difference is that the electron and the nucleus carry electrical charges and, according to classical radiation theory, should emit radiation with the frequency of the orbital motion. The loss of energy through radiation would cause the radius of the orbit to decrease so that the electron would be expected to spiral in toward the nucleus with an ever-increasing angular frequency. The emitted radiation should, therefore, cover a wide range of continuous frequencies; in other words, the spectrum should be a continuum. It is evident that such a theory cannot explain line spectra of the type described in Section 3–1.

(a) The Bohr postulates

The Bohr theory may justifiably be considered the most important advance in the development of the theory of atomic structure. In spite of this, it does not break sufficiently with classical ideas to give the comprehensive theory required. Bohr did, however, formulate two postulates which provide the basis of modern theories. These are:

(1) *The existence of stationary states.* An atomic system may exist only in certain stationary states corresponding to discrete quantities of energy. Further, it can exist in one of these states without emitting radiation, as required by the classical theory. A transition from one state to another is accompanied by a process which either provides or disposes of the difference in energy of the two states. The absorption and emission of radiation are examples of methods through which such transitions can occur.

(2) *The Bohr frequency condition.* Since the energy levels are discrete, energy is absorbed or emitted in units known as *quanta*. The frequency of the light emitted or absorbed during the transition is given by the formula

$$h\nu' = E_2 - E_1, \tag{3–10}$$

where E_2 and E_1 are the energies of the upper and lower states, respectively, and h is Planck's constant. From Eq. (3–3), we obtain the wave number of the emitted or absorbed light as

$$\nu = \frac{\nu'}{c} = \frac{E_2}{hc} - \frac{E_1}{hc}. \tag{3–11}$$

The similarity between Eqs. (3–11) and (3–7) reveals the insight of Bohr in recognizing the correspondence between the empirically derived terms and the discrete energy levels of the atomic system. In a sense, neither of these postulates originated with Bohr. Quantization had been invoked in 1900 by Max Planck in his derivation of the emission law for glowing bodies, and Einstein, in explaining the photoelectric effect, proposed quanta of energy $= h\nu'$. The application of these ideas to atomic structure was by no means straightforward, however, and Bohr's genius lay in recognizing their applicability.

The spectral distribution of the radiation from a heated body (a tungsten lamp filament for example) is a function of the temperature to which it is heated. An iron bar will glow first a dull red, then orange, and finally white, as it is more strongly heated. Such a simple system is difficult to treat theoretically because it is not in equilibrium with its surroundings, but the radiation emitted through a small hole in a heated cavity very closely approaches that of the ideal *blackbody*, or perfect absorber, which would maintain such an equilibrium. Such radiation has been investigated experimentally, and its spectral distribution at a number of temperatures is illustrated in Fig. 3–4. Classical radiation laws predict that the density of radiant energy should be proportional to the square of the frequency, and increase without limit as the wavelength becomes shorter (the "ultraviolet catastrophe"). Planck solved this problem by postulating that the oscillators which give rise to the radiation could acquire energy only in discrete units or quanta whose size depends on the frequency of oscillation, according to

$$E = h\nu'.$$

Combined with the statistical Boltzmann distribution law, this provided a complete explanation of the observed blackbody radiation.

Planck's quantum theory received brilliant confirmation at the hands of Einstein in his explanation of the photoelectric effect. Matter, when irradiated, will eject electrons subject to the following conditions. (1) No emission will occur unless the frequency of the incident radiation exceeds a critical value known as the threshold frequency. (2) The kinetic energy of the ejected electrons depends on the frequency of the radiation, but not on its intensity. In classical terms these conditions are incomprehensible, but they find a ready explanation in Einstein's proposal that the energy of a light beam of frequency ν' exists in units of value $h\nu'$, known as *photons*. If the unit is of sufficient magnitude to overcome the forces binding the electron, it will be absorbed and the electron ejected. The kinetic energy of the electron is simply the difference in magnitude of the energy of the photon $h\nu'$ and the work done to remove the electron; that is,

$$K = h\nu' - W.$$

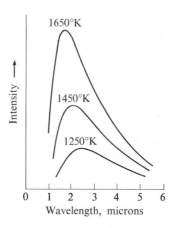

FIG. 3–4. Variations with temperature of the spectral distribution of radiation from a glowing body.

In the derivation of a quantitative theory to describe atomic energy levels, the Bohr theory was less successful. Suitable agreement was achieved between experiment and theory for the hydrogen atom and the hydrogenlike ions; but even with the modifications of Wilson and Sommerfeld, the Bohr theory failed to explain the observed energy levels of the normal helium atom and other systems. In addition, there existed dissatisfaction with the *ad hoc* nature of the quantum conditions of the Bohr theory. Bohr simply proposed, with no justification, that the electron could occupy only orbits of radius r such that the angular momentum is a constant multiple of $h/2\pi$; that is,

$$mvr = \frac{nh}{2\pi}, \qquad n = 1, 2, 3, \ldots. \tag{3–12}$$

That this is simply the mathematical formulation of the stationary state postulate may be shown in the following way.

The total energy is given by

$$E = \Phi + K = -\frac{Ze^2}{r} + \frac{mv^2}{2}. \tag{3–13}$$

Since the Coulomb attraction Ze^2/r^2 is balanced by the force of centripetal acceleration mv^2/r, we have

$$\frac{Ze^2}{r^2} = \frac{mv^2}{r}$$

or

$$mv^2 = \frac{Ze^2}{r}. \tag{3–14}$$

Thus

$$E = -\frac{Ze^2}{2r}. \tag{3–15}$$

From Eq. (3–12),

$$r = \frac{nh}{2\pi mv},$$

or, using Eq. (3–14), we get

$$r = \frac{n^2h^2}{4\pi^2 me^2 Z}.$$

Substituting in Eq. (3–15), we have the total energy as

$$E_n = -\frac{2\pi^2 me^4 Z^2}{h^2 n^2}.$$

The motion of the nucleus may be taken into account by substituting for m the reduced mass, $\mu = (Mm)/(M + m)$, where M is the mass of the nucleus. The present-day theory does not require the imposition of such arbitrary conditions to introduce quantization, but it did necessitate an even more radical break with the classical tradition. It developed simultaneously in two forms: the quantum, or matrix, mechanics of Heisenberg, Born, and Jordan and the wave mechanics formulated by Schrödinger and de Broglie. It is usually introduced in the latter form because it is both mathematically and conceptually simpler.

(b) The classical treatment of physical problems

The use of wave mechanics, even in its most elementary form, involves the introduction of concepts which are quite alien to the student with a background in classical mechanics only. Particularly is this true in the interpretation of the results of wave mechanics, for we must, to a large extent, abandon the notion of a physical picture or at least use it only in a modified form. These difficulties will be better understood if we precede our discussion of wave mechanics with an analysis of the application of classical mechanics to a simple system, the one-dimensional harmonic oscillator.

We wish to derive an explicit equation for the motion of a particle bound to an equilibrium position by a force proportional to its displacement. If x denotes the position of the particle, and the equilibrium position is taken as the origin, then the force acting on the particle is of magnitude $-kx$ where k is a *force constant*, i.e.,

$$F = -kx. \tag{3-16}$$

Newton's second law states that

$$F = m\frac{d^2x}{dt^2}, \tag{3-17}$$

and equating Eqs. (3-16) and (3-17), we obtain

$$m\frac{d^2x}{dt^2} + kx = 0. \tag{3-18}$$

This is a second-order differential equation and its solution will provide us with the desired relation in x and t. Details of the solution are unnecessary here. It is a well-known type of differential equation and may be handled by standard mathematical techniques to give a solution of the form

$$x = x_0 \sin\left[\left(\frac{k}{m}\right)^{1/2} t + \delta\right] \tag{3-19}$$

or, as it is more commonly expressed,

$$x = x_0 \sin[2\pi\nu_0' t + \delta], \tag{3-20}$$

where

$x_0 = $ the amplitude of the oscillation;

$\delta = $ a phase constant determined by the position of the particle at time $t = 0$;

$\nu_0' = $ the frequency of the oscillation.

The student should verify that Eq. (3–19) is a solution by substitution in Eq. (3–18). From Eqs. (3–19) and (3–20), we see that v_0' is related to the force constant by the equation

$$k = 4\pi^2 m v_0'^2. \tag{3–21}$$

Equation (3–20) describes the motion of the particle; to describe the system completely, we need only find an expression for the energy. By definition, the potential energy Φ and the force are related by the equation

$$-\frac{d\Phi}{dx} = F = -kx,$$

so that

$$\Phi = \frac{kx^2}{2} = 2\pi^2 m v_0'^2 x^2.$$

The total energy E of the system is the sum of the kinetic and potential energies and is thus equal to

$$E = K + \Phi = \frac{m}{2}\left(\frac{dx}{dt}\right)^2 + 2\pi^2 m v_0'^2 x^2. \tag{3–22}$$

On substituting Eq. (3–20) for x, we find that E is independent of time and has the value

$$E = 2\pi^2 m v_0'^2 x_0^2. \tag{3–23}$$

Note also that since v_0' is determined by the force constant k through Eq. (3–21), the total energy of the particle defines the amplitude x_0.

For purposes of comparison with the quantum mechanical solution to be obtained in Section 3–3(b), it is interesting to derive an expression for the probability of finding the particle at a given point x at any instant. This will be inversely proportional to the velocity of the particle, that is,

$$\text{Probability} = P = \frac{A}{v} = A\frac{dt}{dx},$$

where A is the constant of proportionality. From Eq. (3–20), we then find that

$$P = \frac{A}{2\pi v_0' x_0 \cos(2\pi v_0' t + \delta)} = \frac{A}{2\pi v_0' \sqrt{x_0^2 - x^2}}. \tag{3–24}$$

To eliminate A we simply impose the condition that the probability of finding the particle between the limits of oscillation x_0 and $-x_0$ must be unity. In other words, we shall normalize Eq. (3–24) by requiring that

$$\frac{A}{2\pi v_0'}\int_{-x_0}^{x_0}\frac{dx}{\sqrt{x_0^2 - x^2}} = 1.$$

Integration gives

$$\frac{A}{2\pi\nu_0'}\left[\left(\sin^{-1}\frac{x_0}{x_0}\right) - \left(\sin^{-1} -\frac{x_0}{x_0}\right)\right] = 1, \quad \text{and} \quad A = 2\nu_0'.$$

The desired probability distribution is therefore

$$P = \frac{1}{\pi\sqrt{x_0^2 - x^2}}. \tag{3-25}$$

Now let us examine the above problem with an emphasis on the method of solution. Stepwise it may be set down as follows: (1) We define the problem mathematically by defining the force F as $-kx$ or the potential energy Φ as $kx^2/2$. (One implies the other.) (2) We apply Newton's second law to produce the differential equation of Eq. (3–18), which describes the motion. (3) We solve the differential equation to give Eq. (3–19), which gives x explicitly as a function of t and the constants of the system. (4) We calculate the energy of the system.

Any problem in classical mechanics may be solved in a manner analogous to that outlined, but as a rule much less easily. The difficulties encountered are of two types. In step (1), the difficulty is to describe a physical system in precise mathematical terms. In the majority of cases it is not possible to do this rigorously, either because of lack of knowledge of all of the forces involved or because taking all of the effects into account would make the problem mathematically impracticable. As an alternative, one introduces assumptions regarding the relative importance of different effects and sets up a physical model which approximates the true system. Common examples from elementary mechanics are the oft-encountered "frictionless" pulley, and the neglect of air resistance in problems in ballistics. It is impossible to overstress the importance of being aware of precisely what assumptions are made in setting up a physical model.

Steps (2) and (4) are generally not problematic, although Newton's law may be more easily employed in one of the more sophisticated forms due to Lagrange or Hamilton. The solution of the differential equation in step (3) may introduce extreme difficulties of a purely mathematical nature. It is at this stage that electronic computers have proved to be of such great value.

3-3. WAVE MECHANICS

Solving a problem by using wave mechanics follows a pattern which is quite similar to that of solving a problem by classical mechanics. The problems of setting up the physical model and solving the differential equation remain, and new ones, mostly difficulties of interpretation, are introduced. They are difficulties largely because of the prejudices built up within us through daily contact with a macroscopic world ruled by classical mechanics. Newtonian mechanics should be regarded as a special case of wave mechanics applicable to macroscopic systems and events. If, on the other hand, we wish to treat atomic or molecular systems, we must use wave mechanics or one of the other forms of quantum mechanics.

In the wave-mechanical treatment of a problem, step (1), the setting up of the physical model, is essentially the same except that we may be dealing with systems more difficult to describe mathematically. The second step is different in that we can no longer apply the familiar laws of Newton but must instead make use of the *Schrödinger equation*. Step (3) will still require the solution of a differential equation but the result will no longer be an explicit function of the spatial coordinates, such as Eq. (3–20). It will be expressed rather in terms of the *wave function*, the interpretation of which is unique to quantum mechanics and will be discussed shortly. The solution of the differential equation will also supply an expression for the energy in a quantized form without the introduction of arbitrary conditions.

(a) The wave nature of the electron

The majority of optical problems, such as refraction, diffraction, etc., may be treated quite successfully by considering light to be electromagnetic waves. On the other hand, even our preliminary analysis of the hydrogen atom spectrum should convince us that light is absorbed or emitted in energy quanta, i.e., in particles which we know as photons. This does not mean that we must revive the old controversy of the corpuscular versus the undulatory theories of light. On the contrary, we know now that both theories are part of a more general theory. In some cases one theory applies, and in others we must invoke the alternative.

The dual nature of light is clearly illustrated by combining the fundamental relationships of Planck,

$$E = h\nu',\tag{3–26}$$

and of Einstein,

$$E = mc^2,\tag{3–27}$$

to give

$$h\nu' = mc^2.\tag{3–28}$$

Or, introducing $\lambda = c/\nu'$ in place of ν', we have

$$\lambda = \frac{h}{mc} = \frac{h}{p}.\tag{3–29}$$

Thus the wavelength λ is associated with photons of mass m and velocity c or momentum $p = mc$.

This relation finds experimental confirmation in the Compton effect in X-ray scattering. In essence, the experiment demonstrates that the loss of momentum suffered by an X-ray photon, when scattered by an electron, is reflected in a change in wavelength of the scattered radiation. The experiment is only possible with

X rays, where λ is small and m large enough compared with the mass of the electron to give a measurable change in wavelength.

Observations such as these led de Broglie, in 1924, to generalize and ascribe a wave nature to the electron as well. Thus he proposed that an electron of mass m and velocity v has associated with it a wavelength given by

$$\lambda = \frac{h}{mv}. \tag{3-30}$$

The wave nature of the electron was demonstrated experimentally in the work of Davisson and Germer on the diffraction of electron beams by crystal lattices. The results were analogous to those observed in the diffraction of X rays by crystals. One important consequence of Eq. (3–30) is that the existence of stationary states, i.e., states of constant momentum as proposed by Bohr, follows immediately and naturally from the existence of line spectra.

(b) The Schrödinger equation

If the electron is to behave as a wave, one might expect there to be a wave equation to describe its motion. The Schrödinger equation, similar to the second-order differential wave equation of classical mechanics, does just this. For this reason, it is often called the Schrödinger wave equation (or simply the wave equation), but such terms tend to overemphasize a similarity which is more apparent than real. The equation can be derived by analogy with the classical wave equation (see, for example, the book by Heitler listed at the end of the chapter), but this can lead to confusion in its interpretation, so we shall not pursue the analogy further here.

Schrödinger's system of mechanics has been justified in the best possible way, by experimental verification. We must accept the Schrödinger equation as a fundamental law of nature, in the same way that we accept the laws of thermodynamics and Newton's laws as applied to macroscopic systems and events.

The Schrödinger equation for stationary states of one dimension is customarily employed in the form

$$\frac{d^2\psi(x)}{dx^2} + \frac{8\pi^2 m}{h^2}[E - \Phi(x)]\psi(x) = 0. \tag{3-31}$$

The potential energy $\Phi(x)$ is formulated in terms of the spatial coordinates in precisely the same way that it would be done classically, and the differential equation is solved for the wave function $\psi(x)$ and the total energy E. The wave function $\psi(x)$ is the wave-mechanical analog of the classical solution [such as Eq. (3–19), which describes the motion of the particle], but it must be interpreted quite differently. In itself, the wave function has no direct physical significance; the square of the wave function $\psi^2(x)$ is interpreted as a probability distribution function. In other words, $\psi^2(x)$ tells us the probability of finding the particle at any given point x, but not where the particle is located at any given instant. It is characteristic of wave mechanics that we must give up hope of describing the behavior of a system in the explicit detail of classical mechanics, and resort instead to a description in terms of the probability distribution function.

Since $\psi(x)$ may be complex, the probability distribution function should properly be written $\psi(x)\psi^*(x) = |\psi(x)|^2$, where $\psi^*(x)$ is the complex conjugate of $\psi(x)$. Because of its physical significance, $|\psi(x)|^2$ must be both real and positive. The probability character of quantum-mechanical descriptions is closely related to the degree of accuracy with which the behavior of a system may be defined by quantum-mechanical methods. The degree of accuracy finds expression in the *Heisenberg uncertainty principle*, which states that it is impossible to specify or determine precisely both the position and the velocity of a particle. If Δx and Δv denote the uncertainty in x and v, respectively, then the principle is expressed in the inequality

$$\Delta x \, \Delta v \geq \frac{h}{4\pi m},$$

or as usually expressed, in terms of the momentum p,

$$\Delta x \, \Delta p \geq \frac{h}{4\pi}. \tag{3–32}$$

The uncertainty is of no consequence in macroscopic measurements because h is very small (6.6×10^{-27} erg/sec) and m is relatively large; but it is obviously of importance when considering electrons ($m = 9.0 \times 10^{-28}$ gm) and other small particles. The uncertainty principle poses interesting problems in philosophy, since it implies intrinsic limits to the precision of experimentation.

To illustrate the technique of the application of the Schrödinger equation and the interpretation of the wave function, we turn again to the one-dimensional harmonic oscillator. As in the classical treatment, we first define the physical model as a particle of mass m displaced in the x-direction from its equilibrium position at the origin and acted upon by a force of magnitude

$$F = -kx. \tag{3–33}$$

By definition,

$$-\frac{d\Phi}{dx} = F$$

and

$$\Phi = \frac{kx^2}{2}. \tag{3–34}$$

The potential energy Φ, as given by Eq. (3–34), can now be substituted in the Schrödinger equation to give the wave-mechanical differential equation of motion,

$$\frac{d^2\psi(x)}{dx^2} + \frac{8\pi^2 m}{h^2}\left[E - \frac{kx^2}{2}\right]\psi(x) = 0. \tag{3–35}$$

Solution of the equation by standard mathematical techniques shows that valid wave functions, i.e., continuous, single-valued, and finite, exist not for all values of the energy but only when E takes the values

$$E(v) = \left(\frac{kh^2}{4\pi^2 m}\right)^{1/2}(v + \tfrac{1}{2}), \tag{3–36}$$

where v (the vibrational quantum number) can take only integral values: $v = 0, 1, 2, 3, \ldots$.

It is important to note that the quantization of the energy has arisen naturally as a requirement of the system and not by an arbitrary postulate, as in the earlier Bohr theory. If we make use of the classical vibrational frequency in place of $k = 4\pi^2 m v_0'^2$, then Eq. (3–36) becomes

$$E(v) = (v + \tfrac{1}{2})hv_0', \qquad v = 0, 1, 2, 3, \ldots. \tag{3–37}$$

Each value of the vibrational quantum number v defines a separate state of the system described by the characteristic energy value and a unique wave function. Unfortunately the wave functions cannot be expressed simply in terms of elementary functions (they involve the Hermite orthogonal functions), and we must content ourselves with a graphical portrayal of their properties. Figure 3–5 shows the energy levels of the harmonic oscillator and the probability distribution functions $\psi^2(x)$ for the first few energy levels. The function $\psi^2(x)$ may be considered the wave-mechanical analog of the classical probability distribution given in Eq. (3–25), but it should be emphasized that this is the only information concerning the position of the particle that wave mechanics provides. There is no wave-mechanical equivalent for the classical expression of Eq. (3–20) which gives x as an explicit function of t.

We may summarize the application of wave mechanics to a physical problem in the following way. (1) We define the problem in precisely the same way as was done classically, by defining the force or potential energy. (2) We formulate the wave mechanical differential equation of motion by substituting Φ in the Schrödinger equation. (3) We solve the differential equation to yield the wave function $\psi(x)$ and an expression for the energy levels E.

In addition to providing a good illustration of the application of wave mechanics, the harmonic oscillator is of considerable importance in the treatment of molecular vibra-

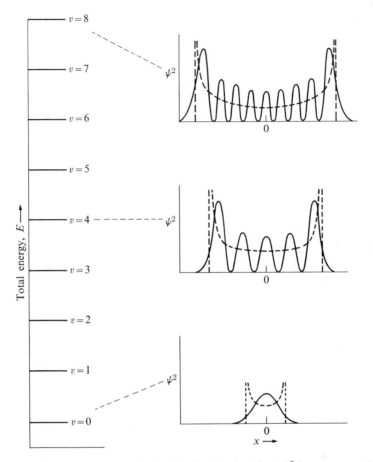

FIG. 3-5. Energy levels and probability distribution functions ψ^2 for the ground state, and some lower excited states of the one-dimensional harmonic oscillator. The dashed lines represent the classical probability distribution functions for oscillators with the same total energy.

tions. The simple model used above represents, to a first approximation, the vibration of a diatomic molecule when m is replaced by μ, the reduced mass of the two atoms. With regard to the energy, it should be noted that even in the lowest vibrational state corresponding to $v = 0$, the system has vibrational energy. This energy $E_0 = h v_0'/2$ is known as the *zero-point energy* and is an important feature of the quantum-mechanical treatment. The radiation emitted or absorbed in transitions between adjacent energy levels is of frequency v_0' and lies in the infrared region of the electromagnetic spectrum.

A further point of interest is revealed when the classical and quantum-mechanical probability distributions, for systems of the same total energy, are compared (Fig. 3-5). In the ground state ($v = 0$) the particle, according to classical mechanics, is most likely to be found at the clearly defined points marking the extremes of its motion. The wave-mechanical probability distribution, on the other hand, has a maximum at the origin.

Furthermore, there is a small but finite probability that the particle may be found outside the classical boundaries. This is a rather remarkable result, because in this region the total energy is less than the potential energy. It does not, however, imply a violation of the law of conservation of energy, because the negative kinetic energy may be explained on the basis of the uncertainty principle. Figure 3–5 also shows that as v increases, the wave-mechanical probability distribution more nearly approximates the classical one. This illustrates the conception of classical mechanics as a special case of quantum mechanics in which the difference in energy between adjacent levels is negligible compared with the absolute energy. In other words, the quantum is so small that there is, for all practical purposes, a continuum of energy levels.

3–4. WAVE MECHANICS OF THE HYDROGEN ATOM

With a knowledge of the fundamentals of wave mechanics, we may now apply this very powerful tool to gain an understanding of the electronic structure of atoms. Again we shall begin with a discussion of the hydrogen atom, since by nature it is the simplest.

The hydrogen atom consists of a nucleus of charge $+e$ which exerts a Coulomb force $-e^2/r^2$ on a single electron of charge e at a distance r. The potential energy of the electron is then $-e^2/r$, and if we take the proton as the center of our system of coordinates, then the Schrödinger equation for the system is

$$\frac{\partial^2 \psi}{\partial x^2} + \frac{\partial^2 \psi}{\partial y^2} + \frac{\partial^2 \psi}{\partial z^2} + \frac{8\pi^2 m}{h^2}\left(E + \frac{e^2}{r}\right)\psi = 0. \qquad (3\text{–}38)$$

This is simply the three-dimensional form of Eq. (3–31), in the Cartesian coordinates x, y, and z, employing partial rather than ordinary derivatives. (The electron-proton distance r can, of course, be expressed in terms of the cartesian coordinates as $r^2 = x^2 + y^2 + z^2$.) The solution of the differential equation, although somewhat involved, is again a purely mathematical problem (see any of the texts on wave or quantum mechanics listed at the end of the chapter), and we shall be concerned only with the results. This same physical model can be applied to hydrogenlike ions (He^+, Li^{2+}, Be^{3+}) simply by taking $\Phi = -Ze^2/r$, corresponding to a nuclear charge of $+Ze$, where Z is the atomic number. The more general form of Eq. (3–38) is usually written as

$$\nabla^2 \psi + \frac{8\pi^2 m}{h}\left(E + \frac{Ze^2}{r}\right)\psi = 0. \qquad (3\text{–}39)$$

The abbreviation

$$\nabla^2 = \frac{\partial^2}{\partial x^2} + \frac{\partial^2}{\partial y^2} + \frac{\partial^2}{\partial z^2} \qquad (3\text{–}40)$$

is commonly used when writing the Schrödinger and similar differential equations.

(a) Hydrogen atom energy levels

It is found that proper solutions of Eq. (3–40) exist only for values of E given by the equation

$$E(n) = -\frac{2\pi^2 m e^4 Z^2}{n^2 h^2} = -\frac{RhcZ^2}{n^2}, \qquad n = 1, 2, 3, \ldots, \qquad (3\text{–}41)$$

where R is the Rydberg constant introduced in Eq. (3–2), and n is known as the *principal quantum number*. This is precisely the same result yielded by the Bohr theory but, as noted earlier, the quantization arises naturally in the solution of the Schrödinger equation. The recognition by Bohr that the spectroscopic terms are actually energy levels is quantitatively confirmed if we put Eq. (3–41) in the form

$$T(n) = \frac{E(n)}{hc} = -\frac{RZ^2}{n^2}, \qquad (3\text{–}42)$$

which is exactly the same as the empirically derived expression of Eq. (3–8) except for the negative sign. The sign implies that the energy of the interacting electron and nucleus is lower than that of the isolated particles; this is a necessary condition, of course, if the hydrogen atom is to be stable. The lowest or *ground state* of the hydrogen atom is that for which $n = 1$ and $E(1) = -Rhc$. If the electron occupies a level for which $n > 1$, it is said to be in an *excited state*, and energy must be supplied to raise the electron from the ground state to the excited state. Such energy may be absorbed as a photon or quantum of light (thus absorption spectra), or the transition may be induced by electrical means in a gaseous discharge. Emission spectra arise from the release of energy in a transition from an excited state to a lower excited state or to the ground state. If energy equal to or greater than that given by

$$|E(1)| = RhcZ^2 \qquad (3\text{–}43)$$

is absorbed by a normal atom (i.e., in the ground state), then the electron is split off, leaving a charged nucleus. The energy $|E(1)|$ is thus known as the *ionization energy*. Any excess energy simply becomes the kinetic energy of the free particles and, since this is not quantized, we speak of a continuum of energy levels for the free particles.

The units in which the atomic energy levels are expressed vary with the origin and use of the data. For spectroscopic purposes, cm^{-1} are the most convenient, but most energy level diagrams include a scale in electron volts. The chemist's favorite unit is the calorie or more commonly the kilocalorie (kcal), and to facilitate comparison, this unit will be used consistently throughout the text. All three units are used in Fig. 3–6, and a table of conversion factors is to be found in Appendix I. The *ionization potential* is simply the potential through which the electron must be raised to free it from the nucleus, and will be equal numerically

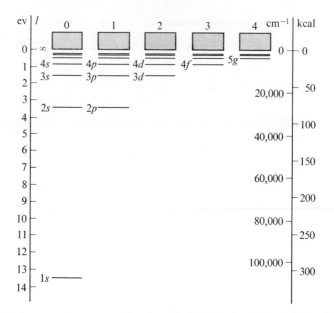

Fig. 3–6. Hydrogen atom energy levels. Each state is designated by the principal quantum number followed by a letter (*s*, *p*, *d*, *f*, *g*) to indicate the values of *l*. The zero of the energy scales corresponds to the particles of infinite separation ($n = \infty$). The shaded portion above $n = \infty$ represents the continuum of energy levels for the free particles.

to the ionization energy in electron volts. The ionization potential should, however, be expressed in volts.

Although Eq. (3–41) is in complete agreement with the energy levels of the hydrogen atom as deduced empirically from the Lyman and Balmer series, etc., a more detailed theoretical treatment reveals that the energy may take values other than those given by Eq. (3–41). In fact, the energy is determined not only by the principal quantum number *n* but also by the *azimuthal quantum number l*, which may take the values $l = 0, 1, 2, \ldots (n - 1)$. Thus, in Fig. 3–6, we see that each level is split into *n* separate levels corresponding to different values of *l*. Spectroscopically, these are designated as *s*-, *p*-, *d*-, and *f*-states for $l = 0, 1, 2$, and 3, respectively. The difference in energy for states of equal *n* but different *l* is very small for the hydrogen atom and appears in the theoretical treatment only when relativity is considered. The effect of this small difference on the spectrum is to introduce a splitting of the lines into a number of closely spaced components of nearly equal wavelength. Because of the close spacing, this fine structure is observed only when instruments of great resolving power are used.

———————

The number of fine structure components observed experimentally is much smaller than might be expected. This situation arises because the transitions are governed by selection rules, and not all possible transitions are allowed. The selection rules can be derived theoretically and show, in complete agreement with experiment, that transitions may occur only between levels where l differs by ± 1.

(b) Hydrogen atom wave functions

In the ground state ($n = 1$), the wave function of the electron is given by the fairly simple function

$$\psi_1 = \left(\frac{1}{\pi a_0^3}\right)^{1/2} e^{-r/a_0}, \tag{3–44}$$

where

$$a_0 = \frac{h^2}{4\pi^2 m e^2}. \tag{3–45}$$

The constant a_0 is of common occurrence in the theoretical study of atomic structure and is, in fact, the radius ($a_0 = 0.529$ A) of the ground-state Bohr orbit of the hydrogen atom. The probability distribution or probability density is then given by

$$\rho_1 = \psi_1^2 = \frac{1}{\pi a_0^3} e^{-2r/a_0}. \tag{3–46}$$

Since only r, the distance of the electron from the nucleus, is involved, we observe at once that the probability distribution in the ground state is spherically symmetrical about the nucleus.

The wave functions corresponding to the other states of the hydrogen atom, that is, $n > 1$, are on the whole much more complicated, so it is important at this juncture that we devise a graphical portrayal of ψ or ψ^2 which will allow us to draw qualitative conclusions without becoming involved in detail. Four possible methods (Fig. 3–7) are the following: (1) graphical plot of how ψ and ψ^2

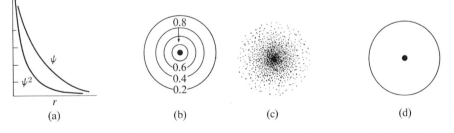

FIG. 3–7. Pictorial methods of representing wave functions: (a) simple plot, along a line, of the variation of ψ and ψ^2 with distance r of the electron from the nucleus; (b) contour map of electron density (ψ^2) in a planar section; (c) charge cloud representation with probability proportional to cloud density; (d) boundary line (surface); a single low-level contour line (surface) enclosing a high proportion of ψ or ψ^2.

TABLE 3–2(b)

RADIAL FACTORS $\psi_{n,l}(r)$ FOR HYDROGENIC WAVE FUNCTIONS

$$\psi_{1,0}(r); \quad \psi(1s) = 2\left(\frac{Z}{a_0}\right)^{3/2} e^{-\sigma/2}$$

$$\psi_{2,0}(r); \quad \psi(2s) = \frac{1}{2\sqrt{2}}\left(\frac{Z}{2a_0}\right)^{3/2} (2 - \sigma)e^{-\sigma/2}$$

$$\psi_{2,1}(r); \quad \psi(2p) = \frac{1}{2\sqrt{6}}\left(\frac{Z}{a_0}\right)^{3/2} \sigma e^{-\sigma/2}$$

$$\psi_{3,0}(r); \quad \psi(3s) = \frac{1}{9\sqrt{3}}\left(\frac{Z}{a_0}\right)^{3/2} (6 - 6\sigma + \sigma^2)e^{-\sigma/2}$$

$$\psi_{3,1}(r); \quad \psi(3p) = \frac{1}{9\sqrt{6}}\left(\frac{Z}{a_0}\right)^{3/2} (4 - \sigma)\sigma e^{-\sigma/2}$$

$$\psi_{3,2}(r); \quad \psi(3d) = \frac{1}{9\sqrt{30}}\left(\frac{Z}{a_0}\right)^{3/2} \sigma^2 e^{-\sigma/2}$$

$$\sigma = \frac{2Zr}{na_0}; \qquad a_0 = \frac{h^2}{4\pi^2 me^2}$$

TABLE 3–2(a)

ANGULAR FACTORS $\psi_l(\theta, \phi)$ FOR HYDROGENIC WAVE FUNCTIONS

$$\psi_0(\theta, \phi); \quad \psi(s) = \left(\frac{1}{4\pi}\right)^{1/2}$$

$$\psi_1(\theta, \phi); \quad \psi(p_x) = \left(\frac{3}{4\pi}\right)^{1/2} \sin\theta\cos\phi$$

$$\psi(p_y) = \left(\frac{3}{4\pi}\right)^{1/2} \sin\theta\sin\phi$$

$$\psi(p_z) = \left(\frac{3}{4\pi}\right)^{1/2} \cos\theta$$

$$\psi_2(\theta, \phi); \quad \psi(d_{z^2}) = \left(\frac{5}{16\pi}\right)^{1/2} (3\cos^2\theta - 1)$$

$$\psi(d_{zz}) = \left(\frac{15}{4\pi}\right)^{1/2} \sin\theta\cos\theta\cos\phi$$

$$\psi(d_{yz}) = \left(\frac{15}{4\pi}\right)^{1/2} \sin\theta\cos\theta\sin\phi$$

$$\psi(d_{x^2-y^2}) = \left(\frac{15}{4\pi}\right)^{1/2} \sin^2\theta\cos 2\phi$$

$$\psi(d_{xy}) = \left(\frac{15}{4\pi}\right)^{1/2} \sin^2\theta\sin 2\phi$$

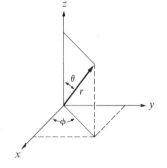

FIG. 3–8. Spherical polar coordinate system.   The wave functions of Table 3–2 are
expressed in terms of these coordinates.

vary with r; (2) contour map of a section through the distribution, showing
contours of constant ψ or ψ^2; (3) charge cloud interpretation; the density of the
cloud is proportional to ψ or ψ^2; (4) boundary surface; one of the contours of
(b) is chosen such that most of the charge (say 90%) is within the boundary.

The charge cloud interpretation in which the electron is regarded as smeared
out over space with a charge density given by ψ^2 is perhaps not a rigorously
correct interpretation of the probability distribution function.   It is nonetheless
an extremely useful concept for pictorial and qualitative purposes, and we shall
frequently make use of it. Thus, when the shape or size of a wave function or orbital
is referred to, it is to be understood that this applies to the shape or size of the
contour figure, as described in (4) above.

In the ground state then, for which the principal quantum number n equals
one, the system has energy as given by Eq. (3–44) and a wave function as shown
in Fig. 3–7.   While we no longer consider the electron to be in a fixed orbit as
proposed by Bohr, the wave function does, in a sense, describe the motion of the
electron, and Eq. (3–44) is thus referred to as an *atomic orbital* (AO).   For $n = 1$,
l can take only the value zero and, carrying over the spectroscopic notation, the
distribution of Eq. (3–44) is called an *s*-orbital and often written $\psi(1s)$.

The solution of the Schrödinger equation for the hydrogen atom is most conveniently worked out in terms of spherical polar coordinates; hence the wave
functions are usually expressed in terms of θ, ϕ, and r as shown in Fig. 3–8.   From
our point of view two important facts emerge from the theoretical treatment.
First, the wave function, corresponding to a particular state and determined by
the quantum numbers n and l, may be written as the product of two functions,
one of which, $\psi_l(\theta, \phi)$, is a function of l and the angular coordinates, and the
other, $\psi_{n,l}(r)$, a function only of n, l, and r.   In other words,

$$\psi = \psi_l(\theta, \phi)\psi_{n,l}(r).$$

Analytical expressions for the hydrogenic wave functions, for the ground and lower
excited states, are listed in Table 3–2.   Second, for the states where l is equal to

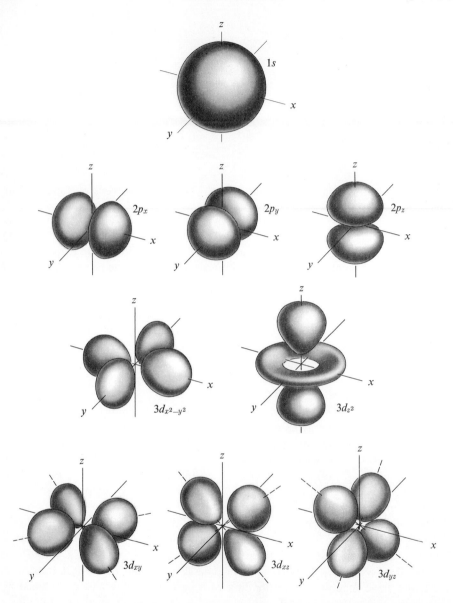

FIG. 3–9. Hydrogenic wave functions or orbitals. The d_{z^2} orbital and the p-orbitals are figures of revolution about the axis of orientation, but the lobes of the remaining d-orbitals are not circular in section. Note also that the two lobes of the p-orbitals are of different sign, and the lobes of the d-orbitals alternate in sign, i.e., opposing pairs are of the same sign. The orbitals are not drawn to scale.

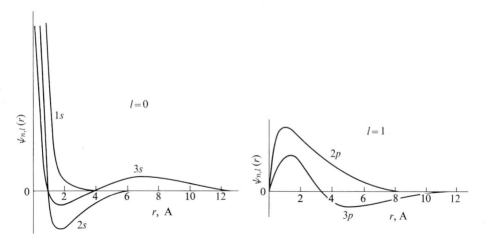

FIG. 3–10. Radial wave functions, $\psi_{n,l}(r)$ for the lower s- and p-states of hydrogen.

or greater than one, there exist several independent wave functions, the number being equal to $(2l + 1)$. Under normal conditions, i.e., in the absence of an external perturbation, orbitals of the same l-value have the same energy, and we speak of the energy level as being *degenerate*. Thus an electron in the $n = 2$, $l = 1$ energy level may occupy any one of three $2p$ orbitals of equal energy.

It can be seen that the shape and orientation of an AO will be largely determined by the angular factor of the wave function, $\psi_l(\theta, \phi)$, and since this is independent of n, we can expect orbitals of the same l but different n to be similar in shape. In later chapters, we shall be concerned with the part AO's play in molecular geometry; therefore the directional properties of these orbitals are of particular importance. To illustrate these properties, contour figures of the basic AO's ($1s$, $2p$, $3d$) are shown in Fig. 3–9. The most important feature of the radial part of the wave function is the fact that it determines the spatial extent of the orbital. This is clearly shown in Fig. 3–10, where it is seen that $\psi_{n,l}(r)$ goes to zero for progressively larger values of r, as n increases. At the same time it will be observed that for some values of n and l, $\psi_{n,l}(r)$ exhibits both maxima and minima, and the shape of the AO will be modified accordingly. In the case of the s-orbital, the oscillating nature of the radial function, for higher values of n, produces spherical shells of alternating sign, as illustrated in Fig. 3–11. There are, in fact, $n - 1$ finite values of r for which $\psi(ns)$ is equal to zero (nodes). Figure 3–11 also shows how the $3p$ orbital differs from the $2p$ as a result of the nodes in the $3p$ radial function. More important, however, is the fact that the directional properties of the angular functions are not significantly altered by the radial functions; if anything, they are more pronounced. This is true not only of the s-, p-, and d-orbitals with which we shall be concerned, but for AO's in general.

The electron charge density or probability distribution, as given by ψ^2, exhibits directional properties much like those of the orbital concerned, although the

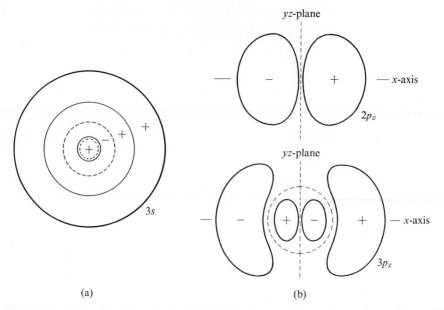

FIG. 3–11. (a) Section through $3s$ orbital, showing positive and negative regions. (b) Sections through $2p_x$ and $3p_x$ orbitals. The dashed lines represent nodes $\psi = 0$, and the solid lines are contour lines except in the case of the s-orbital, where the inner solid lines represent maxima and minima. The orbitals are not shown to scale.

shapes of nonspherical distributions are slightly different. More interesting, however, is the function $4\pi r^2[\psi_{n,l}(r)]^2$, plotted in Fig. 3–12. Since $4\pi r^2$ is the volume of the spherical shell bounded by spheres of radius r and $r + dr$, this expression gives us the probability of finding the electron within such a shell. For spherical charge distributions, $4\pi r^2[\psi_{n,l}(r)]^2$ represents the probability of finding the electron at a distance r from the nucleus. This type of plot shows, even more dramatically than the simple $[\psi_{n,l}(r)]^2$ function, that the electron is usually further from the nucleus in the higher energy states. In the case of nonspherically symmetric charge distributions, the interpretation of the $4\pi r^2[\psi_{n,l}(r)]^2$ function is not quite as straightforward. It still represents the relative probability of finding an electron at r in a given direction, however. Thus we are safe in concluding that, in the $3p$ state, for example, the electron will most often be in the outermost "doorknob" portions of the orbital.

The orbitals of Fig. 3–9 serve very well to illustrate the strongly directional character of the p- and d-orbitals, but it must be realized that these are not the only possible wave functions. For example, if $\psi(p_x)$ and $\psi(p_y)$ are solutions of the Schrödinger equation, then their sum must also be. This can be seen by substituting

$$\psi(p_x + p_y) = \psi(p_x) + \psi(p_y)$$

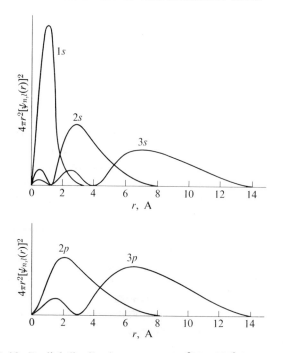

FIG. 3–12. Radial distribution curves, $4\pi r^2[\psi_{n,l}(r)]^2$ for hydrogen.

in the wave equation to give

$$\nabla^2\psi(p_x + p_y) + \frac{8\pi^2 m}{h^2}(E - \Phi)\psi(p_x + p_y) = 0, \qquad (3\text{–}47)$$

or

$$\nabla^2\psi(p_x) + \nabla^2\psi(p_y) + \frac{8\pi^2 m}{h^2}(E - \Phi)\psi(p_x)$$

$$+ \frac{8\pi^2 m}{h^2}(E - \Phi)\psi(p_y) = 0. \qquad (3\text{–}48)$$

Since $\psi(p_x)$ and $\psi(p_y)$ are each individually solutions, that is,

$$\nabla^2\psi(p_x) + \frac{8\pi^2 m}{h^2}(E - \Phi)\psi(p_x) = 0 \qquad (3\text{–}49)$$

and

$$\nabla^2\psi(p_y) + \frac{8\pi^2 m}{h^2}(E - \Phi)\psi(p_y) = 0,$$

their sum is also a solution. More generally, we can express the three possible

p-orbitals as linear combinations of $\psi(p_x)$, $\psi(p_y)$, and $\psi(p_z)$ of the form

$$\psi(p_1) = a_1\psi(p_x) + b_1\psi(p_y) + c_1\psi(p_z),$$

$$\psi(p_2) = a_2\psi(p_x) + b_2\psi(p_y) + c_2\psi(p_z), \qquad (3\text{-}50)$$

$$\psi(p_3) = a_3\psi(p_x) + b_3\psi(p_y) + c_3\psi(p_z).$$

Thus too much importance must not be attached to the orbitals of Fig. 3–9. They should be regarded, rather, as a set of standard orbitals in terms of which orbitals appropriate to the problem at hand may be expressed. This is an extremely important concept and, because of the role of AO's in chemical bonding, it will be much used in a modified and extended form in subsequent chapters. The situation whereby linear combinations of the solutions to a differential equation are themselves solutions is, of course, not unique to quantum mechanics.

At this point the student may well ask: What is the form of the true p_1 orbital of a hydrogen atom? If a hydrogen atom could be isolated in the $2p$ state, what would the charge cloud look like? In the strictest sense, these questions have no significance, because the very fact that we are looking (by means of some experimental technique) implies some form of perturbation and removes the degeneracy and the isolation. From the philosophical point of view, however, the question is capable of provoking a most interesting debate.

We shall sidestep any further discussion of free atoms because our interest lies in their behavior in the presence of other atoms in molecules; and under such conditions, the appropriate orbitals may be chosen, at least qualitatively, through other considerations. It is strange, and perhaps paradoxical, that we can make more definite statements regarding the shape of atomic orbitals when the system is complicated by the presence of an external influence than we can when it is not.

This latter statement is well illustrated by the set of wave functions which apply to the hydrogen atom in a strong magnetic field in the z-direction (Fig. 3–13). Under these conditions, the p-orbitals are complex and take the form

$$\psi(p_{+1}) = \psi(p_x) + i\psi(p_y),$$

$$\psi(p_{-1}) = \psi(p_x) - i\psi(p_y), \qquad (3\text{-}51)$$

$$\psi(p_0) = \psi(p_z),$$

where $i = \sqrt{-1}$. More important, the threefold degeneracy is removed, and each orbital corresponds to a different energy value. Each individual state is designated by a *magnetic quantum number* $m_l = 0$ and ± 1 (or more generally $m_l = -l, -l + 1, -l + 2, \ldots l - 1, l$. Thus, in a magnetic field, each level for which $l = 1$ is split into three levels of slightly different energy.

In optical spectra, the splitting of the levels produces a fine structure known as the Zeeman effect, after its discoverer. The strong influence of spectroscopists on the early development of quantum theory is also reflected in the fact that the

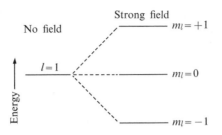

FIG. 3–13. Removal of degeneracy of p-orbitals in strong magnetic field.

orbitals of Eqs. (3–51) are commonly represented in texts on atomic structure. One final point of interest concerns the difference in energy of states of equal l but different m_l. The difference in energy is a function of the magnetic field, but is of such magnitude that transitions between these levels of energy give rise to spectra in the microwave region of the electromagnetic spectrum. The study of these spectra is thus in the realm of electron paramagnetic resonance spectroscopy.

3–5. MANY-ELECTRON ATOMS

In principle, the method of dealing with many-electron atoms, both experimentally and theoretically, is the same as that outlined for the hydrogen atom. Spectra, both optical and X-ray, are the principal source of experimental information, and although these are generally far more complicated than in the case of the hydrogen atom, a semiquantitative treatment alone usually enables us to interpret the spectrum and to derive the electronic structure. For many-electron atoms, an exact solution of the Schrödinger equation is theoretically impossible because of the electron-electron interaction terms, but a number of very effective approximate methods have been devised. The most commonly used and most accurate of these is the Hartree-Fock self-consistent-field method. The methods themselves are too involved to be discussed here, but they yield results which indicate that we may treat many-electron atoms by employing a logical extension of the method employed for the hydrogen atom.

(a) Basic principles of description

In discussing the hydrogen atom, we brought forth a number of principles which we used to describe its electronic configuration. Slightly modified, these principles also form the basis for a description of the electronic structure of many-electron atoms. Summarized briefly, they are: (1) The spatial configuration of each electron is represented by a wave function ψ, called an atomic orbital, such that ψ^2 gives the charge density at any point in the electron cloud. (2) The state of each electron is designated by a set of quantum numbers: n, the principal quantum number, which primarily determines the size of the orbital occupied;

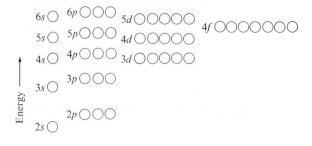

FIG. 3–14. Schematic orbital energy diagram for lighter atoms. Corresponding to each of the quantized energy levels are $2l + 1$ orbitals, represented by circles, each of which may be occupied by two electrons with paired spins (cf. Fig. 3–6).

and l, the azimuthal quantum number, which denotes the shape of the orbital. (3) Associated with each orbital is a characteristic energy, the amount of which may be determined from the Schrödinger equation. For the lighter atoms, the relative order of the energies of each type of orbital is approximately

$$1s < 2s < 2p < 3s < 3p < 4s \approx 3d,$$

as portrayed in Fig. 3–14.

As observed above, the description is qualitatively similar to that derived rigorously for the hydrogen atom. One important difference is noted, however, when the energy levels of Fig. 3–14 are compared with those of Fig. 3–6; orbitals corresponding to the same value of n no longer have the same energy. This dependence of the orbital energy on l is one of the reasons for the complicated spectra of many-electron atoms.

Figure 3–14 gives no indication of the absolute value of the energy levels; as might be expected, this absolute value is very strongly dependent on the nuclear charge. This dependence is illustrated in Fig. 3–15, which shows the variation of the energies of the lower orbitals. We shall have occasion later to discuss this diagram and the experimental source of the information on which it is based, but two points in particular should be noted now. First, we see that the upper energy levels tend to be crowded together, a fact which the logarithmic scale tends to deemphasize. The crowding is especially severe for $4s$ and $3d$ orbitals, which effectively overlap in the region of $20 < Z < 30$. Although not illustrated here, the situation with regard to the $5s$ and $4d$ and the $6s$ and $5d$ orbitals is similar. The second point to note is that the relative order of the energy levels is also a function of Z. Again, the most striking example is the energy of the $3d$ level, which is the same as the $3s$ and $3p$ levels in hydrogen, but is higher than even the

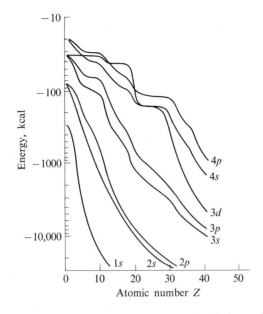

FIG. 3–15. Curves showing approximate dependence of orbital energies on atomic number. The curves are based on experimental data derived from optical and X-ray spectra.

$4s$ for the atoms with $6 < Z < 20$. It recrosses these levels at about $Z = 20$, and eventually drops to the level of the $3s$ and $3p$ orbitals. Not illustrated is the analogous situation which exists with regard to the $4d$, $5d$, and $4f$ orbitals.

(b) Electron interactions; the Pauli principle

Ignoring intranuclear phenomena which involve energies several orders of magnitude larger than those with which we are concerned here, we can say that an atom owes its coherence to the Coulomb attraction between the positively charged nucleus and the negatively charged electron or electrons. In other words, energy is released when the nucleus and the electrons interact to give a stable configuration of lower total energy. As we have seen, this energy can be accurately calculated in the case of the hydrogen atom, because there is only one interaction to be considered, that between the lone electron and the nucleus.

Turning to helium, which is still a relatively simple atom, we find that in addition to the interaction between each electron and the nucleus, the potential function must include the interaction between the two electrons; a total of three terms in all. The Schrödinger equation can still be formulated exactly, but the presence of the interaction term makes it impossible to solve the equation rigorously. With a further increase in atomic number, the potential function rapidly becomes extremely complicated, and we find that with beryllium a total of ten individual interactions must be taken into account. The need for sophisticated methods and for the application of digital computers is obvious.

On the other hand, it would appear from Fig. 3–15 that the nuclear charge is the dominant factor in determining the energy of any particular orbital; this dominance is intuitively reasonable, and may be confirmed theoretically. It is convenient therefore to regard the interelectronic interactions as a perturbation of the negative Coulomb attractive energy. The procedure followed here is certainly not wholly justified from a rigorous theoretical point of view, but is a good enough approximation for the present purpose. A rigorous approach would involve us in a discussion of electronic angular momentum and multiplet theory, which would be out of place here.

We shall regard the total interelectronic interaction energy as made up of two terms: (1) positive Coulomb repulsion energy, and (2) spin correlation energy. The first is the larger of the perturbation terms and results from the electrostatic repulsion between charged particles of the same sign. It is, of course, always positive and tends to raise the total energy of the atom. Qualitatively the effect is often described as one in which the electrons shield one another from the full nuclear charge. One speaks, for example, of the electrons in outer orbitals being shielded from the nucleus by the inner electrons, with the result that the energies of these outer orbitals tend to fall off more slowly with an increase in nuclear charge. A detailed correlation is difficult because of the irregular shape of the orbitals.

Aside from the electrostatic repulsion between electrons, there is a further effect, magnetic in origin, which we must take into account. This magnetic effect arises because, in addition to its orbital motion, the electron behaves as if it were spinning about an axis through its own center. The energy of this motion is also quantized, but the conditions are simple, for the *spin quantum number* m_s may take only the values $m_s = \pm\frac{1}{2}$. In other words, the spin axis may be aligned either parallel to or opposed to some arbitrary direction. Thus it is possible to speak of the *spin* of an electron as aligned parallel to or opposed to an applied magnetic field, but we shall most commonly be concerned with the relative spins of two electrons in close proximity.

It is important to realize that if a reference axis is not defined in some way, then it makes no sense to speak of the spin of an electron. We cannot, for example, make any statement regarding the relative spins of the electrons in two hydrogen atoms unless they come near enough together for the electrons to sense one another, i.e., to interact. We say then that the spins are *correlated*.

The results of the interaction between electron spins may be stated in a number of ways. All of these are expressions of the basic *Pauli exclusion principle* which, like the Schrödinger equation, finds its justification in the validity of the conclusions drawn from it. Mathematically the Pauli principle involves the imposition of special conditions on the wave function, but the results of these restrictions are simply stated, and are so important that the principle is more commonly found in a descriptive form. A statement of the Pauli principle that is convenient for our purposes is simply that electrons with the same spin tend to avoid one another and do not occupy the same region of space. This statement is most significant because it means that in systems of two or more electrons, the spin-spin interaction greatly influences the spatial distribution of the electrons. One immediate consequence is that no more than two electrons may occupy the same AO, and then only if their spins are different. The two electrons, with opposed spins of $+\frac{1}{2}$ and $-\frac{1}{2}$, are then said to be *paired*. Furthermore, the Pauli principle means that paired electrons, with opposed spins, exhibit greater electrostatic interaction than electrons with like spin which tend to avoid one another. This is the source of the second perturbation term: the spin-correlation energy or *exchange energy*. (If we wished to be pedantic, we might regard this effect as a perturbation of the perturbation.) The spin-correlation energy is positive when the electrons are paired and negative when the spins are the same.

Another common way of expressing the Pauli exclusion principle is to state that no two electrons in any atom may have precisely the same set of quantum numbers (n, l, m_l, m_s). This statement of the principle is also valid; but, strictly speaking, it is only so when all of the quantum numbers are defined. In the relatively simple case of hydrogen, for example, we have seen that the presence of a magnetic field is necessary to remove the degeneracy of the three p-orbitals and make m_l a "good" quantum number. In fact, in a strong magnetic field, each of the levels designated by the quantum number m_l is further split into two levels defined by $m_s = \pm\frac{1}{2}$. When the magnetic field is weak or nonexistent, m_l and m_s are replaced by another quantum number defined by quantized vector sums of m_l and m_s. The situation becomes much more involved when polyelectronic atoms are considered.

Both of these interelectronic interactions are, of course, reflected in the experimental orbital energies of Fig. 3–15. It must be kept in mind, however, that the scale of the plot does not permit the showing of a number of small but important irregularities. The figure does show trends with reasonable precision, and the deviations, which are associated with unique configurations, will be dealt with in succeeding sections.

(c) The Aufbau principle and the periodic table

We now have at our command sufficient knowledge of the scheme of AO's and electronic interactions to derive, in a descriptive form, the electronic structure of the ground states of the atoms. This is done by an *aufbau* (building-up) process in which extranuclear electrons will be added to the appropriate orbitals as required in order to balance the nuclear charge.

Direct experimental confirmation of these structures lies in the analysis of atomic spectra, but these spectra are unfortunately too complex to discuss here. We shall, however, find a correlation between these structures and the chemical properties of the atoms which will leave little doubt as to the validity of the electronic configurations. Indeed, we shall see that the periodicity of these properties, as expressed in the periodic table, is a direct result of the electronic configurations.

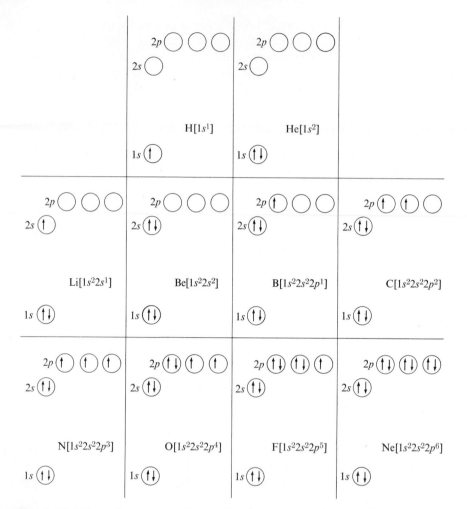

FIG. 3–16. Schematic representation of the electronic structures of the ground states of the elements of the first and second periods. The relative spins of the electrons are indicated by the directions of the small arrows.

In the ground state, the single orbital electron of hydrogen occupies a $1s$ orbital, and the electronic structure is designated H[$1s$]. The two orbital electrons of helium also occupy the $1s$ orbital, but their spins are opposed, in accordance with the Pauli principle. Despite electrostatic repulsion between the electrons, the energy is not raised sufficiently to make single occupancy of the $1s$ and $2s$ orbitals more profitable energetically. The electronic structure of helium is therefore He[$1s^2$]. This and the structures of the remaining elements of the first two periods are illustrated in Fig. 3–16, with arrows to indicate the spins of the electrons. Since the $1s$ orbital will accept no more electrons, we say that, in the case of helium, the $1s$ subshell is filled. Further, since it is the only subshell for $n = 1$ (that is, l can only be zero), the K-shell is completely filled or closed.

In a similar way the structures of lithium and beryllium are derived by adding electrons to the $2s$ orbital, as illustrated in Fig. 3–16. This does not fill the L $(n = 2)$ shell, however, since there remain the $2p$ orbitals. Thus the configuration of boron is obtained by placing the next electron in a $2p$ orbital to give the configuration $B[1s^2 2s^2 2p^1]$. The additional electron in the carbon structure also goes into a p-orbital, but now there is a choice because of the threefold degeneracy. Do both p-electrons occupy the same orbital, or are they in different ones? If they occupy different orbitals, then what are their relative spins? In fact, they do occupy different orbitals, and their spins are the same, i.e., parallel, which is a situation that can be explained on the basis of interelectronic interactions. When we recall our previous discussion of interelectronic interactions, it is apparent that the occupation of different orbitals by the electrons minimizes the repulsive Coulomb interaction energy. Furthermore, with spins aligned, the spin correlation energy is favorable, i.e., negative.

We have, then, two rules to apply when placing electrons in degenerate orbitals. These are as follows: (1) electrons tend, as far as possible, to avoid being in the same orbital; (2) unpaired electrons in degenerate orbitals are in their lowest energy state when their spins are parallel. Previously, similar rules, known as *Hund's rules*, were derived empirically in the analysis of optical spectra.

Thus carbon will have the structure $C[1s^2 2s^2 2p^1 2p^1]$ and nitrogen will be $N[1s^2 2s^2 2p^1 2p^1 2p^1]$, with all the $2p$ orbitals singly occupied. Further electrons which must be added in oxygen, fluorine, and neon will also go into the p-orbitals, but with paired spins. Neon with the configuration $Ne[1s^2 2s^2 2p^6]$ has both the $2s$ and the $2p$ subshells filled, and thus also a completely filled L-shell. This marks the end of the second period. The electronic configurations of the atoms of the third period are derived in an analogous way, by the filling of the $3s$ and $3p$ orbitals. Note, however, that argon does not have a filled M-shell because the $3d$ orbitals remain empty (see Fig. 3–15).

At this point it is important to clarify the meaning of the orbital energies displayed in Fig. 3–15. From an experimental point of view, the orbital energy may be defined as the energy required to remove one electron in the orbital from the neutral atom; it is, therefore, often termed a *one-electron orbital energy*. From a physical point of view, then, Fig. 3–15 tells us the relative energy of the orbitals in the neutral atom with the ground-state configuration. On the other hand, the sum of the terms formed by multiplying each of these orbital energies by the number of electrons in the orbitals does not constitute the total electronic energy of the neutral atom. This statement is made abundantly clear by considering the reverse of the building-up process, i.e., successive ionization. In the case of beryllium, for example, Table 3–3 indicates that 215 kcal are required to remove the first $2s$ electron; 420 kcal the second; 3550 kcal the first $1s$ electron and 5020 kcal the last electron. Because of the decreased shielding with ionization, it is more difficult to remove an electron from a positive ion than from a neutral atom.

TABLE 3–3

IONIZATION ENERGIES OF GASEOUS ATOMS (kcal/mole; 0°K)*

Atomic number	Element	I	II	III	IV
1	H	313.5			
2	He	566.9	1254		
3	Li	124.3	1744	2823	
4	Be	214.9	419.9	3548	5020
5	B	191.3	580.0	874.5	5980
6	C	259.6	562.2	1104	1487
7	N	335.1	682.8	1094	1786
8	O	314.0	810.6	1267	1785
9	F	401.8	806.7	1445	2012
10	Ne	497.2	947.2	1500	2241
11	Na	118.5	1091	1652	2280
12	Mg	176.3	346.6	1848	2521
13	Al	138.0	434.1	655.9	2767
14	Si	187.9	376.8	771.7	1041
15	P	254	453.2	695.5	1184
16	S	238.9	540	807	1091
17	Cl	300.0	548.9	920.2	1230
18	Ar	363.4	637.0	943.3	1379
19	K	100.1	733.6	1100	1405
20	Ca	140.9	273.8	1181	1550
21	Sc	151.3	297.3	570.8	1700
22	Ti	158	314.3	649.0	997.2
23	V	155	328	685	1100
24	Cr	156.0	380.3	713.8	1140
25	Mn	171.4	360.7	777.0	
26	Fe	182	373.2	706.7	
27	Co	181	393.2	772.4	
28	Ni	176.0	418.6	810.9	
29	Cu	178.1	467.9	849.4	
30	Zn	216.6	414.2	915.6	
31	Ga	138	473.0	708.0	1480
32	Ge	182	367.4	789.0	1050
33	As	226	466	653	1160
34	Se	225	496	738	989
35	Br	273.0	498	828	
36	Kr	322.8	566.4	851	
37	Rb	96.31	634	920	

* To a good approximation, the values at 298°K may be obtained
by adding 1.5 kcal per electron removed to the listed values.

TABLE 3–3   (*Continued*)

IONIZATION ENERGIES OF GASEOUS ATOMS (kcal/mole; 0°K)

Atomic number	Element	I	II	III	IV
38	Sr	131.3	254.3		1300
39	Y	147	282.1	473	
40	Zr	158	302.8	530.0	791.8
41	Nb	158.7	330.3	579.8	883
42	Mo	164	372.5	625.7	1070
43	Tc	168	351.9		
44	Ru	169.8	386.5	656.4	
45	Rh	172	416.7	716.1	
46	Pd	192	447.9	759.2	
47	Ag	174.7	495.4	803.1	
48	Cd	207.4	389.9	864.2	
49	In	133.4	435.0	646.5	1250
50	Sn	169.3	337.4	703.2	939.1
51	Sb	199.2	380	583	1020
52	Te	208	429	720	880
53	I	241.1	440.3		
54	Xe	279.7	489	740	
55	Cs	89.78	579		
56	Ba	120.2	230.7		
57	La	129	263.6	442.1	
72	Hf	160	344		
73	Ta	182	374		
74	W	184	408		
75	Re	182	383		
76	Os	200	390		
77	Ir	200			
78	Pt	210	4280		
79	Au	213	473		
80	Hg	240.5	432.5	789	
81	Tl	140.8	470.9	687	1170
82	Pb	171.0	346.6	736.4	975.8
83	Bi	168.1	384.7	589.5	1040
84	Po	194			
85	At				
86	Rn	247.8			
87	Fr				
88	Ra	121.7	234.0		
89	Ac	160	279		

The *total electronic energy* of the beryllium atom is then given by the sum of the four ionization energies or about 9200 kcal. In contrast, using the one-electron orbital energies, one obtains $(2 \times 2800) + (2 \times 220)$ or about 6000 kcal. The difference represents the total interaction energy of the electrons.

Turning to the fourth period, we see in Fig. 3–16 that for potassium and calcium the 4s level is lower than the 3d, and one finds accordingly that these elements have the configurations K[Ne $3s^2 3p^6 4s^1$] and Ca[Ne $3s^2 3p^6 4s^2$]; the symbol Ne represents the neon configuration. For the next ten elements the energies of the 4s and 3d levels are very close together and somewhat lower than that of the 4p level. Thus the first row of transition elements results from the filling of the 3d orbitals. The first transition series presents some interesting problems, but it is clear that over this group of elements, the 3d level gradually drops below the 4s. Thus at the beginning of the series the 4s level is below the 3d, and scandium has the electronic structure Sc[Ne $3s^2 3p^6 3d^1 4s^2$], while copper has the configuration Cu[Ne $3s^2 3p^6 3d^{10} 4s^1$], indicating a reversal of order.

For the middle elements the situation is more complex, and it is noted that chromium, for example, has the configuration Cr[Ne $3s^2 3p^6 3d^5 4s^1$]. It would appear that in this case there is an accidental degeneracy of the 3d and 4s levels, and that Coulombic repulsion and spin correlation determine the configuration. On the other hand, manganese, iron, and cobalt have the $4s^2$ configuration. It is indeed true, as Slater points out, that the question of the relative stability of the 3d and 4s electrons in the iron group is a very subtle one. Under these circumstances, the situation is best understood by comparing the energies of the various possible configurations or states, particularly in regard to the electronic structure of ions. Such information, experimentally derived, is given in the graphs of Fig. 3–17 for titanium and iron.

In the case of titanium, the graphs confirm that the $3d^2 4s^2$ configuration is the more stable one for the ground state. This implies, as stated above, that the 4s level is below the 3d. For iron, on the other hand, there is little difference in energy between the $3d^6 4s^2$ and $3d^7 4s$ states, although the former is the normal ground-state configuration.

Far more interesting are the structures of the positive ions, for it is seen that the lowest energy state for Ti$^+$ is the $3d^2 4s$. Thus, although the 4s level is the more stable in the neutral atom, it is a 4s electron which is removed in the ionization process. This apparent paradox is explained if, in the ion, the 3d level drops to the level of the 4s; that is, if they accidentally become degenerate. The situation is even more dramatic in the case of iron, where the ground-state configuration of Fe$^+$ is $3d^7$, and a complete reversal of order occurs. The doubly positive ions Fe^{2+} and Te^{2+} both exhibit configurations in which only d-orbitals are filled, there being little question that here the d-orbitals are definitely at lower energy than the 4s. It is, in fact, quite generally true that the doubly positive transition metal ions have ground-state configurations in which only d-orbitals are occupied. Both increasing nuclear charge and increasing net ionic charge have the effect

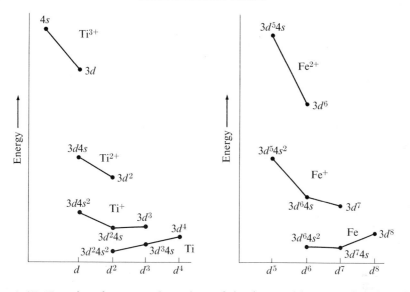

FIG. 3–17. Energies of some configurations of titanium and iron as a function of the number of d-electrons.

of making the energy levels more hydrogenic in order. With zinc, the $4s$ subshell is refilled, and the structures of the remaining elements of the fourth period are derived by regular filling of the $4p$ orbitals.

The procedure for the building up of the configurations of the remaining elements (Table 3–4) is now clear, and a detailed discussion is unnecessary. The second and third rows of the transition elements result, as the first, from the filling of d-orbitals. The same general considerations apply with regard to the relative energy of the d- and the adjacent s-levels, but note that the configurations are not the direct analogs of those of the first transition series. A new feature arises with the filling of the $4f$ orbitals to give the series of rare earths, or lanthanides, but the pattern is straightforward. The configurations of some of the heavier atoms are somewhat uncertain because of the proximity of the energy levels involved.

(d) Wave functions for many-electron atoms

Even when approximate methods are employed, the evaluation of wave functions for many-electron atoms is a lengthy chore. Despite this, the wave functions for many of the lighter atoms and ions have been evaluated, more recently with the aid of digital computers. Fortunately, there is no need for us to consider each atom separately, because in all cases the wave functions obtained are very similar to the hydrogenic functions discussed in Section 3–4(b). In fact, to a good approximation, the dependence on angle is exactly the same, and the only difference is in the radial function. In other words, the orbitals have the same shape and differ only in size.

TABLE 3–4. LONG FORM OF PERIODIC TABLE,
SHOWING GROUND-STATE CONFIGURATIONS OF THE ELEMENTS

First period	1 H $1s^1$									
Second period He +	3 Li $2s^1$	4 Be $2s^2$								
Third period Ne +	11 Na $3s^1$	12 Mg $3s^2$								
Fourth period Ar +	19 K $4s^1$	20 Ca $4s^2$	21 Sc $4s^2 3d^1$	22 Ti $4s^2 3d^2$	23 V $4s^2 3d^3$	24 Cr $4s^1 3d^5$	25 Mn $4s^2 3d^5$	26 Fe $4s^2 3d^6$	27 Co $4s^2 3d^7$	28 Ni $4s^2 3d^8$
Fifth period Kr +	37 Rb $5s^1$	38 Sr $5s^2$	39 Y $5s^2 4d^1$	40 Zr $5s^2 4d^2$	41 Nb $5s^1 4d^4$	42 Mo $5s^1 4d^5$	43 Tc $5s^2 4d^5$	44 Ru $5s^1 4d^7$	45 Rh $5s^1 4d^8$	46 Pd $4d^{10}$
Sixth period Xe +	55 Cs $6s^1$	56 Ba $6s^2$	57* La $6s^2 5d^1$	72 Hf $6s^2 4f^{14} 5d^2$	73 Ta $6s^2 4f^{14} 5d^3$	74 W $6s^2 4f^{14} 5d^4$	75 Re $6s^2 4f^{14} 5d^5$	76 Os $6s^2 4f^{14} 5d^6$	77 Ir $6s^2 4f^{14} 5d^7$	78 Pt $6s^1 4f^{14} 5d^9$
Seventh period Rn +	87 Fr $7s^1$	88 Ra $7s^2$	89† Ac $7s^2 6d^1$							

*Rare earths or Lanthanides Xe +	57 La $6s^2 5d^1$	58 Ce $6s^2 5d^1 4f^1$	59 Pr $6s^2 5d^1 4f^2$	60 Nd $6s^2 5d^1 4f^3$	61 Pm $6s^2 5d^1 4f^4$

†Actinides Rn +	89 Ac $7s^2 6d^1$	90 Th $7s^2 6d^2$	91 Pa $7s^2 6d^1 5f^2$	92 U $7s^2 6d^1 5f^3$	93 Np $7s^2 6d^1 5f^4$

						2 He $1s^2$
5 B $2s^22p^1$	6 C $2s^22p^2$	7 N $2s^22p^3$	8 O $2s^22p^4$	9 F $2s^22p^5$	10 Ne $2s^22p^6$
13 Al $3s^23p^1$	14 Si $3s^23p^2$	15 P $3s^23p^3$	16 S $3s^23p^4$	17 Cl $3s^23p^5$	18 Ar $3s^23p^6$

29 Cu $4s^13d^{10}$	30 Zn $4s^23d^{10}$	31 Ga $4s^23d^{10}4p^1$	32 Ge $4s^23d^{10}4p^2$	33 As $4s^23d^{10}4p^3$	34 Se $4s^23d^{10}4p^4$	35 Br $4s^23d^{10}4p^5$	36 Kr $4s^23d^{10}4p^6$
47 Ag $5s^14d^{10}$	48 Cd $5s^24d^{10}$	49 In $5s^24d^{10}5p^1$	50 Sn $5s^24d^{10}5p^2$	51 Sb $5s^24d^{10}5p^3$	52 Te $5s^24d^{10}5p^4$	53 I $5s^24d^{10}5p^5$	54 Xe $5s^24d^{10}5p^6$
79 Au $4f^{14}5d^{10}$	80 Hg $6s^24f^{14}5d^{10}$	81 Tl $6s^24f^{14}5d^{10}6p^1$	82 Pb $6s^24f^{14}5d^{10}6p^2$	83 Bi $6s^24f^{14}5d^{10}6p^3$	84 Po $6s^24f^{14}5d^{10}6p^4$	85 At $6s^24f^{14}5d^{10}6p^5$	86 Rn $6s^24f^{14}5d^{10}6p^5$

62 Sm $5d^14f^5$	63 Eu $6s^25d^14f^6$	64 Gd $6s^25d^14f^7$	65 Tb $6s^25d^14f^8$	66 Dy $6s^25d^14f^9$	67 Ho $6s^25d^14f^{10}$	68 Er $6s^25d^14f^{11}$	69 Tm $6s^25d^14f^{12}$	70 Yb $6s^25d^14f^{13}$	71 Lu $6s^25d^14f^{14}$
94 Pu $7s^25f^6$	95 Am $7s^25f^7$	96 Cm $7s^26d^15f^7$	97 Bk $7s^26d^15f^8$	98 Cf $7s^25f^{10}$	99 Es $7s^25f^{11}$	100 Fm $7s^25f^{12}$	101 Md $7s^25f^{13}$	102 No $7s^25f^{14}$	103 Lw $7s^26d^15f^{14}$

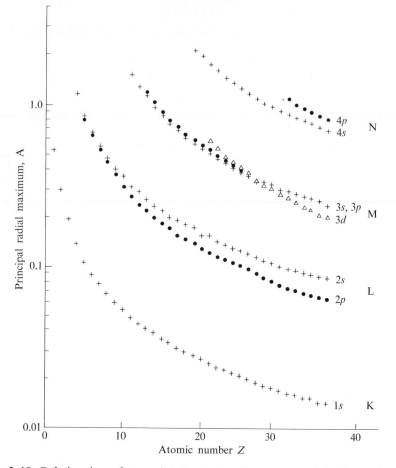

FIG. 3–18. Relative sizes of ground-state atoms. The curves actually depict the position of the main maxima of the radial distribution curves. (See Fig. 3–12.)

The problem of defining the absolute size of an atom or ion was mentioned previously (Section 2–5). In spite of the problem of defining size, a good indication of the relative size of any particular orbital is the radius at which the radial charge density $4\pi r^2[\psi_{n,l}(r)]^2$ has its maximum. Curves analogous to those of Fig. 3–12 for hydrogen provide the information which is conveniently summarized in Fig. 3–18.

There are a number of interesting observations regarding Fig. 3–18. First, curves showing radial maxima for orbitals with the same principal quantum number are very close together. This confirms our previous assertion that the size of an orbital is determined primarily by the value of n and, incidentally, justifies our terminology when we refer to orbitals of the same principal quantum number as "shells." The contraction of a given orbital or shell as the nuclear charge increases is to be expected because of the Coulomb forces involved, and this contraction correlates in a general way with the decreasing energy of these inner orbitals.

The relationship may in fact be expressed quantitatively by a function of the type $r_{max} = C/Z_{eff}$. The effective nuclear charge, Z_{eff}, may in turn be written $Z_{eff} = Z - S$, where S is a screening constant depending on the number of electrons present and the orbitals they occupy. The principle is the same as that embodied in the discussion of ionization energies in the following section, but the screening constants are different.

Qualitatively, it can be seen from the logarithmic scale that there is, for the $1s$ orbital, for example, a tenfold reduction in size in passing from hydrogen (0.53 A) to neon (0.055 A). We note also that in neon itself, the $1s$ orbital or K-shell is much smaller than the L-shell (0.37 A) containing the outer electrons. The rough parallelism of the curves for different shells tells us that this difference in size occurs for all atoms in keeping with the much lower energies of the electrons in the inner shells (compare Fig. 3–15). Again, however, the odd behavior of the d-electrons provides an exception to the rule. Thus, the $3d$ subshell, while approximately the same as the $3s$ and $3p$ orbitals in radius for the first transition series, has about the same energy as the much larger $4s$ orbital, because of the very different shape of the $4s$ and $3d$ orbitals.

Finally, it seems reasonable to expect that the sizes of atoms and ions will be determined by the sizes of the outermost orbitals involved. Thus, referring to the periodic table, we should find, in a given row or period where only a single shell is being filled, a steady contraction when we go from left to right. On the other hand, the beginning of each period involves a new shell, so that a gradual increase

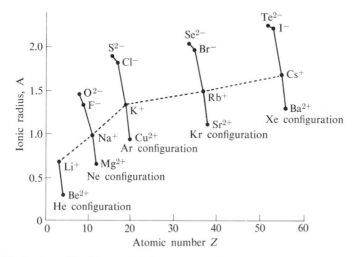

FIG. 3–19. Ionic radii of ions with inert gas configurations, as a function of atomic number. Solid lines follow isoelectronic series and show the contraction with increasing nuclear charge. The dashed line shows the influence of additional shells.

in size with an increase in atomic number is predicted in a column or group. We shall see, in later chapters, that these predictions are in complete accord, qualitatively, with atomic radii empirically derived from molecular structure investigations.

Similar arguments apply to the ionic radii defined in Section 2–3. The ions listed in Table 2–3 which have inert gas configurations are most conveniently considered in isoelectronic series, as in Fig. 3–19. Qualitatively, two effects are noticed. The variation in size with inert gas configuration, e.g., in the series Li^+, Na^+, K^+, Rb^+, Cs^+ is of course analogous to the effect in a group of the periodic table. Within a given isoelectronic series, i.e., for a particular inert gas configuration, the radius falls off rapidly with an increase in atomic number, due to the contraction of the orbitals. The relationship is not a simple one, since both the nuclear charge and the net charge on the ion, i.e., the number of electrons removed, must be taken into account. Pauling's method for deriving ionic radii takes both factors into account in a semi-empirical manner (Section 2–3).

A brief outline of the *Hartree self-consistent field* (*SCF*) *method* for treating many-electron atoms will serve to indicate the magnitude of the calculations involved. In essence, Hartree's SCF method involves solving the Schrödinger equation individually for each electron moving in the combined potential field of the nucleus and of all other electrons. Consideration of the instantaneous interactions with all of the remaining electrons poses an insoluble problem, which is sidestepped by assuming the electron to be acted upon by the average charge distribution of the other electrons. In order to obtain this average in the first place, we guess plausible wave functions and sum the individual charge distributions $\sum \psi^2$. Such a summation gives us a potential which is very nearly symmetrical spherically, and in this approximation the potential is made completely spherical by the fact that we take a spherical average. It is possible for us to solve the wave equation with this potential, and thus to provide what might be termed a "first improved" wave function for the electron concerned. This new function may then be used along with the other trial wave functions to obtain a first improved wave function for a second electron, and so on. Repetition of the process provides a complete set of first improved wave functions or orbitals.

Further improvement in the computed orbitals results when a second cycle of calculations is carried out to give a set of second improved orbitals. In fact, the technique is repeated for a number of cycles until, to a good approximation, there is no further change in the wave functions. The set of orbitals is then said to be self-consistent. Finally, it should be noted that the similarity in shape between these orbitals and the hydrogenic wave functions is not an accident, but is a direct result of the imposition of the spherical potential in the Hartree method.

(e) Electronic configuration and periodic properties

In the process of deriving the electronic configurations of the elements through the building-up method of Section 3–5(c), we made it clear that a correlation existed between these configurations and the periodic table. This being so, it should be possible, on the basis of electronic structure, to explain the characteristic properties of the elements which led to the formulation of the periodic table. To a large extent such an explanation is possible, at least qualitatively, and although in some cases a detailed explanation is lacking, there is no doubt that the gross chemical properties are well understood.

Much of our discussion will center around the energy levels of Fig. 3–15, and the reader is cautioned again to note the logarithmic energy scale and the wide disparity between the energies of the inner and outer shells. The single $3s$ electron in the outer M-shell of sodium, for example, lies at -119 kcal, and the energies of the inner L- and K-shells are about -1000 kcal and $-25,000$ kcal, respectively. Because of this large difference in energy, it is usually only the outermost electrons which participate in bonding, so that the electrons in the outer shell are commonly known as *valence electrons*. That the phenomenon is a general one can be quickly verified by an examination of the first ionization energies of Table 3–3. All but one of these are less than 500 kcal and, if the inert gases are excluded, 400 kcal is the limit.

The relationship between the electronic configuration and orbital energy levels can be expressed quantitatively by a function of the type

$$E = \frac{(Z - S)^2 C}{n^2} ,$$

where C is a constant and n is the principal quantum number. This is an empirical relationship similar to Eq. (3–41) for hydrogenlike ions, with the nuclear charge Z replaced by an effective nuclear charge $(Z - S)$. The screening constants of individual electrons are allotted according to their classifications as inner-shell or same-shell electrons. The expression is a surprisingly accurate one, and is useful in the estimation of ionization energies (see Problem 3–9, for example).

The disparity in energy of the inner and outer shells is also reflected in the experimental source of the data. Thus optical spectra, in the visible and ultraviolet regions, arise from transitions involving the outermost electrons and provide information concerning the normally unoccupied upper energy levels. On the other hand, transitions between the inner shells involve large changes in energy and the correspondingly short wavelengths characteristic of X-radiation. In sodium, for example, if a $1s$ electron is removed by electron bombardment, then an electron will drop down from the $2p$ level, releasing 24,000 kcal or emitting X rays with a wavelength of 11.8 A. The distinction in terms of optical and X-ray spectra is, of course, an arbitrary one, since spectra of intermediate wavelength are also emitted when the quanta are of the appropriate size. Experimental measurements in the intermediate region (vacuum ultraviolet) are very difficult because of atmospheric absorption. Even in the more accessible regions the normal complexities are increased by the presence of the spectra of one or more ions, and in some cases, by double excitation.

The first ionization energies have already been mentioned briefly, but as Fig. 3–20 shows, they exhibit marked periodic properties which merit further attention.

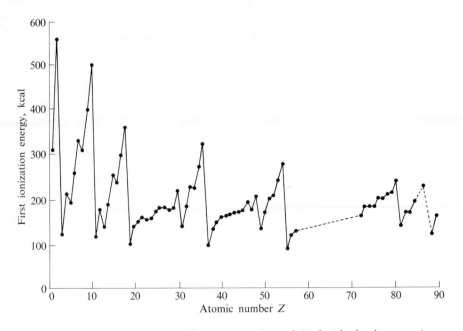

FIG. 3–20. Periodic variations, with atomic number, of the first ionization energies.

These properties are a direct result of the periodicity of the electronic configurations and the regular variation of the orbital energy levels. Thus the ionization
energy of helium is much larger than that of hydrogen because of the sharp drop
in the $1s$ orbital energy occasioned by the doubling of the nuclear charge. In
contrast, the single $2s$ electron of lithium at the beginning of the second period is
removed relatively easily because it is farther from the nucleus and is shielded
from the full charge of the nucleus by the $1s$ electrons in the inner shell.

With increasing atomic number, the ionization energy rises to another maximum
with neon; but despite the fivefold increase in nuclear charge, the ionization
energy of neon is still less than that of helium. One of the reasons for this disparity
is the shielding by the inner electrons, which manifests itself in the more gradual
fall-off of the $2s$ and $2p$ orbital energies. Specific electronic interactions also play
a part. For example, although the three $2p$ electrons in nitrogen are in separate
orbitals, the remaining three in oxygen, fluorine, and neon must go into orbitals
which already contain one electron. The additional repulsion energy and the
adverse spin correlation energy are sufficient to make the ionization energy of
oxygen less than that of nitrogen. Another break in the steady increase occurs at
boron, but this is simply because the $2p$ orbital energy is slightly above that of
the $2s$.

Variations in the ionization energies of the third period may be explained in a
similar fashion, except that here the shielding effects are even more pronounced
because of the additional filled inner shell. As a consequence, the maximum at

argon is still lower than that for the preceding inert gas, neon. In the eighteen-membered fourth period, normal variations are observed in the ionization energies of the first two and last six elements but, as might be expected since d-orbitals are involved, the ionization energies of the transition elements behave differently. As in the case of the electronic configurations, the proximity of the $3d$ and $4s$ orbital energies poses some interesting but subtle questions. The fact that the order of levels may be different in the ion and in the neutral atom, plus the fact that there is a gradual change of role of the d-orbital from an outer to an inner orbital, accounts for the observed variation. In such cases, it is more suitable to think of the ionization energy as the difference in the energy of the ion and the energy of the neutral atom, but a complete discussion is beyond the scope of this text.

Our discussion of the periodic variations of ionization energies would lead us to expect similar behavior on the part of the electron affinities. It is pertinent here to recall that the definition of electron affinity as the exothermicity of the reaction

$$X + e \rightarrow X^-, \qquad E(X) = -\Delta H, \tag{3-52}$$

is contrary to the normal convention whereby the release of energy in a reaction is indicated by a negative sign. (See also Section 4-1.) This unfortunate practice has become too firmly established to be changed without a great deal of confusion, but the difficulty may be eliminated if we regard these as ionization energies of negative ions. Thus the data of Table 3-5 may be interpreted in the same way as that of Table 3-4.

For the most part the ionization energies of the negative ions correlate in the expected manner with those of the neutral atoms. The negative ions of the hydrogen and the alkali metals have low ionization energies or electron affinities, for example, while those of the halide ions are much larger.

An interesting departure from the general rule is that the electron affinities of the second-period elements are all lower than the third-period members of the same group; that is, $E(\text{Li}) < E(\text{Na})$, $E(\text{O}) < E(\text{S})$, and $E(\text{F}) < E(\text{Cl})$. There seems to be no adequate explanation for this phenomenon at the present time. The fact that relatively few electron affinities are listed in Table 3-5 is due to the extreme experimental difficulties encountered in making these measurements. In addition, few of the methods yield an electron affinity directly, and some of the assumptions involved in the final calculations may lead to rather large errors.

Up to this point we have discussed a number of the properties of the elements, properties which are related to electronic configuration and which exhibit a periodic variation. All of these properties, including ionization energy, electron affinity, and others, are instrumental in formulating the overall chemical behavior of the elements. In fact, one of the major aims of this book is to explain chemical properties in these terms, and to bring to light the various correlations which exist. Most of this material will be the subject of study in later chapters, but a few of the principal elemental characteristics, probably already familiar to the student, will be discussed now.

TABLE 3–5

IONIZATION ENERGIES OF SOME GASEOUS NEGATIVE IONS
(kcal/mole, 0°K)*

Ion	I	II
H$^-$	17.2	
Li$^-$	12.5	
Na$^-$	28	
K$^-$	16	
Hg$^-$	35.4	
O^{2-}	-189	33
S^{2-}	-135	55
F$^-$	80.6	
Cl$^-$	85.3	
Br$^-$	80.2	
I$^-$	73.0	

* These values may be corrected to
298°K by adding 1.5 kcal/electron.

The characteristics of the group-one elements, in particular the alkali metal halides, are familiar from the preceding chapter. We can see now why the alkali metals are chemically alike, because the valence-electron configuration is the same in every case: a single s-electron. Further, as reflected in the low first ionization energies of the alkali metals, the lone s-electron is relatively easy to remove. As a consequence, the alkali metals commonly form compounds in which ionic bonding predominates. In contrast, the high second ionization energies (about an order of magnitude higher) emphasize the difficulty in removing electrons from inner shells, and account for the nonexistence of stable multivalent alkali metal ions.

The halogens form another group with remarkably similar properties. In fact, chemically they are probably more alike than the constituents of any other group. Again this results from an identical valence configuration, this one in the form of a p-subshell lacking one electron to make it complete. Compared with the structure of the alkali metals, this structure gives rise to the other extreme; i.e., a large ionization energy and a correspondingly large electron affinity. Consequently, the halogens are often found as monovalent anions in ionic structures. They are obviously not restricted to participation in ionic bonding, however, because their elemental state is diatomic.

The characteristic valences of the other groups of the periodic table may be explained in a similar way. Beryllium and the alkaline earths commonly form divalent positive ions because of the relative ease of removal of the two s-electrons in their valence configuration. On the other hand, oxygen and the other chalkogenides frequently form divalent negative ions by accepting two electrons to fill the deficient p-subshell.

It is important to realize, however, that factors other than the ionization energy and the electron affinity are important in determining the stability of ions. Observe, for example, that the electron affinity of oxygen in producing the divalent ion is negative; i.e., the reaction $O + 2e = O^{2-}$ is endothermic. One might then question the stability of an ionic compound which requires the input of some 156 kcal of energy to produce the negative ion. Especially is this so when one considers that energy, I, is also required to form the positive ion. Such reasoning is faulty in that it does not take into account the energy of interaction of the ions (e.g., crystal energy), and it is this energy, of course, which leads to their stabilization. It can be shown, in fact, that the difference, $I - E$, is always adverse, so that the ions must interact with one another or with their environment in order to preserve their identity. In solution, for example, the stability of the ions relative to the parent atoms is ensured by interaction with the polar solvent molecules.

We also now have an insight into the remarkable inertness of the rare gases.* The very high ionization energies characteristic of the group do not favor positive ion formation, while at the same time the electron affinities must be low. No experimental measurements are available to confirm this, but the complete lack of evidence for stable negative ions of the rare gases is sufficient proof of very low electron affinities for the group. An electron, if accepted, would have to go into an orbital in the next shell, and presumably the nuclear charge is simply not high enough to bind an electron so far out.

The inertness or stability of the rare gas configuration is reflected also in the fact that the ions of the alkali metals and the alkaline earths are isoelectronic with the inert gas preceding them in the periodic table. Similarly, the halogens and the chalkogenides attain inert gas configurations by accepting electrons. Filled shells or subshells are also characteristic of many other ions, and this has led to the association of an extra or special stability with such configurations. Further credence is lent to this argument by the configurations of chromium and copper, where half-filled and filled shells are favored. Although the concept is a useful one, we should realize that the extra stability of filled and half-filled shells is often more apparent than real, and that the reasons for the phenomenon differ from case to case. The half-filled p-subshell of nitrogen, for example, is no more stable than the doubly occupied p-subshell of carbon which precedes it. The break in the upward stability trend of ionization energies actually occurs with oxygen, because of the extra repulsion involved when two electrons occupy the same orbital.

---

* In view of recent developments, it would appear that the rare gases are less inert than has traditionally been assumed. Crystalline $XePtF_6$, prepared by Bartlett, is apparently composed of Xe^+ cations and PtF_6^- anions. Other compounds of Xe and Rn are described in Chapter 5.

The above discussion of chemical properties is a brief one, and much has been left for more detailed treatment in later chapters. In particular, nothing has been said of the relation between covalent bonding and electronic structure. We shall see that here also group properties arise because of the influence of electronic configuration but, because of the phenomenon of hybridization and the involvement, in heavier atoms, of *d*-orbitals, the subject is considerably more complicated and merits a chapter of its own. Similar considerations apply to the larger group of elements which make up the transition series.

Very great interest has been aroused in the chemistry of transition metals in recent years. The characteristic properties (multiplicity of oxidation states, tendency to form complexes, etc.) which are largely due to the presence of unfilled *d*-orbitals will be discussed in Chapter 6. The two remaining groups, the lanthanides and actinides, although they are also marked by characteristic properties, are rather specialized subjects and will not be covered in any detail in this text.

BIBLIOGRAPHY

A

BROWN, G. I., *A Simple Guide to Modern Valency Theory*. London: Longmans Green, 1953.

COULSON, C. A., *Valence*. New York: Oxford, 1961.

DAY, M. C., and J. SELBIN, *Theoretical Inorganic Chemistry*. [New York: Reinhold, 1962.

HEITLER, W., *Elementary Wave Mechanics*. New York: Oxford, 1956.

HERZBERG, G., *Atomic Spectra and Atomic Structure*. New York: Dover, 1944.

HESLOP, R. B., and P. L. ROBINSON. *Inorganic Chemistry*. Amsterdam: Elsevier, 1960.

KETELAAR, J. A. A., *Chemical Constitution*. Amsterdam: Elsevier, 1958.

LINNETT, J. W., *Wave Mechanics and Valency*. London: Methuen, 1960.

OGRYZLO, E. A., and G. B. PORTER, "Contour Surfaces of Atomic and Molecular Orbitals." *J. Chem. Ed.*, April 1963.

PAULING, L., *The Nature of the Chemical Bond*. Ithaca, New York: Cornell, 1960.

RYSCHKEWITSCH, G. E., *Chemical Bonding and the Geometry of Molecules*. New York: Reinhold, 1963.

B

FANO, U., and L. FANO, *Basic Physics of Atoms and Molecules*. New York: Wiley, 1959.

KAUZMANN, W., *Quantum Chemistry*. New York: Academic Press, 1957.

LANDAU, L. D., and E. M. LIFSHITZ, *Quantum Mechanics*. Reading, Mass.: Addison-Wesley, 1958.

PAULING, L., and E. B. WILSON, *Introduction to Quantum Mechanics*. New York: McGraw-Hill, 1935.

SLATER, J. C., *Quantum Theory of Atomic Structure*. New York: McGraw-Hill, 1960.

PROBLEMS

3–1. Describe the Rutherford model of the atom, and state the experimental evidence which substantiates it.

3–2. Calculate the wave number, in cm^{-1}, and wavelength, in A, of the first five lines and the series limit for the Balmer series.

3–3. Why is the Lyman series the only one normally observed in the absorption spectrum of the hydrogen atom? Would you expect the same situation to obtain for gaseous hydrogen in the solar atmosphere?

3–4. The spectrum of mercury vapor shows strong emission at the wavelengths 1650 A, 2536 A, 3650 A, 5460 A, and 7346 A. Calculate the energy, in kcal, associated with each of these transitions, and state in which region of the electromagnetic spectrum the lines lie. Compare these with the energy of the radiation at 1.54 A emitted by copper when it is used as a target in an X-ray tube.

3–5. A necessary condition for the observation of diffraction by crystals is that the wavelength of the radiation used must be of the same order of magnitude as the internuclear distance. Is this criterion satisfied by a beam of electrons accelerated through 100 volts?

3–6. Given that the ionization energy of hydrogen is 313.4 kcal, calculate the ionization energies of He^+, Li^{2+}, and Be^{3+}.

3–7. Outline the scheme of orbitals for many-electron atoms, in terms of subshells, for the K-, L-, M-, and N-shells. Give in each case the total number of electrons which may occupy each shell and subshell.

3–8. Write the electronic configurations for the following species and indicate those which are isoelectronic: S^{2-}, Cd^{2+}, Zr^{2+}, Sc^{3+}, Ne, Pd, Sr, and Al^{3+}.

3–9. Plot a graph of the square roots of the ionization energies versus nuclear charges for the series of ions Li, Be^+, B^{2+}, C^{3+} and Be, B^+, C^{2+}, N^{3+}. Explain the observed relationship.

3–10. Derive an experimental value for the total electronic energies of the atoms H, He, Li, Be.

3–11. Use the wave functions of Table 3–2 to show that: (a) the charge distribution $\rho = \psi^2$ for two electrons occupying p_x- and p_y-orbitals is cylindrically symmetrical about the z-axis, i.e., is independent of ϕ; (b) the charge distribution for a filled or half-filled p-subshell has spherical symmetry, i.e., is independent of both θ and ϕ.

3–12. It has been suggested by Zener that the constant in the empirical function for the repulsive energy $(e^{-s/\rho})$ may be approximated by the expression

$$\rho = \frac{a_0}{\left(\sqrt{\Delta H_{ion}(1)} + \sqrt{\Delta H_{ion}(2)}\right)\sqrt{2a_0/e^2}}$$

where $\Delta H_{ion}(1)$ and $\Delta H_{ion}(2)$ are the ionization energies of the species involved, $a_0 = 0.5292$ A is the radius of the first Bohr orbit, and e is the charge on the electron. Use this expression to calculate ρ for several of the alkali halides, and compare your values with those used in Chapter 2 to calculate crystal energies.

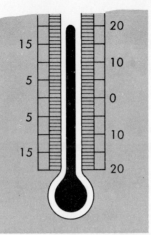

CHAPTER FOUR

Thermochemistry

On an empirical basis, the thermochemical relationships among many different chemical compounds are firmly established. Energy changes accompanying chemical reactions have been measured with a high degree of accuracy and by a variety of experimental methods, so that a vast amount of precise data is available. Since the energy change accompanying a particular reaction in large measure determines the position of equilibrium or extent of reaction, such information is invaluable in all areas of chemistry.

An important aspect of thermochemistry is the insight it provides into problems of chemical bonding; this aspect is so important that the study of thermochemistry logically precedes that of the chemical bond, which we shall come to in Chapter 5. We have already seen in Chapter 2 that the agreement between theoretical and experimental crystal energies of simple ionic crystals lends considerable support to the physical model used in the Born-Mayer treatment of the alkali halides. However, these energies do not lend themselves to direct experimental measurement.

Comparison of calculated and experimental energies provides a key test of the validity of any theory of chemical bonding. Of course, there are many aspects other than energy by which theories of chemical structure may be compared with experiment; nevertheless, the energy comparison is a fundamental one.

As a starting point, after we present some notes on terminology and definitions, we shall discuss Hess' law, and apply it to a number of systems, including the problem mentioned above of the experimentally derived crystal energies. We shall see that this law provides the means whereby a large amount of thermochemical data can be tabulated in compact as well as convenient form. Since thermochemical data are not always available for systems of interest, especially when these interests include the synthesis of new compounds, we shall consider the problem of estimating these data through the use of bond energies. The rather stringent limitations of these methods will be demonstrated by some sample calculations.

4-1. HEAT AND ENERGY

Thermochemistry itself is concerned with the changes in potential energy that accompany chemical reactions or physical processes. When such a reaction or process is carried out under carefully controlled conditions in a calorimeter, this energy change manifests itself in an increase or decrease in the temperature of the system, according to whether heat is evolved or absorbed, respectively, during the reaction. In order for such results to be meaningful, however, it is essential that the products be known (i.e., that the reaction can be defined unambiguously), and that the extent of reaction in terms of moles of reactant be determined. The amount of rise in temperature can be converted to conventional energy units by calibration of the calorimeter with a previously measured reaction, or by comparison with the electrical energy required to reproduce the temperature change.

We distinguish between the heat evolved or absorbed during a process carried out at *constant pressure*, as in a system open to the atmosphere, and that evolved during a process carried out at *constant volume*, such as a gaseous reaction, where the gas is contained in a rigid vessel. In the latter case, the heat absorbed, q, is identified with the energy change or better, *internal energy* change, ΔU, of the system:

$$\Delta U = q \qquad \text{(constant volume)}.$$

Thus if heat is absorbed, q is a positive quantity, as is ΔU, and the reaction is said to be *endothermic*. On the other hand, should q be negative, that is, if heat is evolved, then ΔU is also negative and the reaction is *exothermic*. This particular sign convention is chosen to conform with the idea that in an exothermic reaction, the system is lowered in potential energy. Although the reverse convention has on occasion been used in texts and references, the one given here is now used universally.

When a reaction is carried out at constant pressure and there is a volume change in the reaction, the heat absorbed includes not only the increase in potential energy due to the chemical reaction but also the equivalent of the amount of work done by the system on its surroundings:

$$\Delta U + w = q. \qquad (4\text{-}1)$$

Provided that certain conditions (on which we shall not dwell here) are maintained, this work is given by $p\,\Delta V$, where ΔV is the final volume less the initial volume; hence Eq. (4-1) becomes

$$\Delta U + p\,\Delta V = q \qquad \text{(constant pressure)}. \qquad (4\text{-}2)$$

Because most reactions are carried out at constant pressure, the function on the left-hand side of Eq. (4-2) has its own name, the *enthalpy change*, and symbol, ΔH. Indeed, it is a quantity so frequently encountered that it is known in addition as the *heat of reaction*, a name which, in view of the above discussion, is decidedly ambiguous. It is unfortunate but true, however, that ambiguous or not, the latter term is used far more frequently than the former. Since we shall make no further use of the quantity q discussed above, thereby reducing the ambiguity in names, the terms "enthalpy change" and "heat of reaction" will both be used interchangeably from this point on to refer to ΔH.

Both of the quantities ΔU and ΔH are functions of state only. The implication of this statement is that regardless of how a reaction is carried out, ΔU and ΔH are uniquely defined if the states of the reactants and products are exactly specified. This is a fundamental and important consideration in thermochemistry and thermodynamics, for it establishes exact relationships among the thermochemical properties of different but related reactions.

Note that, in the discussion above, the terms "energy change" and "enthalpy change" were specified, rather than their absolute values. The reason for this is very simple: It is not possible to define energy on an absolute basis. Even if we could so define energy, it would add nothing useful to thermochemistry, because the important quantity in a chemical reaction is the change in a thermodynamic quantity, which, in turn, is independent of any absolute values.

4–2. HEATS OF FORMATION

Despite the fact that absolute energies and enthalpies cannot be determined, it is desirable for purposes of concise tabulation to establish an arbitrary reference scale. This is conveniently done by choosing a particular state of each element and assigning zero enthalpy to it. Thus, following the usually accepted convention, we shall assign zero enthalpy to each element at 298.15°K (25°C) when it is in the standard state of the most stable form of the element at this temperature. Proper definition of the *standard state* involves subtleties which are best left for discussion in Chapter 8. For the present we shall regard standard conditions as denoting one atmosphere pressure for solids and liquids, and ideal-gas (i.e., low-pressure) behavior for gases. Symbolically, the standard state is commonly designated by a superscript °, while the temperature is specified by a subscript. According to our convention, then

$$H^\circ_{298}(Cl_2, g) = 0, \qquad H^\circ_{298}(I_2, s) = 0, \qquad H^\circ_{298}(Br_2, l) = 0, \qquad \text{etc.,}$$

where g, s, and l denote the form of the element as a gas, solid, or liquid, respectively. When isomorphs of the solid state exist, it is necessary to be more specific. In the case of carbon, for example, zero enthalpy is assigned to graphite in its standard state, not to diamond. Note also that the standard enthalpy of an element at some temperature other than 298°K will not be zero.

We can now define the *heat of formation*, ΔH_f, of a substance as the change in enthalpy accompanying the formation of the substance from its constituent elements in their standard states at 298°K. The heat of formation of gaseous carbon dioxide, for example, is the enthalpy change for the reaction

$$C \text{ (graphite)} + O_2(g) = CO_2(g); \quad \Delta H = \Delta H_f(CO_2, g).$$

To be precise we should also specify the temperature of the product, but we shall not do this unless it differs from 298°K.

Clearly, we can define standard states for compounds as well as for the elements. Thus, if the reactants and the products are all in standard states, then the enthalpy change for the reaction

$$\tfrac{1}{2} H_2(g) + \tfrac{1}{2} Cl_2(g) = HCl(g)$$

defines the *standard heat of formation*, ΔH_f° (HCl, g), of gaseous HCl. More generally, if in any reaction the products and reactants are in their standard states, we may denote the enthalpy change as the standard enthalpy (change) of the reaction. We shall, in fact, confine ourselves almost exclusively to enthalpy changes under standard conditions.

The standard heats of formation of a great number of chemical compounds have been determined, often with considerable accuracy, not only by calorimetric means, but by many diverse methods. In fact, it is actually a rare case in which a heat of formation can be measured directly. Some of the indirect methods will be discussed in the following section of this chapter, and others will be dealt with still later.

A representative, but by no means complete, selection of standard heats of formation is tabulated in Appendix II. The order in which they are given is alphabetical according to the symbol of the "principal" element, an ambiguous term the meaning of which will be apparent after an inspection of the table. These data, when presented in the form of standard heats of formation, provide the means to compress a considerable body of thermochemical information into a small and orderly table.

4–3. HESS' LAW

The progress of chemistry might well have been impeded instead of enhanced by thermochemistry had it been necessary to measure experimentally the heat of reaction of every chemical system studied. Fortunately, this is not the case at all, and we shall show that it is required only that the standard heats of formation of each compound in the reaction in question be known. Then the standard heat of reaction or standard enthalpy change can be deduced to an accuracy of the least accurate heat of formation.

The principle involved was enunciated by Hess in 1840. In modern terms the statement implies that enthalpy and internal energy changes are functions of state only. In practical terms it means that if a reaction can be carried out, even if only in principle, by a series of steps, the overall enthalpy change is the sum of the enthalpy changes of the individual steps. Further, if a reaction can be carried out by two different paths, the enthalpy changes by either path must be identical, provided only that the initial and final states are identical. We shall develop the use of Hess' law in two different ways, the first of which is useful as an introduction (although it is somewhat unwieldy), while the second makes more use of symbols and therefore represents a more compact and less time-consuming method.

It is apparent, even after only a little consideration, that Hess' law is a valuable tool which has wide application. As an illustration, consider its use in deriving a value for the standard heat of formation of HI. This cannot be measured directly in a calorimeter, but it is possible to determine experimentally the standard heat of formation of HCl according to the reaction,*

$$\tfrac{1}{2}H_2(g) + \tfrac{1}{2}Cl_2(g) = HCl(g); \qquad \Delta H_f^\circ = -22.06 \text{ kcal.} \qquad (4\text{-}3)$$

In addition, one can measure experimentally the heat of the reaction,

$$\tfrac{1}{2}Cl_2(g) + HI(g) = HCl(g) + \tfrac{1}{2}I_2(s); \qquad \Delta H^\circ = -28.26 \text{ kcal.} \quad (4\text{-}4)$$

Or, reversing the latter, we obtain

$$HCl(g) + \tfrac{1}{2}I_2(s) = \tfrac{1}{2}Cl_2(g) + HI(g); \qquad \Delta H^\circ = 28.26 \text{ kcal.} \qquad (4\text{-}5)$$

Applying Hess' law, we add Eqs. (4-3) and (4-5), or subtract Eq. (4-4) from Eq. (4-3), and obtain

$$\tfrac{1}{2}H_2(g) + \tfrac{1}{2}I_2(s) = HI(g); \qquad \Delta H_f^\circ = 6.20 \text{ kcal.} \qquad (4\text{-}6)$$

The heats of the reactions are added in the same way as the equations, and the latter are treated algebraically, with cancellation of equivalent items on both sides of the equals sign.

Alternatively, Eqs. (4-3) and (4-5) may be written in the perhaps more familiar, but less desirable form

$$\tfrac{1}{2}H_2(g) + \tfrac{1}{2}Cl_2(g) = HCl(g) + 22.06 \text{ kcal,}$$

and

$$HCl(g) + I_2(s) = \tfrac{1}{2}Cl_2(g) + HI(g) - 28.26 \text{ kcal.}$$

---

* The use of an equals sign in writing the chemical equation, in place of the double arrow, $\rightleftharpoons$, which indicates an equilibrium, is common practice. It is a concession to the fact that, when we apply Hess' law, we handle chemical equations as algebraic equations. The two symbols may thus be considered equivalent.

(Note the change of sign when the heat of reaction is included in the equation.) Adding the equations gives

$$\tfrac{1}{2}H_2(g) + \tfrac{1}{2}I_2(s) = HI(g) - 6.20 \text{ kcal},$$

the same result as before.

The above example also leads us to an alternative, but equivalent, statement of Hess' law. It is readily seen that Eq. (4–4) is equal to Eq. (4–3) minus Eq. (4–6), or in terms of the heats of reaction,

$$\Delta H° = \Delta H_f°(\text{HCl, g}) + \tfrac{1}{2}\Delta H_f°(I_2, s) - \Delta H_f°(\text{HI, g}) - \tfrac{1}{2}\Delta H_f°(\text{Cl}_2)$$

$$= \Delta H_f°(\text{HCl, g}) - \Delta H_f°(\text{HI, g}). \qquad (4\text{–}7)$$

More generally, for the reaction

$$aA + bB + \cdots = xX + yY + \cdots,$$

the standard heat of reaction is given by

$$\Delta H° = x\,\Delta H_f°(X) + y\,\Delta H_f°(Y) + \cdots - a\,\Delta H_f°(A) - b\,\Delta H_f°(B), \qquad (4\text{–}8)$$

that is, by the sum of the standard heats of formation of the products less that of the reactants. This immediately shows the value of the heats of formation. So long as the requisite heats of formation are available, the enthalpy change in any reaction can be deduced to within the accuracy of the least accurate piece of data.

(a) Some applications of Hess' law

No organic compound can be prepared in pure form by direct reaction of its component elements, nor can the reverse reaction be carried out except in a few particular cases, so that the heats of formation must always be obtained by indirect methods. The most useful technique involves the determination of the enthalpy change for the combustion of the compound in oxygen. All substances containing only carbon, hydrogen, and oxygen burn under appropriate conditions to give carbon dioxide and water as the sole final products. Methanol, for example, burns in oxygen according to the equation

$$CH_3OH(g) + \tfrac{3}{2}O_2(g) = CO_2(g) + 2H_2O(l). \qquad (4\text{–}9)$$

The heat of combustion under standard conditions, $\Delta H_{comb}°$, is -182.61 kcal/mole of alcohol. The application of Hess' law in the form of Eq. (4–8) yields

$$\Delta H_{comb}° = \Delta H_f°(CO_2, g) + 2\,\Delta H_f°(H_2O, l) - \Delta H_f°(CH_3OH, g). \qquad (4\text{–}10)$$

Note that since the standard heat of formation of oxygen is by definition zero, it need not be included. Substitution of the standard heats of formation of H_2O and CO_2 (Appendix II) into Eq. (4–10) gives, for the standard heat of formation of methanol vapor, -48.08 kcal/mole. This method is, in fact, just what was used to determine this information in tabulated thermochemical data.

One of the principal difficulties with the combustion method lies in the extreme exothermicity of the reactions, so that a high degree of accuracy is required. This feature is demonstrated clearly for the compound benzene, $C_6H_6(g)$, which has a heat of combustion under standard conditions of -789.08 kcal/mole. From this result, the standard heat of formation, as shown in Appendix II, is 19.82 kcal/mole. However, an error of 0.01% in the determination of the heat of combustion would result in an error of nearly 0.5% in the calculated heat of formation. For this reason, combustion calorimeters are carefully calibrated, usually by carrying out the combustion of pure samples of benzoic acid, $C_6H_5COOH(s)$, for which the heat of combustion has been determined to be 6.3179 kcal/gm, in a number of very careful studies in different laboratories.

Organic compounds which contain elements other than carbon, oxygen, and hydrogen require special techniques. As an example, a trace of nitric oxide is added to sulfur-containing compounds to catalyze the complete oxidation of sulfur to sulfuric acid. In addition, the combustion calorimeter is rotated to bring all of the product sulfuric acid into aqueous solution at a uniform known concentration.

The examples above illustrate the manipulations of thermochemical data with the aid of Hess' law, but they are mainly concerned with obtaining the standard heats of formation themselves. More important applications, from our point of view, are those which employ the tabulated data to yield experimental information for comparison with an atomic- or molecular-based theory. Many such applications, relating to bonding in the solid, liquid, and gaseous phases will be found throughout the text. The Born-Haber crystal energies, discussed in Chapter 2, are typical, and we shall discuss this application in detail here.

We wish to derive an experimental value for the crystal energy of NaCl as defined by the equation

$$Na^+(g) + Cl^-(g) = NaCl \text{ (cryst)}; \quad \Delta H^\circ_{cryst}(NaCl).$$

Applying Hess' law, the crystal energy will be given by

$$\Delta H^\circ_{cryst}(NaCl) = \Delta H^\circ_f(NaCl, \text{cryst}) - \Delta H^\circ_f(Na^+, g) - \Delta H^\circ_f(Cl^-, g).$$

The standard heat of formation of crystalline NaCl is usually to be found in tables of thermochemical data (Appendix II), but those for gaseous sodium and chloride ions are found less commonly. We can, nevertheless, derive these quantities from more fundamental ones. The reaction

$$Na(s) = Na^+(g) + e; \quad \Delta H^\circ_f(Na^+, g),$$

may be written in two steps as

$$Na(s) = Na(g); \quad \Delta H_f^\circ(Na, g),$$

and

$$Na(g) = Na^+(g) + e; \quad \Delta H_{ion}^\circ(Na, g).$$

We therefore have

$$\Delta H_f^\circ(Na^+, g) = \Delta H_f^\circ(Na, g) + \Delta H_{ion}^\circ(Na, g).$$

The former quantity may be found in the thermochemical tables of Appendix II, while the latter is listed in Table 3–3. Because of their spectroscopic origin, ionization energies are usually tabulated for 0°K but they may be corrected to 298°K by adding 1.5 kcal per electron removed.

For the chloride ion we wish to find $\Delta H_f^\circ(Cl^-, g)$, as defined by the reaction

$$\tfrac{1}{2}Cl_2(g) + e = Cl^-(g); \quad \Delta H_f^\circ(Cl^-, g).$$

This also may be written in two steps as

$$\tfrac{1}{2}Cl_2(g) = Cl(g); \quad \Delta H_f^\circ(Cl, g),$$

and

$$Cl(g) + e = Cl^-(g); \quad -\Delta H_{ion}^\circ(Cl^-, g).$$

We then obtain

$$\Delta H_f^\circ(Cl^-, g) = \Delta H_f^\circ(Cl, g) - \Delta H_{ion}^\circ(Cl^-, g).$$

Again the required data are listed in Appendix II and Table 3–5.

We find, finally, that the crystal energy is given by the expression

$$\Delta H_{cryst}^\circ(NaCl) = \Delta H_f^\circ(NaCl, cryst) - \Delta H_f^\circ(Na, g) - \Delta H_{ion}^\circ(Na, g)$$
$$- \Delta H_f^\circ(Cl, g) + \Delta H_{ion}^\circ(Cl^-, g).$$

Substituting values from the tables gives

$$\Delta H_{cryst}^\circ(NaCl) = -98.23 - 25.9 - 119.9 - 29.01 + 86.8 = -186.2 \text{ kcal.}$$

Because of the cumulative error resulting from the mathematical operations, the figure in the first decimal place must be suspect and is not quoted in Table 2–6.

While the above procedure appears to be long and involved, an examination will reveal that we have simply broken down the reaction in question into a number of steps for which the heats of reaction are available. Experience enters in determining the proper steps, but the student will quickly become acquainted with the data he can expect to find in thermochemical tables. Many reactions crop up so frequently that the enthalpy or heat involved is given a special name and symbol. Some of those used above are:

Crystal energy $= \Delta H_{cryst}$,

Ionization energy $= \Delta H_{ion} = I = IP$ (Ionization potential),

Heat of sublimation $= \Delta H_{sub}(Na) = \Delta H_f(Na, g)$,

Dissociation energy $= D(Cl_2) = 2 \Delta H_f^\circ(Cl, g)$,

Electron affinity $= E(Cl) = \Delta H_{ion}(Cl^-, g)$.

The application of the term "Born-Haber cycle" to the above method for calculating ionic crystal energies arises from the presentation of the reactions in the form

$$Na^+(g) + Cl^-(g) \xrightarrow{\Delta H_{cryst}^\circ(NaCl)} NaCl \text{ (cryst)}$$

$$-\Delta H_{ion}^\circ(Na, g) \downarrow \qquad \downarrow \Delta H_{ion}^\circ(Cl^-, g) \qquad\qquad \uparrow \Delta H_f^\circ(NaCl)$$

$$Na(g) + Cl(g) \xrightarrow[-\Delta H_f^\circ(Cl, g) \, -\Delta H_f^\circ(Na, g)]{} Na(s) + \tfrac{1}{2}Cl_2(g).$$

This form is, of course, simply a shorter method of writing the many reactions involved. In fact, its brevity makes it a less desirable form of presentation for students not adept at this type of calculation.

(b) Stability

One of the most overworked and misused words in chemistry is "stability." Yet it has a clear unambiguous meaning in the thermodynamic sense. We are not in a position, at this point, to introduce the idea of true thermodynamic stability. For the present, we shall treat stability on an energetic basis only, reserving the more complete aspect of the problem for Chapter 8.

The heat liberated in an exothermic reaction implies that the products have a lower enthalpy than the reactants; hence we may state that the products are energetically stable with respect to the reactants. The comment that a particular substance is stable or unstable is without meaning unless it is qualified by a statement of the possible decomposition products and the conditions obtaining during the reaction. To illustrate this point, consider liquid hydrogen peroxide, H_2O_2, with a standard heat of formation of -44.88 kcal/mole. Reversing the process of formation, we can say that the decomposition of peroxide into its constituent elements according to the reaction

$$H_2O_2(l) = H_2(g) + O_2(g)$$

is endothermic by 44.88 kcal. Hydrogen peroxide is therefore energetically stable with respect to the elements in their standard states. On the other hand, the tendency of H_2O_2 to decompose spontaneously, sometimes with explosive force, is well known. The decomposition products are not hydrogen and oxygen, however, but water and oxygen.

Reference to Appendix II reveals that the reaction

$$H_2O_2(l) = H_2O(l) + \tfrac{1}{2}O_2(g)$$

is exothermic by 23.44 kcal. Hydrogen peroxide is therefore decidedly unstable with respect to decomposition into water and oxygen.

While it is true that most reagents found on laboratory shelves do have negative heats of formation under standard conditions, the example of hydrogen peroxide illustrates the fact that a negative heat of formation is no guarantee that a substance is safe from decomposition. At the same time, a positive heat of formation does not imply that a substance decomposes quickly. Many of the substances commonly found in the laboratory, such as $NO_2(g)$, $NO(g)$, $N_2O(g)$, and $C_2H_2(g)$ have positive heats of formation.

We realize, then, that while thermochemistry provides data regarding the energetic stability of a compound relative to a particular mode of decomposition, it gives no information concerning the rate of the reaction. Highly exothermic reactions often require a catalyst or initiator in order for the reaction to proceed at a reasonable rate. Liquid hydrogen peroxide, for example, if very pure and stored in a scrupulously clean glass container, may be kept indefinitely. Most impurities catalyze the decomposition, however, and the presence of organic matter often leads to explosive decomposition.

4–4. BOND ENERGIES

Despite the fact that vast amounts of thermochemical data have already been amassed, it is desirable to have some way of predicting thermal data, since new compounds are continuously being synthesized and discovered. Before we go on to look at this problem, let us point out that such methods of prediction as are available are largely empirical. Hess' law we know to be exact, and calculations of enthalpy changes based on it are as reliable as the experimental data from which they are derived. However, this reliability does not apply for the empirical methods to be discussed now, even though the experimental data used in their formulation are quite reliable.

It would be ideal if a certain energy could be assigned to each specific bond in a molecule, independent of the nature of the other bonds. As we shall see, it is not possible to do so with any degree of precision. However, within stringent limitations, rough estimates of thermochemical quantities may be made, based on reasonable values for various bond energies.

(a) Bond dissociation energies

The concept of a bond dissociation energy is well established and clearly defined, although relatively few values have been established experimentally, and those often with poor accuracy. The simplest example of a bond dissociation energy is found in the formation of two atoms from a diatomic molecule; as, for example,

$$H_2(g) = 2H(g).$$

The bond dissociation energy is the enthalpy change in this reaction: $D(H—H) = 104.18$ kcal/mole. Although such bond dissociation energies are often quoted for the reaction at $0°K$, those given here refer to the standard conditions, that is, $298°K$. The bond dissociation energies of diatomic molecules can generally be determined very accurately because they are evaluated from spectroscopic rather than thermal data.

Often, however, the spectroscopic results can be interpreted in a number of ways. For example, spectroscopic studies of nitrogen have at various times been interpreted to give the following values for $D(N—N)$: 170.18, 197.60, 225.96, and 272.0 kcal/mole. It is only recently that the controversy has been resolved with the adoption of the third value, namely

$$D(N—N) = 225.96 \text{ kcal/mole.}$$

It is interesting that even rather crude thermal data allow a choice to be made from among a number of ambiguous but extremely precise spectroscopic values.

Another case in point is that of fluorine. For a long time the spectroscopic value $D(F—F) = 63.5$ kcal/mole was accepted, in part because it fitted in well with the other halogens. In the last decade, however, a sufficient number of concordant thermal results have led to its revision downward to 37.8 kcal/mole. A list of bond dissociation energies of diatomic molecules is given in Table 4–1.

For molecules other than diatomic ones, bond dissociation energies are more difficult to obtain and are far less accurate. The bond dissociation energy in water is the enthalpy change in the reaction

$$H_2O(g) = H(g) + OH(g),$$

for which the value $D(HO—H) = 119.7$ kcal/mole has been obtained. This is a typical example, in that the reaction cannot easily be investigated by ordinary thermochemical methods because the products, hydrogen atoms and hydroxyl radicals, have but a fleeting existence. The hydroxyl radical itself has a bond dissociation energy $D(O—H) = 101.5$ kcal/mole. This is our first indication that it is not rigorously correct to assign an energy to a particular "bond"; the bond dissociation energies in the water molecule and in the hydroxyl radical are not the same.

TABLE 4-1

BOND DISSOCIATION ENERGIES, $D(X—X)$, OF SOME
DIATOMIC MOLECULES (kcal/mole, 298.15°K)

Molecule	Dissociation energy	Molecule	Dissociation energy
O_2	118.32	S_2	102
H_2	104.18	Se_2	64.7
OH	101.5	Te_2	53.4
F_2	37.8	N_2	225.08
HF	134.6	NO	150.10
Cl_2	58.02	P_2	116.9
HCl	103.16	As_2	90
ClF	60.6	Sb_2	69
Br_2	46.08	Bi_2	39.7
HBr	87.46	C_2	144
BrF	56.0	CO	256.47
BrCl	52.3	CH	81
I_2	36.08	B_2	69
HI	71.37	Li_2	26.41
ICl	50.3	Na_2	18.01
IBr	42.5	K_2	12.24
At_2	22.4	Rb_2	11.66
SH	85	Cs_2	10.71

In the methane molecule, CH_4, there are four stepwise bond dissociation energies. Of these only two are known with any certainty at the present moment (although the others may well have been established by the time this book is in print). The first one, involving the formation of a methyl radical and a hydrogen atom,

$$CH_4(g) = CH_3(g) + H(g),$$

has been measured by several different experimental techniques as $D(CH_3—H) = 103$ kcal/mole. The last one,

$$CH(g) = C(g) + H(g),$$

is known from spectroscopic data to be 81 kcal/mole. All that is known for certain about the other two is their sum. From the heats of formation of methane, of hydrogen atoms, and of carbon atoms (all as gases), the heat of atomization $\Delta H°_{atom}$ of methane, that is, the heat of the reaction

$$CH_4(g) = C(g) + 4H(g),$$

can be calculated by Hess' law to be 397.1 kcal. It is clear, however, that the heat of atomization will also equal the sum of all of the bond dissociation energies,

$$\Delta H^{\circ}_{\text{atom}} = D(\text{CH}_3\text{—H}) + D(\text{CH}_2\text{—H}) + D(\text{CH}\text{—H}) + D(\text{C}\text{—H}). \quad (4\text{-}11)$$

Given the first and last bond dissociation energies as well as the heat of atomization, we can solve Eq. (4-11) for the sum $D(\text{CH}_2\text{—H}) + D(\text{CH}\text{—H}) = 213$ kcal. The values 89 and 124 kcal, respectively, have been suggested, but the question is still very much open to dispute and, what is more important, to further experiment.

(b) Bond energies

It is clear from the discussion of the previous section that the heat of atomization of any compound can be calculated if its standard heat of formation and the heats of formation of its constituent atoms are known. On the other hand, the standard heat of formation can be deduced if the heat of atomization is known or can be estimated.

In the atomization of water vapor, two O—H bonds are ruptured per molecule. With this information, we can compute an average bond energy in the molecule. This quantity, which we will refer to as the bond energy to distinguish it from the bond dissociation energy, is abbreviated $E(\text{O—H})$. Although it does not have the direct physical significance of the bond dissociation energy, we shall find it a very useful quantity. Its value is found by halving the heat of atomization of water vapor; therefore $E(\text{O—H}) = 110.6$ kcal. As is quite evident in a comparison of $E(\text{O—H})$ with $D(\text{HO—H})$ and $D(\text{O—H})$, the bond energy and the bond dissociation energy are definitely not the same. It is only for a diatomic molecule that they are identical.

From the heat of atomization of methane, we can calculate $E(\text{C—H})$ simply by dividing by four the number of C—H bonds in the molecule. We find $E(\text{C—H}) = 99.3$ kcal. As we shall see shortly, better agreement with experimental data on high molecular-weight hydrocarbons is obtained if we choose a somewhat smaller value for $E(\text{C—H})$, in spite of the fact that it leads to a heat of atomization for methane which is too small. The next member of the homologous series of hydrocarbons is ethane, C_2H_6. Its heat of atomization, deduced from standard heats of formation, is 674.6 kcal/mole. This should be equivalent to the appropriate sum of bond energies,

$$\Delta H^{\circ}_{\text{atom}}(\text{C}_2\text{H}_6, \text{g}) = E(\text{C—C}) + 6E(\text{C—H}).$$

With the value of $E(\text{C—H})$ found in methane, we determine $E(\text{C—C})$ to be 78.8 kcal.

Now we are in a position to check the internal consistency in the determination of heats of atomization from bond energies. The heat of atomization of propane,

C_3H_8, should, if the method is to work, be equal to

$$\Delta H^{\circ}_{\text{atom}}(C_3H_8, g) = 2E(C—C) + 8E(C—H),$$

which yields 952.0 kcal, with the values derived above from ethane and methane for the bond energies. From the heat of formation of propane (Appendix II) we determine the heat of atomization to be 954.21 kcal. This error of slightly more than two kcal is more significant when we compare the estimated standard heat of formation of -22.6 kcal with the correct value, -24.82 kcal.

An empirical formula for the standard heat of formation of saturated linear hydrocarbons, C_nH_{2n+2}, has been developed in the form

$$\Delta H^{\circ}_f(C_nH_{2n+2}, g) = -10.41 - 4.926n \text{ kcal/mole}. \tag{4-12}$$

This equation gives excellent results, especially when n is greater than four. In terms of heats of atomization, Eq. (4–12) can be converted to

$$\Delta H^{\circ}_{\text{atom}} = 114.6 + 280.0n \text{ kcal}, \tag{4-13}$$

but the heats of atomization can also be given in terms of bond energies, as

$$\Delta H^{\circ}_{\text{atom}} = (n - 1)E(C—C) + (2n + 2)E(C—H). \tag{4-14}$$

Setting Eq. (4–13) equal to Eq. (4–14), we find that

$$2E(C—H) - E(C—C) = 114.6 \quad \text{and} \quad E(C—C) + 2E(C—H) = 280.0,$$

whereupon we can solve for $E(C—C)$ and $E(C—H)$, for which are found the values 82.7 and 98.7 kcal, respectively. On rounding these off, we have a suitable pair of bond energies,

$$E(C—C) = 83 \text{ kcal}$$

and

$$E(C—H) = 99 \text{ kcal},$$

which we shall adopt for the general case. Estimates based on these and other bond energies are only approximate. We cannot reasonably expect to get results to within much more than a few kilocalories even when the circumstances are favorable.

More refined empirical equations, similar to Eq. (4–12), have been developed to take into account, for example, the difference in enthalpies of formation found for isomeric molecules (see the data on the three isomeric C_4H_8 molecules in Appendix II), but such refinements are beyond the scope of this text.

TABLE 4–2

BOND ENERGIES, $E(X—X)$, FOR SINGLE BONDS
(in kcal/mole)

Bond	Energy	Bond	Energy	Bond	Energy
O—O	33	S—S	63	As—As	40
H—H	104	S—H	88	As—H	61
H—O	111	S—Cl	66	As—F	115
F—F	37	S—Br	51	As—Cl	69
F—O	45	Se—Se	44	As—Br	57
F—H	135	Se—H	67	As—I	42
Cl—Cl	58	Se—Cl	59	Sb—Sb	34
Cl—O	50	Te—Te	33	Sb—Cl	75
Cl—H	103	Te—H	57	C—C	83
Cl—F	61	N—N	38	C—O	82
Br—Br	46	N—H	93	C—H	99
Br—H	88	N—F	66	C—F	116
Br—F	57	N—Cl	48	C—Cl	78
Br—Cl	52	P—P	41	C—Br	66
I—I	36	P—H	76	C—I	57
I—H	71	P—Cl	76	C—N	70
I—Cl	50	P—Br	64		
I—Br	43	P—I	51		

There is still another method of arriving at the carbon—carbon bond energy. The heat of sublimation of graphite at 298°K is now generally accepted to be 170.89 kcal/mole. If we combine this enthalpy change with the standard heat of formation of diamond, we find for the reaction

$$C(\text{diamond}) = C(\text{gas}), \qquad (4\text{–}15)$$

an enthalpy change of 170.44 kcal/mole, which is the heat or enthalpy of sublimation of diamond. In a diamond crystal, each carbon atom is covalently bonded to four other carbon atoms (Chapter 7). Therefore, when reaction (4–15) occurs, two carbon—carbon bonds are broken for each atom formed. By halving the enthalpy of sublimation of diamond, we arrive at

$$E(\text{C—C}) = 85 \text{ kcal,}$$

which is in reasonably good agreement with that found in hydrocarbons.

By procedures similar to those discussed above, a set of bond energies, given in Table 4–2, can be assigned. Extension of these methods leads to the multiple bond energies in Table 4–3.

TABLE 4-3

MULTIPLE BOND ENERGIES, $E(X{=}X)$ AND $E(X{\equiv}X)$
(in kcal/mole)

Bond	Energy
C=C	148
N=N	100
C=N	147
C=O	164–174
C=S	114
C≡C	194
N≡N	225
C≡N	207–213

(c) Estimation of thermochemical data

In order to arrive at satisfactory estimates of standard heats of formation through bond energies, the molecule (vapor phase) must fit the following requirements: (1) The molecule must be representable by a single reasonable valence bond structure. (2) The atoms in the molecule must have their normal covalence, e.g., three for nitrogen, four for carbon, etc.

The classical case of a molecule for which a single valence bond structure cannot be written is that of benzene. The closest we could come would be a Kekulé formula with three single and three double carbon—carbon bonds. The heat of atomization should, according to this structure, be given by

$$\Delta H^\circ_{\text{atom}} = 3E(\text{C—C}) + 3E(\text{C}{=}\text{C}) + 6E(\text{C—H}).$$

From the bond energies in Tables 4–2 and 4–3, we calculate: $\Delta H^\circ_{\text{atom}} = 1287$ kcal, which in turn gives 51 kcal/mole for the standard heat of formation of benzene vapor. When we compare this estimate with the correct standard heat of formation given in Appendix II, we find the estimate to be over 30 kcal too endothermic. It is generally true that a molecule which is best described in terms of delocalized molecular orbitals or resonance structures (see Chapter 5) rather than a single valence bond structure is more stable (i.e., its heat of formation is more exothermic), than would be predicted from bond energies.

The bond energy $E(\text{P—Cl})$ given in Table 4–2 was derived from the standard heat of formation of $PCl_3(g)$. If we disregard the second rule and attempt to calculate the standard heat of formation of $PCl_5(g)$ from this bond energy, we find: $\Delta H^\circ_f(PCl_5,g) = -160$ kcal/mole. Since the observed value is -88.7 kcal/mole, we see that our estimate is too exothermic by over 70 kcal. This behavior is characteristic of a compound having a larger valence than normal.

It is difficult at present to find experimental thermochemical data on inorganic compounds by which the method of bond energies can be adequately tested.

Consider the compound Se_2Cl_2, which has one Se—Se bond and two Se—Cl bonds. The heat of atomization is given by

$$\Delta H^\circ_{atom} = 2\,\Delta H^\circ_f(Se, g) + 2\,\Delta H^\circ_f(Cl, g) - \Delta H^\circ_f(Se_2Cl_2, g),$$

and also approximately by

$$\Delta H^\circ_{atom} = E(Se\text{—}Se) + 2E(Se\text{—}Cl).$$

The latter bond energies, given in Table 4–2, were evaluated from the standard heats of formation of Se_6 and $SeCl_2$, respectively. Substitution of the known thermochemical data leads to

$$\Delta H^\circ_f(Se_2Cl_2, g) = -5 \text{ kcal/mole}.$$

The corresponding value in Appendix II is -20.0 kcal/mole, but this value is for the liquid. The boiling point of this substance is not known, but would probably be of the order of 150°C (S_2Cl_2 boils at 138°C). The enthalpy of vaporization would, by Trouton's rule, be about 10 kcal/mole. Therefore, we find an estimated standard heat of formation of the liquid of -15 kcal/mole, a value which is reasonably close to the experimental value.

There is some meager evidence that the compound H_2Se_2 may exist, but no evidence to support the existence of the corresponding tellurium compound. Although, of course, there are no experimental thermal data available, we can at least get some idea of the magnitude of their heats of formation, as well as that for H_2S_2. From the bond energies in Table 4–2, we find for the heats of atomization

$$\Delta H^\circ_{atom}(H_2S_2) = 239 \text{ kcal}, \qquad \Delta H^\circ_{atom}(H_2Se_2) = 178 \text{ kcal},$$

$$\Delta H^\circ_{atom}(H_2Te_2) = 147 \text{ kcal},$$

with the assumption that they would all have the same structure as the sulfur compound (i.e., with one S—S and two S—H bonds). From these we calculate

$$\Delta H^\circ_f(H_2S_2, g) = -2 \text{ kcal/mole}, \qquad \Delta H^\circ_f(H_2Se_2, g) = 25 \text{ kcal/mole},$$

$$\Delta H^\circ_f(H_2Te_2, g) = 50 \text{ kcal/mole}.$$

These calculations show that although H_2S_2 has a small, negative heat of formation, the heats of formation for H_2Se_2 and H_2Te_2 are large and positive, indicating that, although H_2S_2 can be prepared, the latter two might be synthesized only with difficulties.

Consider next the compounds PH_3, PCl_3, P_2H_4, and P_2Cl_4. Thermochemical data are available only for the first two, and these are found in Appendix II. A calculation of the two unknown standard heats of formation gives

$$\Delta H^\circ_f(P_2H_4, g) = 14 \text{ kcal/mole} \qquad \text{and} \qquad \Delta H^\circ_f(P_2Cl_4, g) = -79 \text{ kcal/mole}.$$

These results fit reasonably well with the experimental information, for example, that P_2H_4 decomposes spontaneously and so also does P_2Cl_4. The latter result does not at first seem compatible with the fact that the tetrachloride has a large, negative heat of formation. However, it does not decompose into the elements, but into PCl_3 and solid phosphorus; thus

$$3P_2Cl_4(g) = 4PCl_3(g) + 2P(s),$$

for which we find $\Delta H° = -29$ kcal. Hence our estimated thermal data do predict that P_2Cl_4 is unstable according to this decomposition.

Application of this method has largely been restricted to organic compounds because carbon usually exhibits its "normal" covalence, and also because of the tendency toward catenation. The formation of extended systems of carbon—carbon bonds leads to a great many organic compounds involving only a few bond energies. Provided that we steer clear of those compounds which do not obey the rules given above, the estimates for inorganic as well as organic compounds should be satisfactory. This kind of estimation of thermochemical properties can be of great value to a chemist who is synthesizing new compounds; especially since, in the last few decades, interest in volatile inorganic compounds has developed rapidly.

BIBLIOGRAPHY

A

BARROW, G. M., *Physical Chemistry*. New York: McGraw-Hill, 1961.
NASH, L. K., *Elements of Chemical Thermodynamics*. Reading, Mass.: Addison-Wesley, 1962.

B

COTTRELL, T. L., *The Strengths of Chemical Bonds*. London: Butterworth, 1958.
GAYDON, A. G., *Dissociation Energies*. London: Chapman and Hall, 1953.
LEWIS, G. N., and M. R. RANDALL (revised by K. Pitzer and L. Brewer), *Thermodynamics*. New York: McGraw-Hill, 1961.
SKINNER, H. A., *Modern Aspects of Thermochemistry*. London: The Royal Institute of Chemistry, 1958.

PROBLEMS

4-1. Calculate the enthalpy changes for these reactions under standard conditions:

(a) $ICl(g) + Cl_2(g) = ICl_3(s)$

(b) $2NO_2(g) + 4HCl(g) = 2NOCl(g) + 2H_2O(g) + Cl_2(g)$

(c) $C_3H_6(g) + H_2 = C_3H_8(g)$

(d) $Hg(l) + HgCl_2(s) = Hg_2Cl_2(s)$

(e) $TiCl_4(l) + 2H_2O(g) = TiO_2(s) + 4HCl(g)$

(f) $SiH_4(g) + 4HF(g) = SiF_4(g) + 4H_2$

4-2. When graphite is sublimed, molecular species such as C_2, C_3, etc., are formed, as well as carbon atoms. In what way will the standard heat of formation of carbon atoms be in error if the experimental enthalpy of sublimation is not corrected to take into account the formation of these molecules?

4-3. Show that if all four bond dissociation energies of methane were available, as well as the standard heat of formation of methane and the dissociation energy of hydrogen, the enthalpy of sublimation of graphite could be calculated.

4-4. Verify the bond energies given in Table 4-2 for ClF, BrF, IF and ICl; then, using these bond energies, estimate the standard heats of formation of ClF_3, BrF_3, BrF_5, IF_5, IF_7, and ICl_3. Comment on any differences from the experimental values in Appendix II. (Note that the data for ICl_3 are for the solid.)

4-5. The standard heat of formation of gaseous hydrogen peroxide was derived from measurements of the heat of vaporization (12.34 kcal/mole) and the heat of decomposition of the liquid (-23.44 kcal/mole) into liquid water and oxygen. Given that

$$\Delta H_f^\circ(H_2O, l) = -68.32 \text{ kcal/mole},$$

derive a value for $\Delta H_f^\circ(H_2O_2, g)$.

4-6. Calculate the standard heat of formation of n-heptane gas from its heat of combustion (-1160.0 kcal/mole) and compare the result with that calculated either on the basis of Eq. (4-12) or through bond energies. [Combustion gives $H_2O(l)$.]

4-7. It is proposed to synthesize compounds of the type N_2X_4, in which X is a halogen. The structures are assumed to be symmetrical, with one N—N bond and four N—X bonds. With which halogen would you suggest starting? On a purely thermochemical basis, would you expect the synthesis to be successful?

4-8. A thin layer of chromium metal is frequently used to protect other metals from corrosion. Is this property, e.g., inertness to air, one which would be predicted from thermochemical data? Explain.

4-9. Using thermochemical calculations as a basis, which of the gases, CH_4, CF_4, BF_3 and B_2H_6, would you choose as fuels for burning in air?

4-10. Use the data of Appendix II to derive a value for the N—N bond energy in N_2O_4, the dimer of NO_2.

4-11. Employ the Born-Haber cycle to calculate the crystal energies of the alkaline earth oxides. Compare the experimental values with those calculated in Problem 2-7, using the Born-Mayer equation.

4-12. Use the Born-Haber cycle to calculate the crystal energies of the compounds listed in Problem 2-8. Compare the experimental and theoretical values.

4-13. Assuming the binding energy to be purely electronic, calculate the total electronic energy of H_2, using the data of Table 3-3 and Table 4-1. What proportion of the total electronic energy is the bond dissociation energy?

4-14. Use the data of Appendix II to calculate the bond dissociation energies of the gaseous diatomic alkali halide molecules. Check your answers against the values in Table 2-8.

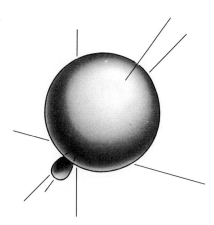

CHAPTER FIVE

Molecular Structure

In discussing the electronic structure of molecules we shall adopt an approach rather different from that used in the case of atoms. Clearly we are faced with a much more complex problem, not only because of the great variety of molecules, but also because of the polycentric nature of the individual structures. We are concerned here, as we were in the case of atoms, with the electronic energy of the molecule; but it is more important, particularly from the point of view of the chemist, to investigate the process by which the atoms interact to form molecules. In other words, we must explain the composition, the geometry, and the binding energy of molecules. It is necessary then to examine what is known experimentally concerning these properties.

The question of composition leads immediately to the concept of valence and the characteristic valences exhibited by the elements. More important still is the fact that one may associate characteristic valences with the groups of the periodic table, since this implies a relation to the electronic structure of the atoms. In the case of ionic valences the relationship is a fairly straightforward one (Section 3–5), but the reasons for the tetravalency of the carbon group elements, the trivalency of the nitrogen group, etc., are less obvious. It is significant also that, to a large extent, there exists a group geometry. This is observed in the pyramidal configurations associated with the nitrogen group elements, such as NH_3, PCl_3, AsF_3, $SbBr_3$, etc., and the angular configurations of molecules involving the oxygen group of elements, such as OH_2, SCl_2, SeH_2, $TeBr_2$, etc. On the other hand, the situation is complicated by the dual or triple valency exhibited by some elements. Even multiple valency seems to be a group property, however, both in regard to the valency and the molecular geometry. The pentahalides of the phosphorus group, for example, are all similar in structure.

We must take into account not only the group properties, but also another experimental discovery of great significance. This is the concept of the chemical bond or, more properly, the localized chemical bond. Evidence that the bond between two atoms is largely determined by these two atoms to the exclusion of others in the molecule has already been presented in the form of average bond energies. We shall see shortly that a similar situation exists with regard to bond lengths. Since it forms the basis of most theories of bonding in polyatomic molecules, the concept of the localized bond has an importance which cannot be overemphasized.

A discussion of crystal or molecular structure as a whole, unlike the discussion of the rather select group of crystals in Chapter 2, requires the application of quantum mechanics. To a large extent, this means a discussion of the covalent or electron-pair bond but, in principle at least, current theories also provide for ionic character in a bond. These theories are then an improvement over the classical treatment rather than just an alternative. On the other hand, the accomplishments of these theories are largely qualitative. Because of the complexity of the calculations, only a very few molecules, mostly diatomic ones, have been studied in any detail. We shall therefore be primarily concerned with relative bond strengths and with the shapes of molecules. For the most part, the discussion will center around free molecules in the gas phase, since in this way we can avoid intermolecular effects, but the term "molecule" will also be applied to molecules or ions which exist as discrete units in solids. The packing of these units, and infinite arrays such as chain or layer structures, will be left until Chapter 7.

5–1. SYMMETRY AND EMPIRICAL CONSIDERATIONS

The Concise Oxford Dictionary defines symmetry as "the beauty resulting from the right proportion between the parts of a body or any whole." Such a definition is equally applicable to a flower or to a molecule, but in the latter case the beauty lies less in the inherent shape than in the opportunity symmetry offers for concise description and for the simplification of theoretical methods. In fact, it is probably true to say regarding symmetry that no other single tool has been of greater assistance in the development of structural chemistry. Although the student will not fully appreciate the usefulness of symmetry until he encounters the more sophisticated and advanced theoretical procedures of molecular structure, we can lay a practical foundation here for the study of symmetry, by placing emphasis on the descriptive aspect. Thus the first section of this chapter may be considered an introduction to the language of structural chemistry.

(a) Symmetry and coordination

A discerning reader, viewing the illustrations of the H_2O and BF_3 molecules in Fig. 5–1, will immediately note regularities in the dimensions and say that the molecules have symmetry. In what systematic manner are we to describe the

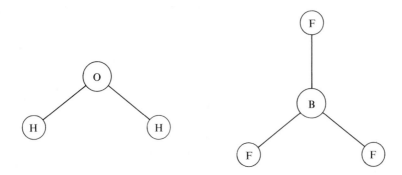

FIG. 5–1. Schematic representation of the structure of H_2O and BF_3.

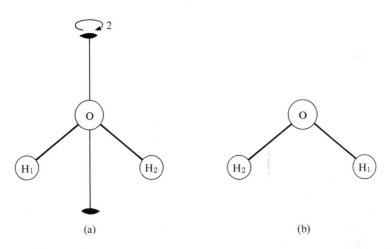

(a)   (b)

FIG. 5–2. The twofold symmetry axis in H_2O. Rotation of 180° about the axis produces configuration (b) from (a).

symmetry? The most elegant means of doing this is in terms of the symmetry elements possessed by the molecule, and the symmetry operations associated with these elements.

Consider first the water molecule, and imagine that we are able to label the hydrogen atoms as shown in Fig. 5–2(a). Suppose now that we rotate the molecule about an axis lying in the plane of the molecule and bisecting the HOH angle ($\angle HOH$) so that the hydrogen atoms 1 and 2 are interchanged. In practice we cannot, of course, distinguish between the hydrogen atoms, so that configuration (b) is actually indistinguishable from (a). Thus we say that we have carried out a *symmetry operation*, and that the axis of rotation is a *symmetry axis*, or more generally, a *symmetry element*. In this particular case there is a twofold symmetry axis, or axis of rotation, and the operation is a rotation through $2\pi/2$.

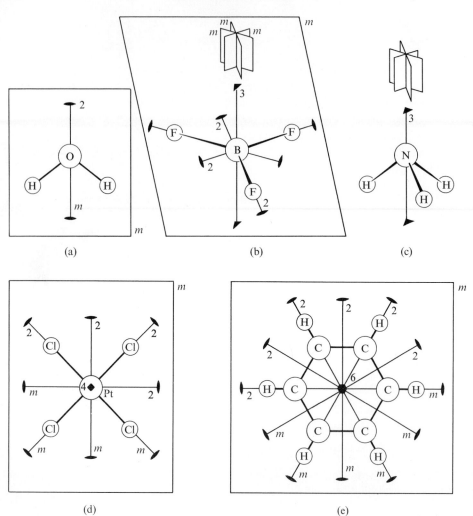

FIG. 5–3. Examples of symmetry in molecules: (a) H_2O, (b) BF_3 trigonal planar, (c) NH_3 trigonal pyramidal, (d) $PtCl_4^{2-}$, square planar, (e) C_6H_6, hexagonal planar. Mirror planes are labeled *m*, while axes of rotation are labeled with the symbols: two-fold, ▲ threefold, ■ fourfold, ● sixfold.

More generally, the operation of rotation through $2\pi/n$ is associated with an *n*-fold axis. Thus the BF_3 molecule of Fig. 5–1 possesses a threefold symmetry axis because a rotation through $2\pi/3$ produces a configuration indistinguishable from the initial one. The adjective *trigonal* is associated with threefold symmetry and, since all four atoms lie in a plane, we speak of BF_3 as having a *trigonal planar* configuration. It should also be observed that BF_3 possesses three subsidiary twofold axes perpendicular to the principal axis. The complete symmetry of

H_2O, BF_3, and other molecules with still higher symmetry axes is shown in Fig. 5–3.

In contrast to BF_3, the NH_3 molecule, while still having a threefold axis, is not planar but has a configuration usually referred to as a *trigonal pyramid*. In terms of symmetry elements, we distinguish between BF_3 and NH_3 by stating that BF_3 possesses a *mirror plane*, or plane of reflection, perpendicular to the threefold axis. The associated operation is reflection in the plane of the mirror and, since the top of the molecule is the same as the bottom, it produces a final configuration indistinguishable from the initial one. A less trivial operation is the reflection associated with one of three vertical mirror planes passing through the threefold axis, for this interchanges two of the fluorine atoms. Note that these vertical planes are also present in the NH_3 molecule, but that the twofold axes are not.

The total number of symmetry elements shown for BF_3 is greater than the number actually required to describe the symmetry; i.e., some of them are superfluous or redundant. This is a common occurrence in highly symmetrical molecules such as we are considering here, and it is possible to formulate general rules regarding these redundancies. Thus the combination of two mirror planes at right angles implies a twofold axis along the line of intersection. This is observed not only in BF_3, but in H_2O, and some of the other molecules illustrated as well.

Only one additional symmetry element will be introduced: the *center of symmetry* or inversion center. The associated operation of *inversion* is essentially reflection in the center, and requires that a line joining symmetrically related atoms be bisected by the inversion center. The dimer of NO_2 (at least in the solid phase) is an example of a molecule which possesses a center of symmetry (Fig. 5–4).

Before going on to more complicated molecules, let us regress for a moment to consider the more or less trivial cases of diatomic and linear molecules (Fig. 5–5). Common to all examples is a rotational axis of order ∞ collinear with the axis of the molecule, but they may possess other symmetry as well. Homonuclear (only one type of atom) diatomic molecules and linear molecules such as CO_2 also possess a mirror plane perpendicular to the axis of the molecule, but heteronuclear (different atoms) diatomic molecules do not. This provides yet another example

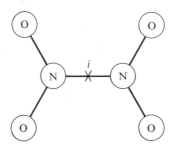

Fig. 5–4. Illustration of the inversion center or center of symmetry (*i*) in planar N_2O_4. A line drawn between symmetrically equivalent atoms is bisected by the inversion center.

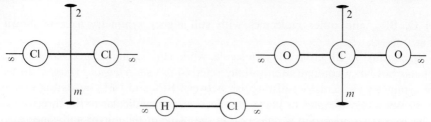

FIG. 5–5. Rotational axes of order ∞: (a) homonuclear diatomic molecule, Cl_2, (b) heteronuclear diatomic molecule, HCl, (c) linear triatomic molecule, CO_2.

of a redundancy of symmetry elements, since the combination of the mirror plane and the rotational axis of order ∞ implies the presence of a center of symmetry and an infinite number of twofold axes perpendicular to the axis of the molecule.

Of rather special interest is the *tetrahedral* configuration so often associated with the carbon atom but common also to many other elements ($[NH_4]^+$, $[PCl_4]^+$, $SnBr_4$, etc.). The tetrahedral configuration, while relatively simple, exhibits a very high degree of symmetry, some of which is difficult to visualize. Drawn inside a cube, as in Fig. 5–6, the symmetry elements are more easily discerned. In particular, one can now see clearly the four threefold axes of the ammonium ion (one collinear with each N—H bond) which are characteristic of tetrahedral symmetry.*

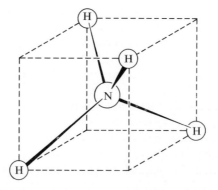

FIG. 5–6. Tetrahedral coordination in NH_4^+.

Fourfold coordination is also achieved in the square planar configuration exemplified by $[PtCl_4]^{2-}$ in Fig. 5–7(a). In common with the tetragonal or square pyramid of (b) and the regular octahedron of (c), the principal axis of symmetry is fourfold. An interesting point arises with these configurations when the four

---

* The nonclassical scholar should be wary of confusing the terms tetrahedral (Greek: *tetra*, four; *hedra*, base) and *tetragonal* (Greek: *tetra*, four; *gonos*, angled). As it is currently used, "tetragonal" denotes the presence of a single fourfold symmetry axis.

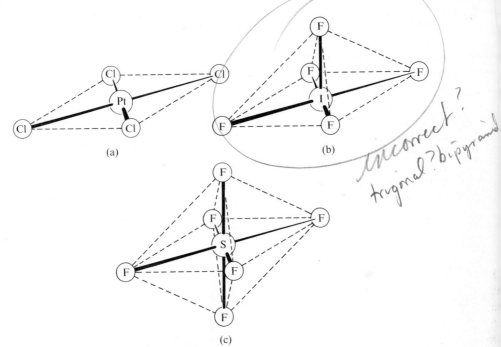

incorrect?
trigonal? bipyramid

FIG. 5-7. Configurations with fourfold symmetry axes: (a) $PtCl_4^{2-}$, square planar, (b) IF_5, square pyramid, (c) SF_6, octahedral.

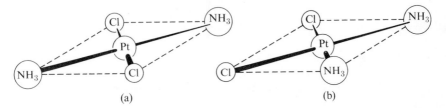

FIG. 5-8. Geometrical isomers of square planar $Pt(NH_3)_2Cl_2$: (a) trans, (b) cis.

coordinating species are not identical, as in $Pt(NH_3)_2Cl_2$. This molecule, although planar, does not have a fourfold axis of symmetry and, as Fig. 5-8 shows, there are two possible structures with the same stoichiometric formula. These are known as *geometrical isomers* and are labeled *cis* or *trans* depending on whether similar species are adjacent to or opposite each other. The existence of geometrical isomers of $Pt(NH_3)_2Cl_2$ is an important piece of evidence in confirming the structure of the compound, since it rules out the possibility of tetrahedral co-ordination where geometrical isomerism is not possible. The phenomenon of isomerism is of particular importance in the study of coordination compounds, and is discussed at some length in Chapter 6.

We have covered a great deal of material very briefly in this section, and it would pay the student well to review, objectively, what he has learned. He should first of all be able to describe the structure of a molecule in brief precise terms by making use of the symmetry elements which we have defined. Second, by employing the accepted nomenclature for the common configurations, he will be able to lend a further conciseness to his powers of description.

Finally, if the student has an inquiring scientific mind, he will be asking himself a number of questions. Why does NH_3 adopt a pyramidal configuration when the threefold coordination of BF_3 gives rise to a planar structure? If the coordination is fivefold, what determines whether the structure will be the square pyramid of IF_5 or the trigonal bipyramid of PCl_5 (Fig. 5–9)? What, indeed, determines the degree of coordination? These are questions which we shall endeavor to answer in the remainder of this chapter.

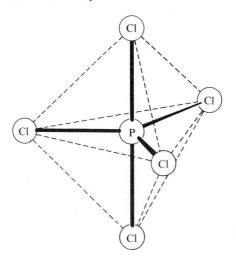

Fig. 5–9. Fivefold coordination in trigonal bipyramidal PCl_5.

(b) Methods of structure determination

To attempt a description of even the principal methods of structural investigation in one small section of this text is a rather pretentious undertaking. We must, of necessity, restrict ourselves to essentials. For the problem at hand, the essentials will consist mainly of a description of the type of information each method provides, and an objective evaluation of the quality of this information. We shall attempt to give a concise description of the physical basis of each method; but for detail, the reader is referred to more specialized texts, in particular the excellent book by Wheatley.

Before turning to the methods themselves, we should ascertain precisely what information is desired. Our primary interest is in the relative positions of the nuclei involved, expressed in terms of internuclear distances or bond lengths and bond

TABLE 5-1

THE CAPABILITIES OF THE VARIOUS EXPERIMENTAL METHODS USED
FOR THE DETERMINATION OF MOLECULAR STRUCTURE
(From Wheatley, *Molecular Structure*)

Method	Molecular parameters	Molecular symmetry
Pure rotation spectra	✓	✓
Vibration spectra	X	✓
Rotational Raman	✓	✓
Vibrational Raman spectra	X	✓
Electron diffraction	✓	✓
X-ray diffraction	✓	✓
Neutron diffraction	✓	✓
Classical stereochemistry	X	✓
Dipole moments	X	✓
Magnetic measurements	X	✓
Nuclear magnetic resonance	✓	✓

In the above table ✓ = yes, and X = no.

angles. In the case of H_2O, for example, a description of the molecular structure would consist of a statement of the O—H bond length and the ∠HOH (HOH angle). This problem has two aspects, however: the symmetry of the molecule and the actual dimensions of it. While some methods provide both pieces of information, a number of them give only the symmetry. The vibrational spectrum of H_2O, for example, clearly reveals that the molecule is bent rather than linear, but the actual dimensions are best obtained from the rotational spectrum. Table 5-1 summarizes the capabilities of the principal methods of structural investigation in this regard. Finally, the remark above concerning the relative positions of nuclei does not mean that the structural chemist is indifferent to the distribution of the electrons. On the contrary, it is simply that (except in special cases) accurate information of this sort is beyond the scope of present techniques.

By far the greatest part of the information available on molecular structure has been obtained with the aid of spectroscopic or diffraction methods. These are in fact still the definitive methods, but there is a variety of other techniques, some of them quite new, others of classical stature, which provide important and sometimes crucial pieces of information in a structural investigation. Accordingly, it is convenient to divide our discussion into three parts, under the headings of spectroscopic methods, diffraction methods, and miscellaneous methods.

We saw in Section 3-1 that the electronic line spectra of atoms are a direct result of the quantization of the electronic energy of atoms, a spectral line being exhibited when an atom absorbs a discrete quantum of energy (i.e., a photon of frequency $\nu' = \Delta E/h$), and is raised to an excited state; or when it emits an

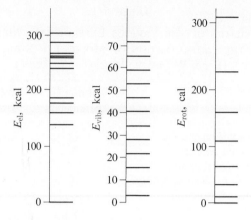

FIG. 5–10. Electronic, vibrational, and rotational energy levels of CO. Note that a different scale is used in each case.

energy quantum or photon and drops to a lower excited state or the ground state. Precisely the same reasoning may be applied to molecular spectra except that we must take into account not only the electronic energy but also the energy associated with rotation and vibration of the molecule. Thus we may, to a good approximation, regard the total energy as the sum of three independent terms,

$$E_{\text{total}} = E_{\text{electron}} + E_{\text{vib}} + E_{\text{rot}}.$$

Each type of energy is quantized, but the size of the quantum is quite different in each case. The separation between the rotational energy levels (i.e., the magnitude of the rotational quantum) is quite small, of the order of 5 to 10 cal, while the vibrational quantum is about one hundred times larger. An electronic transition involves a still greater amount of energy, about 100 kcal. Thus for a given electronic state there is a series of vibrational energy levels, while for a given vibrational state the molecule may exist in one of a series of rotational states. The scheme is illustrated in Fig. 5–10, which shows the energy levels of a diatomic molecule.

Transitions which occur between pairs of rotational levels, the electronic and vibrational states of the molecule remaining unchanged, give rise to a *pure rotational spectrum*. Because the size of the quantum is small, rotational spectra are observed at very long wavelengths, and form the subject of study of far-infrared and microwave spectroscopy. Analysis of observed spectra yields directly the rotational energy levels from which the principal moments of inertia of the molecule may be calculated. These in turn may be used to obtain bond lengths and interbond angles. The rotational transitions are usually studied in absorption and, since great accuracy is possible in the measurements, it is possible to obtain very accurate molecular parameters in this way. The problem usually lies in having more unknown parameters than experimental observables.

With diatomic molecules the problem does not arise, because there is one moment of inertia and only a single parameter, the bond length. However, in the case of a linear triatomic molecule such as N_2O, there is still only one moment of inertia but two parameters, the N—N and N—O bond lengths. (The moment referred to is about an axis perpendicular to the bond; the angular momentum of the electrons is ignored.)

This general problem of having more unknowns than experimental observables is one frequently met with in structural investigations, and is usually countered by making use of isotopic substitution. The substitution technique is based on the assumption that the replacement of an atom by one of its isotopes does not affect the bonding; hence the molecular dimensions remain the same. In effect, isotopic substitution means that we regard the electronic problem as completely separable from those of rotation and vibration, as in fact we did when we expressed the energy as the sum of three independent terms. Formally, this statement is known as the *Born-Oppenheimer approximation*.

In applying the technique to N_2O, one might prepare a sample of NNO^{18} or, alternatively, replace one or more of the N^{14} atoms with N^{15}. In all cases, the bond lengths would remain the same, but the change in mass would alter the moment of inertia and provide an additional piece of information. While the use of N^{15} and O^{18} and many other isotopes is still rather expensive, deuterium substitution in hydrogen-containing compounds has become almost commonplace. In this regard, it should be mentioned that isotopic substitution may have a profound effect on the symmetry of the molecule. Thus, while D_2O and H_2O have the same symmetry, a single substitution to give HDO eliminates all symmetry but the mirror plane in the plane of the molecule.

A *pure vibrational spectrum* would be observed if a molecule underwent a transition from one vibrational level to another without changing its electronic state or rotational energy. For a diatomic molecule, absorption would occur primarily at a single frequency, corresponding to the frequency of vibration of the nuclei. For small amplitudes of vibration, the motion is very nearly simple-harmonic, and may be described in terms of the masses of the nuclei and the strength of the bond as expressed in the force constant [see Section 3–3(b)]. Note that, while there is a qualitative correlation between the force constant and the bond energy, we need not expect it to be either simple or accurate, since the former represents the force required to stretch the bond slightly, while the latter is the energy needed to break it. (One is a function of the depth of the potential well and the other of its first derivative near the equilibrium distance. See Figs. 1–2 and 1–3.)

A vibrational spectrum such as that discussed may be observed in the solid phase, but in the gas phase a change in rotational energy always accompanies a vibrational transition. In other words, one looks at transitions from the rotational levels of one vibrational state to the rotational levels of another vibrational state. The *vibration-rotation spectrum* thus consists of a band of lines much like the pure rotational spectrum, but shifted to the region of the frequency of vibration. An example of such a spectrum is given in Fig. 5–11. While in principle one can ob-

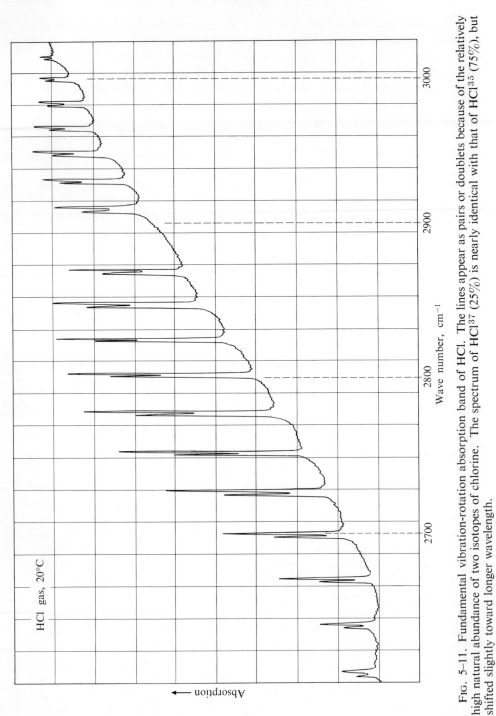

Fig. 5–11. Fundamental vibration-rotation absorption band of HCl. The lines appear as pairs or doublets because of the relatively high natural abundance of two isotopes of chlorine. The spectrum of HCl^{37} (25%) is nearly identical with that of HCl^{35} (75%), but shifted slightly toward longer wavelength.

tain as much information from vibrational-rotational spectra as from pure rotational spectra, the analysis of a band spectrum is considerably more involved and is complicated by rotational-vibrational interaction. (The moments of inertia are slightly different in two different vibrational states, for example.) These factors tend to make the data obtained from vibrational-rotational spectra somewhat less accurate than those obtained from pure rotational spectra.

In the case of polyatomic molecules, the situation is considerably more complicated, because many more vibrations and corresponding frequencies of absorption are possible. In fact, there are $3n - 6$ ($3n - 5$ in the case of linear molecules) frequencies at which absorption may occur, where n is the number of atoms in the molecule. The frequencies of these vibrations depend, in a rather complicated way, on the masses of the atoms and on the geometry of the molecule, but usually they are not very sensitive to small changes in the bond lengths or bond angles. On the other hand, the presence of symmetry in a molecule may make some of the frequencies of absorption the same, or it may prohibit absorption altogether. Vibrational spectroscopy, therefore, can provide valuable clues to the symmetry of the molecule in question.

Much the same considerations apply to electronic spectra of the molecule. As we might expect, each electronic transition is accompanied by rotational and vibrational transitions, so that the spectrum consists of a series of bands. These are studied in both emission and absorption and, in recent years, have been of especial value, as far as structure is concerned, in the investigation of short-lived species such as free radicals, ions, etc. Not only are such species often produced under conditions which favor electronic excitation, but in addition, electronic spectra are relatively more intense, and the methods of detection more sensitive, than vibrational or rotational spectra.

One aspect ignored in the above discussion is the selection rules governing the allowed transitions. Not all of the possible transitions (in fact, relatively few) are observed in infrared vibrational or rotational spectra, but the detailed selection rules tend to be rather complicated. There are, however, two gross selection rules overriding all others. These are: (1) a vibrational infrared spectrum will be observed only when the dipole moment changes during the vibration concerned, and (2) a rotational infrared or microwave spectrum will be observed only when the molecule possesses a permanent dipole moment. These rules mean, for example, that homonuclear diatomic molecules (H_2, N_2, O_2, etc.) do not normally absorb in the infrared or microwave regions.

On the other hand, the selection rules for *Raman spectra* or Raman scattering are dependent on the polarizability of the molecule involved, with the result that Raman and infrared spectra tend to complement one another (see Fig. 5–12). The process of light scattering is a two-stage one involving, first, absorption of a quantum of the incident radiation and, second, the re-emission of a light quantum in the scattering direction. Much of the scattered radiation is due to the re-emission of quanta equal in magnitude to those absorbed. This radiation (Rayleigh scattering) is, therefore, of the same frequency as the incident light.

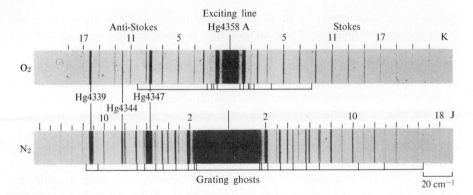

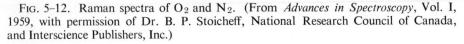

FIG. 5–12. Raman spectra of O_2 and N_2. (From *Advances in Spectroscopy*, Vol. I, 1959, with permission of Dr. B. P. Stoicheff, National Research Council of Canada, and Interscience Publishers, Inc.)

If, however, the scattered radiation is subjected to spectroscopic analysis, it will be found that additional weaker lines exist on the low (Stokes) and high (anti-Stokes) frequency sides of the exciting line. Stokes' lines, which are the stronger, arise from the simultaneous absorption of a vibrational and/or rotational quantum, while the anti-Stokes lines are due to the simultaneous emission of a vibrational and/or rotational quantum during the scattering process.

Apart from the selection rules, the analysis of Raman spectra is very similar to that of infrared spectra, and the same considerations apply regarding information as to symmetry and dimensions. In the past, most Raman studies were restricted to the liquid phase, where a high proportion of the incident light is scattered, but in recent years improved instruments with greater resolution and sensitivity have been employed to record gas phase rotational spectra. These give results of a quality comparable to that of infrared or microwave spectra.

The diffraction techniques also depend on scattering phenomena, but only coherent (i.e., of the same wavelength) scattering is of interest, so that the problem may be treated classically. The theoretical background is much the same in all cases, but each method has a unique character which makes it suitable to a particular application. By far the most commonly used method of investigating molecular structure is *X-ray diffraction*, but it is employed almost exclusively with solids.

Electron diffraction, on the other hand, finds its greatest usefulness in the study of molecules in the gas phase, for several reasons. Because of the charge on the electrons of the incident beam, the electrons are scattered more strongly than X rays, and have little penetrating power. Therefore they are suitable for use only with very thin crystals, or with gases at low pressure. Electron diffraction also offers certain advantages over X-ray diffraction in the detection of lighter atoms, because the scattering power of the individual atoms does not vary as widely with electrons as it does with X rays. With X rays, the scattering power is approxi-

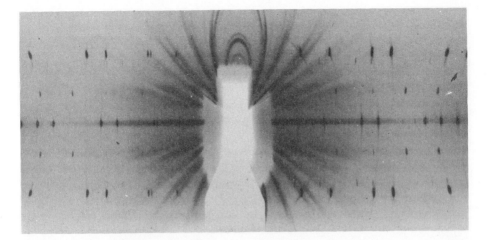

Fig. 5–13. X-ray diffraction photograph (of NaCl) obtained by the rotation technique.

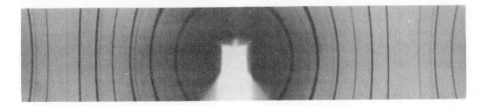

Fig. 5–14. X-ray powder photograph of NaCl.

mately proportional to the number of orbital electrons; hence it is very difficult to detect a light atom such as hydrogen in the presence even of carbon atoms.

It is with light atoms that *neutron diffraction* comes into its own, for in this case the scattering is a property of the nucleus rather than of the orbital electrons. The technique has thus been very useful in the study of compounds containing the hydrogen atom (ice, ammonium halides, etc.). On the other hand, it presents such formidable experimental difficulties that it is rarely used for a complete structure determination, but is employed to find the position of hydrogen atoms in structures otherwise known from X-ray investigations. Notable among the experimental problems is that of obtaining a strong beam of monochromatic neutrons from the continuum available at normal pile operating temperatures.

A single crystal and its associated crystal lattice may be thought of as the three-dimensional analog of the diffraction grating. Thus the diffraction photograph of a single crystal, using a collimated beam, consists of a two-dimensional array of spots (Fig. 5–13). If a finely powdered sample of randomly oriented crystallites is used instead of a single crystal, then the spots degenerate into a series of arcs, as in Fig. 5–14.

To reproduce the powder photograph, imagine a large number of photographs like Fig. 5–13 superimposed, with a common center but randomly rotated. The lines of the power photo are quite sharp but, if the crystallites are made very small, the pattern becomes diffuse and has fewer features. This is the sort of pattern produced by an amorphous substance and, in the extreme, by free molecules in the liquid or gaseous phase. Thus an electron diffraction pattern has the appearance of Fig. 5–15. No matter what the type of pattern recorded, to make full use of the data, it is necessary to record not only the positions of the spots or arcs, but their relative intensities as well.

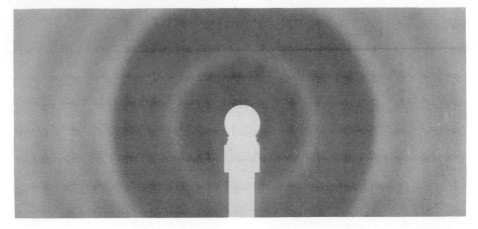

FIG. 5–15. Electron diffraction pattern of 1, 3, 5, 7-cyclo-octatetraene. (The authors are grateful to Dr. Kenneth W. Hedberg, Dept. of Chemistry, Oregon State Univ., for supplying this photograph.)

The amount of information provided directly by any diffraction technique is limited to interatomic vectors or distances, depending on the particular method. Because of the unknown phase relationship of the diffracted beam, it is necessary to adopt an indirect approach in which the calculated diffraction pattern for a trial structure is compared with the observed pattern. The trial structure is arrived at by combining the interatomic vectors with a knowledge of structural chemistry; but once a measure of agreement is obtained, the process becomes an iterative one of refinement. The closer one comes to the true structure, the better the picture provided by the experimental data. One form in which this information may be portrayed is the *Fourier electron density map*. An example of a final Fourier map is shown in Fig. 5–16. (See also Fig. 2–14.) This is not the only method of refinement, but it is probably the preferred one.

The most common use of X-ray powder photographs today is as a method of qualitative analysis. Because of the ease with which such photographs are obtained, the method is particularly suited to this application, and a large library of photographs has been established. While largely superseded by single-crystal techniques for structural investigation, it is still used when single crystals are im-

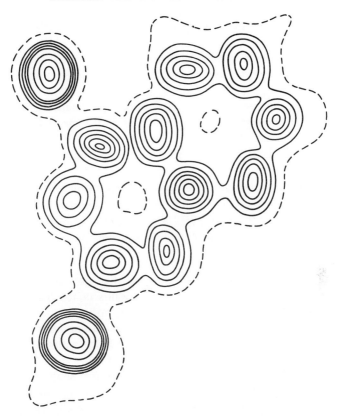

FIG. 5–16. Fourier electron density map of 1:3 dichloronaphthalene. The molecule does not lie exactly in the plane of the projection. (The authors are indebted to Dr. J. Trotter, Chemistry Dept., Univ. of British Columbia, for this Fourier map.)

possible to obtain because of reactivity or instability of the compound under investigation. Even then the powder method is restricted to relatively simple structures.

Similarly, electron-diffraction photographs provide little information directly because of the random orientation. If the symmetry of the molecule is known, however, it is possible to obtain very accurate internuclear distances. In this sense, it is similar to rotational spectroscopy.

Little will be said at this point concerning other methods of investigating molecular structure, although some methods will be mentioned in later discussions. Many of these techniques are concerned with the magnetic properties of molecules, however, and a few general observations are pertinent. Any substance which possesses no permanent magnetic dipole is said to be diamagnetic, and will, if placed in an inhomogeneous magnetic field, tend to move from a stronger to a weaker part of the field. A paramagnetic substance, possessing permanent dipoles, will exhibit the opposite effect in an inhomogeneous magnetic field. The permanent magnetic dipoles are, for the most part, those associated with the spin of un-paired electrons, although some nuclei also possess a small dipole. Quantitatively the effect may be measured in bulk by observing the effect of a magnetic field on the mass (Gouy balance), so that the number of unpaired electrons in a molecule may be estimated.

An alternative technique is that of electron-spin resonance (ESR), which in-vestigates the effect of the imposed magnetic field on the energy levels available to the unpaired electron [see, for example, Section 3–4(b)]. Because of the interac-tions with the nuclei, ESR also provides information regarding the environment of the electron.

Nuclear magnetic resonance (NMR) studies are of a similar nature, but concern the much smaller magnetic dipole of the nucleus (about $\frac{1}{1000}$ that of an unpaired electron). The technique has been particularly useful in locating light atoms, such as fluorine and hydrogen, which possess a nuclear magnetic moment.

(c) Bond lengths

Having discussed the shapes of molecules, we shall now consider the question of size, and look at some of the quantitative results of the methods of Section 5–1(b). This will not be simply a tabulation, but rather a study of some of the empirical relationships which have developed apace with our ever growing knowl-edge of molecular structure. It is these facts, combined with the configurational data of Section 5–1(a), which any theory must set out to explain.

All of the bond lengths or internuclear distances (we shall employ the terms interchangeably) will be quoted only to 0.01 A, without any statement of error. The latter will rarely be higher than ± 0.03 A, and is usually less, depending on the method employed, the symmetry of the molecule, and the care exercised experi-mentally. For these reasons, it is difficult to make generalizations, but many bond lengths are now being reported to 0.001 A, and the C—C distance in diamond is quoted at 1.54452 A $\pm$ 0.00014 at 18°C. It is interesting, in connection with these very precise measurements, that we need not expect perfect agreement among values obtained by different methods because, in effect, they measure different things. By X-ray diffraction, for example, we can determine the electron distribution from which the positions of the nuclei are inferred, while neutron diffraction permits us to measure the position of the nuclei themselves. Thermal motion of the atoms adds a further complication: e.g., spectroscopic methods determine an average value of $1/s^2$, that is, $1/s_e = \sqrt{(1/s^2)_{av}}$, while nuclear mag-netic resonance gives an average of $1/s^3$, that is, $1/s_e = \sqrt{(1/s^3)_{av}}$.

Recalling from Chapter 4 the approximate constancy of bond energies from molecule to molecule, it is logical that we should look for an analogous phe-nomenon in connection with bond lengths. As the examples of Table 5–2 show, it is indeed true that the length of the bond between a given pair of atoms is often the same (or very nearly so) in many different molecules. To be sure, there are limitations on the general rule relating to the multiplicity of the bond; even taking

TABLE 5–2

SOME SELECTED BOND LENGTHS
(in angstroms)

Bond	Molecule	Bond length
O—H	Hydroxyl radical, OH	0.97
O—H	Water, H_2O	0.96
O—H	Hydrogen peroxide, H_2O_2	0.97
O—H	Methanol, CH_3OH	0.96
O—H	Formic acid, CHOOH	0.96
C—C	Diamond	1.54
C—C	Ethane, C_2H_6	1.54
C—C	Ethanol, C_2H_5OH	1.55
C—C	Propane, C_3H_8	1.54
C—C	Isopropyl alcohol, $(CH_3)_2CHOH$	1.54
C—C	n-hexane, C_6H_{14}	1.53
C—S	Diethyl sulfide, $(C_2H_3)_2S$	1.81
C—S	Perfluoro dimethyl sulfide, $(CF_3)_2S$	1.83
C—S	Ethylene sulfide, C_2H_4S	1.82
C—S	Ethane-thiol, C_2H_5SH	1.81

these into account, there are exceptions. What is surprising is that there are not more exceptions. It is really rather remarkable that the bond between a pair of atoms is not more affected by other atoms which are nearby.

While recognizing the recurrence of certain bond lengths, we must at the same time accept the fact that a given pair of atoms may apparently enter into more than one type of bonding arrangement. There is ample evidence of this, some of which is given in Table 5–3. Similar observations may be made with regard to the dissociation energies of these bonds. In fact, insofar as information is available, the correlation between bond energy and bond length is very good.

Some of these data find ready qualitative explanation in terms of the Lewis electron-sharing concept of the covalent bond. Thus the C—C bonds in ethane, ethylene, and acetylene are stated to be single, double, and triple bonds, corresponding to the sharing of two, four, and six electrons, respectively. Other examples given here present a greater problem. For instance, the removal of an electron from O_2 to give O_2^+ apparently strengthens the bond somewhat, while removal of an electron from N_2 weakens the bond. Phenomena such as these set a rather formidable task for the theoreticians.

The success achieved in assigning a characteristic radius to ions leads us to try the same thing with atoms which engage in covalent bonding. Such a step is suggested also by the very localized nature of covalent bonds. The hypothesis may

TABLE 5-3

VARIATIONS IN C—C, O—O AND N—O BOND LENGTHS

Bond	Molecule	Bond length, angstroms	Bond dissociation energy, kcal/mole
C—C	Ethane, C_2H_6	1.54	83
	Graphite	1.42	
	Benzene, C_6H_6	1.39	
	Ethylene, C_2H_4	1.34	128
	C_2 (short life species)	1.31	140
	Acetylene, C_2H_2	1.20	230
O—O	Hydrogen peroxide	1.48	48
	O_2^{2-} in BaO_2	1.49	
	O_2^- in KO_2	1.28	
	Ozone, O_3	1.28	
	O_2^+ (short life species)	1.12	
	Oxygen molecule O_2	1.21	118
N—O	NO_3^- in N_2O_5	1.24	
	NO_2^- in $NaNO_2$	1.24	
	Nitrous oxide, N_2O	1.19	
	Nitrogen dioxide, NO_2	1.19	73
	NO_2^+ in N_2O_5	1.15	
	Nitric oxide, NO	1.15	150
	NO^+ (short life species)	1.06	

be very quickly checked by making use of the data of Table 5–4. Thus a covalent radius may be obtained for the halogen atoms by halving the internuclear distance in the corresponding halogen molecule. If now these are subtracted from the bond lengths of the appropriate hydrogen halides, we should get a constant figure representing the radius of the hydrogen atom. The results (in the third column of Table 5–4) confirm our premise, but indicate that $r(F)$ as derived from F_2 is somewhat larger than usual.

The same fact is suggested by the cross-checks with the diatomic interhalogen compounds. The reader will appreciate, however, that it is possible to carry the derivation process further to obtain a complete set of covalent radii such that, in most cases, the sum of two radii will be approximately equal to the internuclear distance for the two atoms covalently bonded. Such a set of radii was first formulated by Pauling in 1932 and is reproduced with only minor changes in Table 5–5. The changes are, of course, a result of the more extensive and more accurate structural information now available.

TABLE 5–4

BOND LENGTHS FOR SOME DIATOMIC MOLECULES

(in angstroms)

Molecule	Bond length	Derived radius	Sum of radii
F_2	1.42	F 0.71	
Cl_2	1.99	Cl 1.00	
Br_2	2.28	Br 1.14	
I_2	2.67	I 1.34	
HF	0.92	H 0.21	
HCl	1.27	H 0.27	
HBr	1.41	H 0.27	
HI	1.61	H 0.27	
ClF	1.63		1.71
BrCl	2.14		2.14
BrF	1.76		1.85
ICl	2.32		2.34
H_2	0.74	H 0.37	

TABLE 5–5

COVALENT RADII

(in angstroms)

Multiple-bond factors					H 0.29
Double, 0.86 Triple, 0.78	B 0.88	C 0.77	N 0.70	O 0.66	F 0.64
		Si 1.17	P 1.10	S 1.04	Cl 0.99
Double, 0.91 Triple, 0.85		Ge 1.22	As 1.21	Se 1.17	Br 1.14
		Sn 1.40	Sb 1.41	Te 1.37	I 1.33

Although the above radii apply to single covalent bonds, there is nothing, in principle, to prevent one from deriving double and triple bond radii where appropriate. It is unnecessary to tabulate the multiple-bond radii, since they may be obtained from the single-bond radii by the application of the simple factors given in Table 5–5. In the majority of cases, bond lengths predicted by using these radii are in good agreement with the experimental results. Care must be exercised,

TABLE 5-6

SOME SELECTED C—Cl BOND LENGTHS
(in angstroms)

Molecule	Bond length
CBr_2Cl_2	1.75
CCl_4	1.77
C_2Cl_6	1.76
$(CH_3)_2CCl_2$	1.78
C_6Cl_6, hexachlorobenzene	1.71
$C_6H_4Cl_2$, o-dichlorobenzene	1.71
m-dichlorobenzene	1.69
C_6H_5Cl, chlorobenzene	1.69

however, because often the multiplicity of the bond is by no means clear (Table 5-3). The theoretical discussion of Sections 5-2 and 5-3 will help to clarify this point.

Even in relatively simple molecules a number of rather marked exceptions to the additivity rule of atomic radii have been observed. Attention has already been drawn to the case of F_2, but one may cite also the following: the O—O bond length in H_2O_2 (calculated = 1.32 A, observed = 1.47 A); the N—N bond length in N_2H_4 (calculated 1.40 A, observed = 1.47 A); and the internuclear distance in H_2 (calculated = 0.58 A, observed = 0.74 A). Various attempts have been made to eliminate these discrepancies by introducing correction factors into the simple additivity relationship, but none have met with far-reaching success.

Schomaker and Stevenson, for example, use larger radii for O, N, and F and then subtract a correction factor proportional to the difference in electronegativity [Section 5-2(e)] of the bonded atoms. This scheme successfully accounts for most of the major discrepancies listed, but gives rise to others, unless a rather complicated and to some extent arbitrary set of rules and proportionality factors is employed. Clearly more than electronegativity must be taken into account.

From a purely practical point of view, the prediction of an unknown bond length is best accomplished by a survey of analogous bonds in other molecules of similar structure. As an example, consider the selected C—Cl bond lengths of Table 5-6. It is evident from these data that the internuclear distance in substituted hydrocarbons is approximately 1.76–1.77 A, somewhat larger than the 1.70 A or so indicated for chlorobenzene compounds. We should be on fairly safe ground, therefore, in predicting the C—Cl bond length in, say, p-dichlorobenzene to be 1.69 A, as experiment indeed verifies. One might also note that the presence of adjacent chlorine atoms, much larger than hydrogen atoms, tends to lengthen the C—Cl bond. Considerations such as these play an important part in the preliminary stages of most structural investigations.

5–2. DIATOMIC MOLECULES

The application of quantum mechanics to molecular structure in all its various aspects is one of the most popular and challenging fields of study in modern chemistry. It is symptomatic of the problems involved that, despite concerted effort and significant advances, we must still be content, in large measure, with qualitative agreement between experiment and theory. With molecular structure, as with atomic structure, it has been necessary to formulate approximate methods of treatment, and for the same reasons.

Two approaches in particular stand out: molecular orbital (MO) theory and the valence-bond (VB) treatment. The latter is the older, having been developed by Heitler and London in 1927, only one year after Schrödinger's introduction of the wave equation; but the MO approximation, associated with Hückel and Mulliken, is gaining prominence, largely because of its application in the field of spectroscopy and the greater ease with which it lends itself to calculations. As its name implies, the MO approach allots electrons to molecular orbitals similar in many respects to atomic orbitals, except that they are polycentric, due to the presence of more than one nucleus.

The VB method, on the other hand, pictures the formation of a molecule as arising from the bringing together of complete atoms which, although interacting, retain a large part of their individual character. In a sense, the two approximations are complementary, but at the same time they have much in common and, in many cases, lead to the same conclusions in different ways. It is generally conceded that the MO theory is conceptually the simpler; hence we shall begin with this and, for the other reasons stated above, place somewhat greater emphasis on this approach.

(a) The hydrogen molecule; MO approximation

Our purpose in outlining the problems involved in the theoretical study of molecular structure and in introducing the principal methods of overcoming them can best be accomplished by considering the hydrogen molecule. This system consists of two nuclei (protons) and two electrons which will interact according to Coulomb's law, as shown in Fig. 5–17. The potential energy Φ may then be written

$$\Phi = -e^2\left(\frac{1}{r_{a1}} + \frac{1}{r_{a2}} + \frac{1}{r_{b1}} + \frac{1}{r_{b2}}\right) + \frac{e^2}{r_{12}} + \frac{e^2}{R_{ab}}. \tag{5–1}$$

As we do in the case of many-electron atoms, we may rigorously formulate the Schrödinger equation appropriate to the problem by substituting Φ as given by Eq. (5–1) into the general equation. The complexity of the problem, again in common with the problem of many-electron atoms, prohibits rigorous solution of the Schrödinger equation and forces us to devise approximate methods.

The relative simplicity of MO theory lies in the fact that the basic principles of the treatment are largely the same as those relevant to atoms. We know from

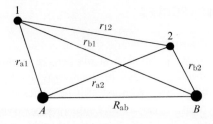

FIG. 5–17. Schematic illustration of the interaction between two protons (A and B) and two electrons (1 and 2).

molecular spectra that the electronic energy levels are quantized; hence it is reasonable to assume that the orbital approximation may be applied to molecules as well as atoms. Thus each electron is described by a wave function or MO, but now the orbitals are polycentric, and not monocentric as in the case of an atom. The interpretation of ψ and ψ^2 remains the same, with ψ^2 measuring an electron probability density, and the same methods (Fig. 3–7) may be employed in representing ψ or ψ^2. Each ψ and the energy value with which it is associated is characterized by a set of quantum numbers, including m_s, the spin quantum number which may take only the values $\pm\frac{1}{2}$. Once the orbitals have been determined, we may employ an Aufbau process, assigning two electrons per orbital, in keeping with the Pauli principle, to build up the structure of the molecule.

As an alternative to rigorous solution of the wave equation, the energy and the wave function may be determined with the aid of the *variation principle*. A detailed application of the principle is out of place here, but the principle itself is important enough to warrant description. The Schrödinger equation for a one-particle system, i.e.,

$$\nabla^2\psi + \frac{8\pi^2 m}{h^2}(E - \Phi)\psi = 0,$$

may be rewritten as

$$\left(\Phi - \frac{h^2}{8\pi^2 m}\nabla^2\right)\psi = E\psi$$

or

$$H\psi = E\psi. \tag{5–2}$$

The quantity $H = \Phi - (h^2/8\pi^2 m)\nabla^2$ is called the quantum mechanical Hamiltonian by analogy with the classical Hamiltonian $H = \Phi + K$. It should be noted that it is not a simple multiplicative factor but is an operator, since ∇^2 means the wave function is to be differentiated. The form of Eq. (5–2) is particularly convenient, for in application to many particle systems H need only be changed to

$$H = \Phi - \frac{h^2}{8\pi^2}\sum_{\substack{\text{all} \\ \text{particles}}}\frac{\nabla^2}{m}.$$

To obtain an expression for the total energy, we multiply both sides of Eq. (5–2) by ψ and rearrange it to give

$$E = \frac{\psi H \psi}{\psi^2}.$$ (5–3)

The expression is still not suitable, however, because ψ is a function of the spatial coordinates and E is not. The problem is overcome by integrating Eq. (5–3) over the spatial coordinates, so that the final expression is

$$E = \frac{\int \psi H \psi \, d\tau}{\int \psi^2 \, d\tau}.$$ (5–4)

In a cartesian coordinate system, $d\tau = dx \, dy \, dz$.

When we use Eq. (5–4) to obtain the energy E, it is necessary to formulate a suitable wave function ψ. This is not as formidable a task as at first appears, because Eq. (5–4) is less sensitive than might be expected to the function chosen for ψ. In other words, the energy calculated is usually more accurate than the wave function employed. Furthermore, Eq. (5–4) has the rather remarkable property of never giving an energy which is lower than the true energy. (The state of zero energy of molecules, as in the case of atoms, is that of infinitely separated particles, so that the energy of the molecule is negative.) This means that if a number of functions are tried for ψ, that giving the lowest energy is the best. Let us also point out that this approach can be elaborated on by inserting one or more parameters in the function and adjusting these to minimize the energy.

The problem facing us then in treating the hydrogen molecule is to fashion a plausible bicentric molecular orbital for the two electrons. To do this we may reason that when an electron is closer to one nucleus (say A) than to the other, then the significant forces acting on the electron will be much the same as those operative in the isolated atom A, and in this region the MO must resemble the AO of the isolated atom. Similar considerations will apply to nucleus B, so we are justified in assuming that, to a good approximation, the MO may be represented by a combination of the two AO's of the type

$$\Psi = \psi_A + \lambda \psi_B.$$

The constant λ denotes the degree to which one AO is favored over the other and is, in effect, a measure of the polarity of the MO. The expression is therefore applicable to diatomic molecules generally, and is furthermore an illustration of a common technique for formulating MO's: that of the *Linear Combination of Atomic Orbitals* (LCAO). In the case of the ground state of the hydrogen molecule, there is little doubt that the proper atomic orbitals to be employed are the $1s$ ones, but in more complicated molecules the situation is not as simple. This matter will be discussed in the next section.

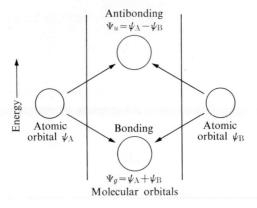

FIG. 5–18. Energy relation between two AO's ψ_A and ψ_B and the bonding Ψ_g and antibonding Ψ_u MO's which may be formed from them in a homonuclear diatomic molecule.

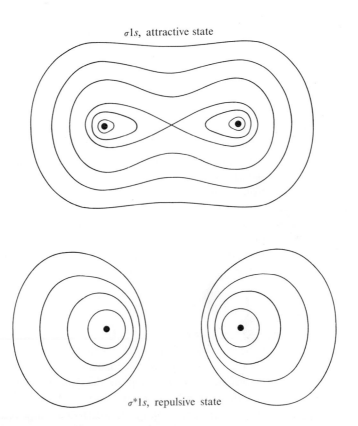

FIG. 5–19. Contours of constant electron density in the charge distributions of the bonding (Ψ_g^2) and antibonding (Ψ_u^2) states of H_2.

Using the ground-state $1s$ orbitals of the hydrogen atom in formulating the MO, we then have

$$\Psi = H_A(1s) + \lambda H_B(1s).$$

Applying the variation method, we then use this wave function to calculate the energy as given by Eq. (5–4), and find that the energy is a minimum for $\lambda^2 = 1$ or $\lambda = \pm 1$. There are, in other words, two allowed MO's; they are usually written

$$\Psi_g = H_A(1s) + H_B(1s) \quad \text{and} \quad \Psi_u = H_A(1s) - H_B(1s). \quad (5–5)$$

One of these MO's, Ψ_g, has a lower energy than that of the AO's (Fig. 5–18), and leads to the formation of a stable molecule. It is termed, therefore, a *bonding MO*. The other allowed MO has an energy higher than that of the AO's, and is an *antibonding MO*. The subscripts g and u reflect the prominence of German as the scientific language at the time of the development of the theory, and stand for *gerade* (even) and *ungerade* (odd). These symbols refer to the symmetry of the MO's.

The form of the charge distribution for the MO's of the hydrogen molecule is illustrated in Fig. 5–19 and Fig. 5–20. The latter diagram in particular shows the buildup of charge between the nuclei, a buildup which is characteristic of the bonding or attractive state. In the repulsive state the charge density between the nuclei is very small, and bonding does not occur. In both cases the orbitals have rotational symmetry about the axis of the molecule. In order to distinguish them

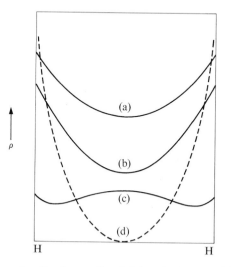

FIG. 5–20. Electron density along a line joining the two nuclei in the hydrogen molecule. Part (a) represents the density in the stable molecule (Ψ_g^2), (b) shows the sum of the charge densities of the individual atoms, that is, $\psi_H^2 + \psi_H^2$. Part (c) shows difference between curves (a) and (b), illustrating the charge buildup between the nuclei, and (d) shows charge distribution in the repulsive state (Ψ_u^2).

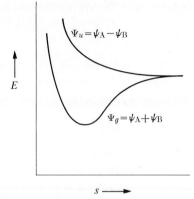

FIG. 5–21. Potential energy curves for the attractive
(Ψ_g) and repulsive (Ψ_u) states of H_2.

from other MO's (to be discussed later) which do not have this property, they are designated σMO's. An asterisk is added to indicate an antibonding MO. It is common practice, also, to follow the symmetry designation of the MO with symbols to indicate the AO's from which it is constructed.

The lower-energy MO ($\sigma 1s$) will, in the case of hydrogen, be occupied by two electrons with their spins paired in accordance with the Pauli principle. That this is indeed a bonding MO is confirmed by the calculated potential energy curve shown in Fig. 5–21. For the attractive case, the potential energy curve exhibits a minimum, indicating the existence of a stable molecule. On the other hand, the energy of the repulsive state has no such minimum, so that the molecule formed would be unstable and would dissociate spontaneously. Using $1s$ AO's in the LCAO approximation, Coulson calculated the dissociation energy and equilibrium internuclear distance of the H_2 molecule to be 61.2 kcal and 0.84 A, respectively. These values do not appear very impressive when we compare them with the observed values of 103.2 kcal (0°K) and 0.74 A, but to view the results in their proper light we must consider that the dissociation energy is but a small part of the total electronic energy. Thus we arrive at the value of 61.2 kcal by subtracting the calculated energy of the hydrogen molecule (-688.4 kcal) from that of two isolated hydrogen atoms ($2 \times -313.6 = 627.2$ kcal). The simple MO treatment has thus successfully accounted for some 93% of the total electronic energy. This is a situation which obtains generally, and accounts for the difficulty in calculating bond energies with any accuracy. (See Problem 4–13.)*

By modifying the simple $1s$ orbitals used in forming the MO for the hydrogen molecule, it is possible to improve on the initial results. The LCAO approximation is, in fact, only a convenient tool, and one may employ any appropriate function.

---

* Coulson has likened the problem to that of weighing the captain of a ship by determining the difference in displacement of his ship when he is, or is not, on board.

The LCAO approach, apart from the fact that it provides a starting point, is useful because it is not difficult to see intuitively how the simple combination may be modified to give improved agreement with experiment. We may argue, for example, that the simple $1s$ orbital of one of the atoms is distorted or polarized by the presence of the nucleus of the other. In addition, we may take into account the screening influence of the electrons on each other. By taking these and other factors into consideration, it has been possible to arrive at calculated values of 95.0 kcal and 0.71 A for the dissociation energy and the equilibrium internuclear distance, respectively. (Note that the improved MO has given a lower energy in accordance with the variation principle.) These are more respectable values than those obtained using the simple $1s$ AO's, but they still fall short of the accuracy attained with the VB method.

The above discussion has dealt only with the ground state of the hydrogen molecule, but the method may be adapted to the consideration of excited states by employing excited AO's ($2s$, $2p$, etc.) to formulate the MO's. In every case the combination results in two MO's, one of which is repulsive, while the other may be attractive.

(b) The hydrogen molecule; VB approximation

The VB treatment of bonding, in contrast to the MO method, begins with the separate atoms and attempts to estimate the interaction which results as they are brought together. The VB method, being somewhat more susceptible to refinement than the MO method, is often capable of greater accuracy, but the labor involved in the calculations has limited the number of molecules to which it has been applied. The case of the H_2 molecule is a graphic illustration of the excellent agreement with experiment which may be attained.

We shall begin by imagining two hydrogen atoms far enough apart so that no appreciable interaction occurs. Supposing that we may label the electrons and nuclei, the wave functions for the separate atoms would be given by $\psi_A(1)$ and $\psi_B(2)$. A very useful theorem of quantum mechanics then allows us to write the total wave function for the separated atoms as a simple product:

$$\Psi = \psi_A(1)\psi_B(2). \tag{5–6}$$

If now the atoms are brought closer together, there is little doubt that the wave function of Eq. (5–6) would be modified by interaction, but we might expect it to be essentially correct. At any rate it would be worthwhile calculating the energy by the variation method before proceeding to a more complicated wave function. If this is done (Fig. 5–22), the energy curve does exhibit a minimum, indicating that a molecule is formed, but the calculated bonding energy of about 6 kcal is far too small. Since, as stated previously, the variation method generally gives an energy value of much greater accuracy than the wave function employed, our choice in Eq. (5–6) must be badly in error. Evidently some essential feature has been ignored.

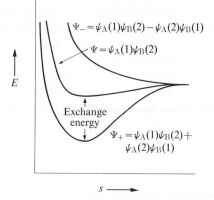

$$\Psi_- = \psi_A(1)\psi_B(2) - \psi_A(2)\psi_B(1)$$

$$\Psi = \psi_A(1)\psi_B(2)$$

Exchange energy

$$\Psi_+ = \psi_A(1)\psi_B(2) + \psi_A(2)\psi_B(1)$$

E

$s \longrightarrow$

FIG. 5-22. Curves showing VB potential energy for the H_2 molecule.

To reveal this error, we must recall that in setting up the wave function of Eq. (5–6) we supposed that the electrons, labeled 1 and 2, could be associated with nuclei A and B, respectively. We know, however, that the electrons are in fact indistinguishable, so that we are incapable of telling which electron is associated with which nucleus. This means that $\psi_A(2)\psi_B(1)$ and $\psi_A(1)\psi_B(2)$ are equally acceptable wave functions, and that the true wave function is likely to be some combination of the two. We might try

$$\Psi = C_1\psi_A(1)\psi_B(2) + C_2\psi_A(2)\psi_B(1). \qquad (5\text{–}7)$$

The parameters C_1 and C_2 impart a general form to Eq. (5–7), but in the case of the H_2 molecule, because of symmetry, the two component wave functions must contribute with equal weight. As before, the weight is proportional to the square of the coefficients, therefore

$$C_1^2 = C_2^2 \quad \text{and} \quad C_1 = \pm C_2, \qquad (5\text{–}8)$$

and there are two possible wave functions,

$$\Psi_+ = \psi_A(1)\psi_B(2) + \psi_A(2)\psi_B(1), \qquad (5\text{–}9)$$

and

$$\Psi_- = \psi_A(1)\psi_B(2) - \psi_A(2)\psi_B(1). \qquad (5\text{–}10)$$

Calculation of the energies associated with these states reveals that Ψ_- represents a repulsive or nonbonding state. In fact, it corresponds to the state in which the two electrons involved have the same spin, so that the repulsive effect is to be expected on the basis of the Pauli principle. On the other hand, the energy curve for the Ψ_+ state has the required minimum for bonding at a separation of 0.80 A. The calculated bond energy is 72.4 kcal, which is in much better agreement with experiment than the energy calculated from Eq. (5–6).

TABLE 5–7

SUMMARY OF VB CALCULATIONS ON H_2

Approximation	s_e	Bond dissociation energy
Heitler-London	0.80 A	66.4 kcal
H-L with screening	0.76	80.8
H-L with screening and ionic terms	0.77	86.3
James and Coolidge, 13-term polynomial	0.74	102.8
Observed	0.74	103.2*

* See Section 4–1. The value quoted in Table 4–2 (104.2 kcal) is for 298.15°K, while the appropriate quantity for comparison with the calculated energy is that for 0°K, which is listed above.

The notion of the indistinguishability of the electrons is obviously an important one. It is known as the *exchange* phenomenon, and was introduced by Heitler and London, whose names are consequently associated with this treatment. The additional binding energy which arises as a result of the inclusion of this concept in the theory is known as the *exchange energy* (Fig. 5–22). This terminology must not be construed to imply that any physical exchange of the electrons takes place, or that an electron resides part of the time near one nucleus and part of the time near the other. We need only consider the rather arbitrary manner in which we have constructed the wave functions of Eqs. (5–9) and (5–10) to see that such an idea is meaningless. We can only say that the greater freedom allowed the electrons by the wave functions of Eqs. (5–9) and (5–10) results in a lowering of the value of the calculated energy, hence the wave functions thus arrived at are a better approximation to the true wave function.

The Heitler-London wave functions can be improved by considering refinements such as screening effects and polarization of the AO's, with corresponding improvement in the calculated binding energy (Table 5–7). The electron density curves derived from these wave functions (Ψ_+ and Ψ_-) are very similar to the analogous ones for the MO's (Fig. 5–18). One rather important improvement concerns the question of ionic configurations. That is, there is a possibility that both electrons will be simultaneously near one of the nuclei so that we must consider also the ionic wave functions $\psi_A(1)\psi_A(2)$ and $\psi_B(1)\psi_B(2)$. The total wave function then becomes

$$\Psi = \psi_A(1)\psi_B(2) + \psi_A(2)\psi_B(1) + \lambda'[\psi_A(1)\psi_A(2) + \psi_B(1)\psi_B(2)], \quad (5–11)$$

or more conveniently

$$\Psi = \Psi_{cov} + \lambda'\Psi_{ion}. \quad (5–12)$$

The constant λ' is, of course, a measure of the degree to which the ionic structures contribute to the bonding. Since, in applying the variation method, we can adjust λ' to give the lowest and therefore best energy, we have a means of judging the extent of the ionic character of the bond. For H_2, λ' is 0.17, and the ionic contribution to the total binding energy only 5.5 kcal.

The inclusion of the ionic terms in the wave function is actually a quantitative application of the *resonance* concept. Thus we speak of resonance between the pure covalent structures represented by H—H and the ionic structures H_A^+—H_B^- and H_A^-—H_B^+. The contribution to the binding energy which results from the inclusion of these terms is thus spoken of as ionic *resonance energy*. As we shall see later, this concept is of fundamental importance in the VB approximation. We must be careful when using the word "resonance" (just as with the word "exchange," discussed previously) not to impart a physical significance to the resonance phenomenon. It is quite wrong to think of these covalent and ionic structures as actually existing, with the molecule assuming one or the other structure for lengths of time determined by λ'.

Finally, to illustrate the accuracy attainable with the VB approach, Table 5–7 includes the values of James and Coolidge. They employed a wave function with no less than thirteen terms.

(c) Homonuclear diatomic molecules; MO treatment

The MO Aufbau process used to derive molecular electronic configurations is quite analogous to the process used for atoms. We must, however, ascertain first which AO's may be combined to form MO's, and what the shape and relative energies of the MO's are. Details of the theory reveal that, in deciding which AO's, ψ_A and ψ_B, will combine we may be guided by three rules: (a) The energies of the AO's ψ_A and ψ_B in their respective atoms must be of comparable magnitude. (b) The charge clouds (and therefore the orbitals themselves) must overlap one another as much as possible. (c) The AO's ψ_A and ψ_B must have the same symmetry relative to the internuclear axis.

The first rule is of no consequence in homonuclear diatomic molecules because obviously we shall combine identical AO's from the two atoms. In the case of heteronuclear bonds, rule (a) means that outer electron orbitals of one atom will not combine with inner electron orbitals of another. This is intuitively reasonable when one considers how strongly bound the electrons are in these inner AO's [Section 3–5(e)]. It is also plausible to expect a large amount of overlap for the successful combination of AO's, for obviously such conditions will lead to the greatest amount of interaction. The amount of overlap can, in fact, usually be used as a measure of the strength of the bond.

The symmetry requirement of rule (c) refers to the sign $+$ or $-$ of ψ in the region about the nucleus. An *s*-orbital is positive in all outer regions, but (as seen in Fig. 5–23) the two lobes of a *p*-orbital are of opposite sign. If, therefore, an *s*-orbital overlaps a p_z-orbital (the *x*-axis is in the direction of the internuclear axis), there is equal overlap of the positive *s*-orbital with the positive and negative

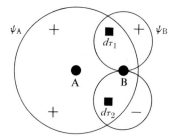

FIG. 5–23. Overlap of an s-orbital with a p_z orbital. Because there are equal portions with positive and negative sign, the overlap integral $\int \psi_s \psi_{p_z} \, d\tau$ vanishes.

regions of the p-orbital, so that the total overlap as represented by integral $\int \psi_s \psi_{p_z} \, d\tau$ (the overlap integral) is zero. Reasoning in this way we are able to draw up, in Table 5–8, a list of the allowed combinations of AO's in the LCAO method. Similar considerations may be applied to combinations of d-orbitals in which adjacent lobes are of opposite sign, but we shall not consider in detail, at this point, any diatomic molecules in which d-orbitals play a part.

TABLE 5–8

ALLOWED COMBINATIONS OF AO'S IN LCAO METHOD

	Allowed	Forbidden
s	s, p_x	p_y, p_z
p_x	s, p_x	p_y, p_z
p_y	p_y	s, p_x, p_z
p_z	p_z	s, p_x, p_y

As with the s AO's used in forming the $\sigma 1s$ and $\sigma^* 1s$ MO's for the hydrogen atom, the combination of any other pair of AO's leads to the formation of a bonding MO and an antibonding MO. This is a general principle which can be quite validly applied to polyatomic as well as diatomic molecules. The scheme of MO's, and the AO's from which they are derived, is shown schematically in Fig. 5–24; each circle represents an orbital which may be occupied by two electrons with paired spins. Some difficulties arise as to the sequence of the orbitals in regard to energy, because the energies of the $\sigma 2p$ and $\pi 2p$ MO's are close together. Molecular spectra indicate a reversal of the sequence at about nitrogen, with the $\sigma 2p$ the lower energy MO in the diatomic molecules of the heavier elements. As we shall see, however, this problem does not introduce any major difficulties; our discussion will also make clear the reason for the degeneracy of the $\pi_y 2p$ and $\pi_z 2p$ orbitals.

With the scheme of Fig. 5–24 as our guide, we may now proceed with our molecular Aufbau process, and derive the electronic structure of some simple

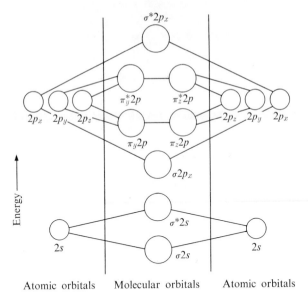

FIG. 5–24. Pairing of AO's by the LCAO method to form bonding and antibonding MO's in homonuclear diatomic molecules. Two electrons with paired spins may occupy each MO. The π-type bonding and antibonding MO's are doubly degenerate.

diatomic molecules. We have already described H_2 as $H_2[(\sigma 1s)^2]$, so that the extra electron in He_2^+ must go into the antibonding $\sigma*1s$ MO to give the configuration $He_2^+[(\sigma 1s)^2(\sigma*1s)^1]$. The helium molecule ion should therefore exist, and has in fact been observed spectroscopically.

On the other hand, the neutral molecule with the configuration $He_2[(\sigma 1s)^2(\sigma*1s)^2]$ has an equal number of bonding and antibonding electrons, a condition which leads to no bond formation, in agreement with experiment. Theoretically, this arises because the antibonding MO is above the energy of the parent AO's by a slightly greater amount than the bonding MO is below it. This nonbonding condition can also be shown pictorially, by summing the charge distributions of the bonding and antibonding MO's shown in Fig. 5–19. It can be seen that the charge buildup between the nuclei for the bonding orbital will be canceled by the very low charge density between the nuclei for the antibonding orbital, so that the overall result will be much like the charge distribution of two isolated helium atoms.

In Li_2, with the MO configuration

$$Li_2[(\sigma 1s)^2(\sigma*1s)^2(\sigma 2s)^2],$$

the combination of the filled $\sigma 1s$ and $\sigma*1s$ MO's will, as in He_2, be largely the same as the $1s$ AO's of the isolated atoms. In effect, the electrons are essentially localized on their respective nuclei and take no part in the bonding. This is indicated by an alternative method of writing the configuration,

$$Li_2[KK(\sigma 2s)^2],$$

where the KK means that the inner shell electrons are approximately normal atomic K-shells.

The Be_2 molecule will have the configuration

$$Be_2[KK(\sigma 2s)^2(\sigma*2s)^2],$$

and, since there are two bonding and two antibonding electrons, the molecule would not be expected to be stable. There is, in fact, no experimental evidence for the existence of a stable Be_2 molecule.

In the case of B_2, there are six electrons outside the KK shell to allot to MO's. It is known, furthermore, that there are two unpaired electrons with parallel spins in the ground-state configuration. Since four electrons will occupy the $(\sigma 2s)$ and $(\sigma*2s)$ MO's, the remaining two with parallel spins must be in the degenerate $(\pi_y 2p)$ and $(\pi_z 2p)$ MO's. The configuration will therefore be

$$B_2[KK(\sigma 2s)^2(\sigma*2s)^2(\pi_y 2p)^1(\pi_z 2p)^1].$$

The presence of the unpaired electrons eliminates the alternative $(\sigma 2p)^2$ configuration and establishes the sequence of the energy levels.

That the $\pi_y 2p$ and $\pi_z 2p$ orbitals are degenerate can be seen in Fig. 5–25. By convention, the atomic x-axes are taken to be coincident with the molecular axis, so that the overlap of identically oriented $2p_z$ orbitals leads to the formation of

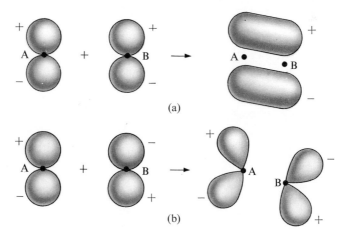

(a)

(b)

FIG. 5–25. (a) Schematic illustration of the formation of a "sausage" or π-type bonding MO from the overlap of p-orbitals. (b) Antibonding π-MO.

a bonding MO with two lobes of opposite sign. If the $2p_z$ orbitals are oriented in opposition, the result is an antibonding MO with a nodal plane perpendicular to the axis of the molecule, as in the case of the σ antibonding MO. Clearly the situation is identical in the case of the $\pi_y 2p$ MO's, except for a rotation of 90° about the axis of the molecule. The energies of the $\pi_y 2p$ and $\pi_z 2p$ MO's are therefore the same. In addition, the charge distribution for a pair of electrons in the $\pi 2p$ MO's of Fig. 5–26 is cylindrically symmetrical about the axis of the molecule, in accord with the symmetry of the molecule. (See Problem 5–16.)

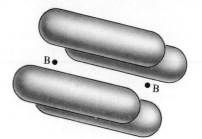

FIG. 5–26. Bonding π MO's in B_2.

A further point of interest in regard to the B_2 molecule concerns the fully occupied $\sigma 2s$ and $\sigma^* 2s$ MO's. Since this combination, as discussed previously, gives rise to a configuration very nearly the same as a pair of $2s$ AO's, we have the phenomenon of paired electrons in the valence shell which contribute little or nothing to the bonding. Such pairs of electrons are known as *lone pairs*.

The ground-state configuration of the C_2 molecule has been a matter of controversy for a number of years, but the latest evidence favors the configuration

$$C_2[KK(\sigma 2s)^2(\sigma^* 2s)^2(\pi_y 2p)^2(\pi_z 2p)^2].$$

There is, however, very little difference in energy (1.7 kcal) between this configuration and the alternative $(\pi_y 2p)^2(\pi_z 2p)^1(\sigma 2p)^1$, which has also been proposed.

In the case of the diatomic nitrogen molecule, there are ten electrons in the valence shell, and the electronic configuration is

$$N_2[KK(\sigma 2s)^2(\sigma^* 2s)^2(\pi_y 2p)^2(\pi_z 2p)^2(\sigma 2p)^2].$$

The configuration is unique because all of the $2p$ bonding MO's and none of the antibonding ones are filled. We might then expect the molecule to be strongly bonded.

As Table 4–1 shows, the dissociation energy of N_2 is the highest of all of the diatomic molecules of the second-period elements. This observation also points the way to a method by which we may define the bond multiplicity more precisely. Thus the *bond order* is defined as one-half of the difference between the number of electrons in bonding MO's and the number of electrons in antibonding MO's.

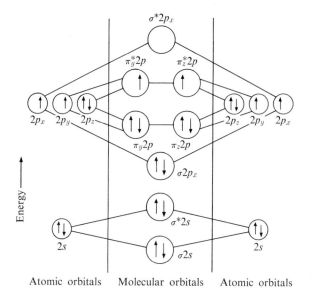

FIG. 5–27. Electronic configuration of the O_2 molecule.

This gives a bond order of three for N_2 ($s_e = 1.095$ A), two for C_2 ($s_e = 1.31$ A), one for B_2 ($s_e = 1.59$ A), and zero for Be_2. Nitrogen, it will be noted, has the highest possible bond order, and the removal or the addition of an electron will weaken the bond. Thus in N_2^+, with a bond order of only 2.5, the internuclear distance is 1.116 A. The bond length in N_2^- is not known, but the effect of the electrons in antibonding MO's is observed in O_2, which has both a longer bond and a smaller dissociation energy than N_2.

The configuration of O_2 is shown schematically in Fig. 5–27 as

$$O_2[KK(\sigma2s)^2(\sigma^*2s)^2(\sigma2p)^2(\pi_y2p)^2(\pi_z2p)^2(\pi_y^*2p)^1(\pi_z^*2p)^1].$$

In O_2, as in B_2, Hund's rules are operative, so that the π_y^*2p and π_z^*2p MO's are singly occupied by electrons with parallel spins, a condition that should give rise to paramagnetism. The explanation of this long-known property of O_2 was one of the early triumphs of MO theory. Also, O_2 and its associated series of ions are convenient for illustrating the correlation between bond order and bond length. Since in O_2 there are eight electrons in bonding MO's and four in anti-bonding MO's, the bond order is two. Consider now the situation which results when electrons are added or removed to form O_2^-, O_2^{2-}, and O_2^+. The added electrons will go into antibonding orbitals, so that in O_2^- the bond order will be 1.5 while in O_2^{2-} it is reduced to one. On the other hand, the electron removed in forming O_2^+ will come from an antibonding orbital, leaving an excess of five bonding electrons to give a bond order of 2.5. These results are summarized in

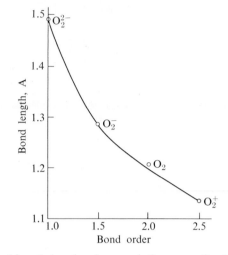

FIG. 5–28. Bond-length bond-order correlation curve for the O—O bond.

Table 5–3, while Fig. 5–28 illustrates the correlation between bond length and bond order.

The fluorine molecule, F_2, with the configuration

$$F_2[KK(\sigma 2s)^2(\sigma^*2s)^2(\sigma 2p)^2(\pi_y 2p)^2(\pi_z 2p)^2(\pi_y^* 2p)^2(\pi_z^* 2p)^2],$$

is also of special interest because, although the bond order is nominally one, there are indications that the bond is anomalously weak. Recall, for example, that the bond length in F_2 is considerably longer than predicted on the basis of the covalent radius of fluorine [observed s_e(F—F) = 1.42 A, $2r$(F) = 1.28 A]. In addition, the bond dissociation energy is much lower than expected, by comparison with the other halide diatomics (Chapter 4). The trend of increasing D(X—X) with decreasing atomic number

$$D(\text{I—I}) < D(\text{Br—Br}) < D(\text{Cl—Cl}),$$

is broken with F_2, which has about the same bond dissociation energy as I_2 does.

Corresponding diatomic series for the nitrogen and oxygen group elements do not exhibit this anomaly. The explanation would appear to lie in our oversimplified definition of bond order. Thus, in saying that the bond order in F_2 is one, we assume that the filling of the π^* MO's cancels the bonding of the corresponding π MO's, so that only the $\sigma 2p$ orbitals are effective. This would be roughly correct if the π^* MO's and the π MO's were equally above and below the energy of the p AO's but, if the energy of the π^* MO's were somewhat higher than this, they would more than cancel the bonding π MO's, and the effective bond order would be something less than one.

The structures of homonuclear diatomics of the elements of other periods may be formulated by applying the principles exemplified above. Thus S_2, like O_2, is paramagnetic, and probably has the configuration

$$S_2[KKLL(\sigma3s)^2(\sigma^*3s)^2(\sigma3p)^2(\pi_y3p)^2(\pi_z3p)^2(\pi_y^*3p)^1(\pi_z^*3p)^1].$$

As before, the $KKLL$ means that the inner shell electrons are essentially localized on their respective nuclei in more or less normal AO's. A precise statement as to the degree to which these participate in the bonding is impossible without detailed calculations; but the K-electrons, at least, must be effectively unshared, and might justifiably be regarded as nonbonding electrons. The same is probably true to a large extent for the L-electrons.

For $n = 3$, however, it would seem best to regard the electrons as shared, and acting either in a bonding or antibonding capacity. On the other hand, less is known experimentally and theoretically about the heavier molecules. It will be shown in Section 5–3(e) that many of the heavier atoms make use of d-orbitals in bonding, and if we ignore this fact in describing S_2, it may be a dangerous over-simplification.

(d) Homonuclear diatomic molecules; VB treatment

In the sense that it describes bonds in terms of the pairing of electrons, the VB approach may, in the first instance, be considered an extension of the elementary Lewis concept of bond formation. On the other hand, the detailed VB treatment reveals many new aspects, such as the necessity for opposed spins in the pairing of the electrons and the importance of the exchange phenomenon. In addition, the VB method has achieved the sophistication of quantitative mathematical confirmation. Nevertheless, its similarity to the Lewis method is close enough for the electron "dot" and bond "line" diagrams familiar to the Lewis-octet theory to be commonly used in qualitative VB treatments.

In essence, then, the VB approach pictures the bond as forming from the pairing or coupling of electrons (one from each atom) whose spins are antiparallel. This pairing process is represented by the joint wave function

$$[\psi_A(1)\psi_B(2) + \psi_A(2)\psi_B(1)].$$

It is, of course, necessary that the electrons involved be unpaired in the original atoms, so that we have immediate limitations on the valence or number of bonds which may be formed by any given atom. Those electrons in the valence shell which are already paired in the isolated atom are the lone pairs of the VB approach.

Finally, in deciding the question as to which electrons should be paired, we may refer again to the overlap criterion. As with LCAO combinations to form MO's, the greater the overlap of the AO's occupied by the electrons, the stronger the bond. The reader should observe at this point that as we make our discussion more qualitative the distinction between the MO and VB approaches tends to disappear, while their similarities become more prominent.

In keeping with this tendency, we shall find that the application of the VB approach leads to results which are, in the least, very similar to those of the MO description. Thus, since there are no unpaired electrons in the isolated He atom, bonding between ground-state helium atoms is not possible. The lithium atom has a single unpaired $2s$ electron in the valence shell; hence the σ bond in Li—Li is formed by pairing two of these.

Since there are no unpaired electrons in the beryllium atom, the VB approach supports the idea of the nonexistence of a stable beryllium molecule, in agreement with MO theory and experiment.

Also in agreement with MO theory are the predicted single and double bonds in B_2 and C_2, respectively. On the other hand, it is less obvious from the VB argument why there should be two unpaired electrons in B_2. A similar situation arises in the case of O_2, and will be discussed more fully later in this section.

In the case of nitrogen, there are three unpaired electrons occupying the $2p_x$, $2p_y$, and $2p_z$ AO's, so that a triple bond symbolized by

$$: N \equiv N :$$

will be formed. One of these will be a σ bond, resulting from the pairing of the $2p_x$ orbitals along the internuclear axis, while the other two, π bonds, are formed by overlap of the $2p_y$ and $2p_z$ orbitals. These σ and π bonds are nearly identical to the σ and π MO's, and in the limit of refinement must be the same. As a result, the terms "bond" and "orbital" are often used interchangeably in this connection.

Up to this point, all of the molecules we have treated by the VB approach have required only electron-pair bonds in describing their electronic configuration. It is obvious, however, that in considering H_2^+ or He_2^+ we shall have to modify the concept. Thus the bond in H_2^+ is called a *one-electron bond*, and its stabilization relative to $H + H^+$ arises through the resonance between two structures, in which the electron is associated with one nucleus or the other:

Similar considerations apply to He_2^+, where the resonance between the structures

$$He : \quad . \, He \quad \text{and} \quad He \, . \quad : He$$

leads to a lowering of the energy relative to $He + He^+$, and the formation of a *three-electron bond*. In this case, we cannot speak of any pairing of electrons between the nuclei because of the exclusion principle. Rather we have a pairing on one nucleus or the other. The electrons are indistinguishable, of course, but since only one really plays a part in the resonance phenomenon, it is not surprising that the one- and three-electron bonds have roughly the same energy.

The binding energies for the three types of bonds in H_2^+, H_2 and He_2^+ are:

$$D(H_2^+) = 61 \text{ kcal}, \qquad D(H_2) = 103 \text{ kcal}, \qquad D(He_2^+) = 58 \text{ kcal}.$$

Empirically then, we may say that one- and three-electron bonds are about half the strength of the electron-pair bond. These conclusions are in agreement with theoretical calculations.

In applying the VB method to the oxygen molecule, we run into some difficulties, for one would expect the coupling of the two unpaired electrons in each of the isolated atoms to give the structure

$$: \overset{\cdot\cdot}{O} = \overset{\cdot\cdot}{O} :$$

with a double bond. This is in accord with the MO approach, but such a description does not account for the strong paramagnetism resulting from the presence of two unpaired electrons in the molecule. On the basis of the maximum overlap criterion, one of the bonds should be a σ bond formed by pairing of the $2p_x$ electrons, while the other would be a π bond resulting from the coupling of the $2p_y$ or the $2p_z$ electrons. A lengthy argument has been given to show that paramagnetism arises because of the choice permitted ($2p_y$ or $2p_z$) in forming the π bond, but the more commonly advanced explanation utilizes the three-electron bond. The alternative structure would then be

$$: O \vdots\vdots O :$$

with a normal single and two three-electron bonds. Such a structure would have a binding energy much the same as that with the double bond, but would be difficult to justify without a prior knowledge of the paramagnetism.

Similar reasoning may be applied to the oxygen molecule ions. Thus the structure of O_2^+ would be pictured as

$$[: O \overset{\cdot\cdot}{=} O :]^+,$$

while the superoxide ion would have the structure

$$\left[: \overset{\cdot\cdot}{\underset{\cdot\cdot}{O}} \cdots \overset{\cdot\cdot}{\underset{\cdot\cdot}{O}} : \right]^-.$$

In a similar way, we may assign to the peroxide ion, O_2^{2-}, the structure

$$\left[: \overset{\cdot\cdot}{\underset{\cdot\cdot}{O}} - \overset{\cdot\cdot}{\underset{\cdot\cdot}{O}} : \right]^{2-}.$$

The VB approach is thus able to account for the bonding in homonuclear diatomics in a qualitative manner, but it has been necessary to devise two other types of bonds (one- and three-electron bonds) in addition to the ordinary electron-pair bond. Furthermore, in a series such as that of the oxygen molecule and its ions, it is not at all obvious what effect the removal or addition of electrons has. In the MO approach, on the other hand, no new mechanism of bonding is required to account for one- and three-electron bonding.

(e) Heteronuclear diatomic molecules

Two new and important factors arise when the MO and VB theories of bonding are applied to heteronuclear diatomic molecules. Since the atoms being bonded have different electronic configurations, it is no longer obvious which orbitals should be combined by the LCAO method to form the MO's. In the VB approach, the analogous question arises as to which electrons should be paired in bond formation. The other feature unique to heteronuclear bonds is that the ionic contribution may play a large part in the bonding. This aspect has received considerable attention, particularly from the VB point of view.

Dealing first with the question of which orbitals to use in the LCAO method, let us look at the relatively simple case of HCl. The choice here is not too difficult, for we can immediately rule out combinations of the hydrogen $1s$-orbital with any of the inner-shell orbitals of Cl ($1s$, $2s$, $2p$) or even the $3s$, because the energies of these are much too low. Of the remaining chlorine AO's, $3p_x$, $3p_y$, $3p_z$, the criterion of maximum overlap leads us to choose the $3p_x$, along the internuclear axis. The structure of HCl would therefore be

$$HCl\{Cl(1s)^2(2s)^2(2p)^6(3s)^2(3p_y)^2(3p_z)^2[H(1s) + \lambda\, Cl(3p_x), \sigma]^2\}$$

or

$$HCl\{Cl(K)(L)(3s)^2(3p_y)^2(3p_z)^2[H(1s) + \lambda\, Cl(3p_x), \sigma]^2\} \ .$$

The bonding MO has rotational symmetry about the bond axis; hence it is of the σ type.

In contrast to the homonuclear case, λ is no longer equal to ± 1, but it still has two values, one of which gives a bonding and the other an antibonding MO. In HCl, only the bonding MO is occupied. The actual value of λ is determined by the extent to which the electrons in the MO favor the region of one nucleus more than the other, and is in fact related to the experimentally measured dipole moment. In this case, because of the greater electronegativity of Cl, we expect $\lambda > 1$, and expect the MO to be "fatter" on the side of the Cl nucleus.

It is perhaps an oversimplification to assume that only the chlorine $3p_x$ orbital plays a part in the bonding, but there are no hydrogen AO's of π symmetry with energy low enough to combine with the chlorine $3p_y$ and $3p_z$ orbitals. In fact, the first excited state of HCl involves a σ MO compounded of the hydrogen $2s$ and the chlorine $4s$ AO's. It seems safe, therefore, to assume that the chlorine $3p_y$ and $3p_z$ and probably also the $3s$ electrons are nonbonding lone pairs localized about the chlorine nucleus.

At this point it is instructive to reconsider, objectively, the arguments we have been using to derive the electronic configurations of molecules. When the LCAO method was first employed, we pointed out that it was just a convenient way of formulating a molecular wave function in terms of AO's. On the other hand, the success of this approach in application to homonuclear diatomic molecules leads us to attach a more formal significance to the orbital pairing process. It is, in fact, this aspect of MO theory which is responsible for its similarity to the VB method. The principle is an important and very useful one in the description of polyatomic as well as diatomic molecules. Some care is necessary in making use of the technique, but the essentials are not difficult to master. The most important of these relate to the symmetry and the relative energy of the orbitals involved. For effective combination, the AO's must both be of σ symmetry or both of π symmetry, and they must furthermore have approximately the same energy. Both of these considerations are well illustrated in the description of HCl given above.

The case of HCl also illustrates the deficiency of this type of description: oversimplification in the description of the MO's. This is a problem which will become even more important as we study other heteronuclear diatomic molecules and encounter hybridization in polyatomic molecules. It is useful, therefore, to introduce a modified nomenclature which tends to emphasize the molecule as a unit.

To do this, let us consider the electronic configuration of NO and SO. Nitric oxide is isoelectronic with O_2^+ and N_2^-, so that it is reasonable to expect the scheme of MO's to be similar to that found for these two molecules. The same considerations apply to SO, which has the same number of electrons in the valence shell as O_2 and S_2, but where the AO's being combined come from different atomic shells. To designate the MO's in heteronuclear diatomic molecules, it is therefore more appropriate to use the symbols

$$z\sigma, \quad y\sigma, \quad x\sigma, \quad w\pi, \quad v\pi, \quad u\sigma.$$

These symbols designate the order of the energy levels and the symmetry without making any explicit statement of the AO's involved. It is understood, however, that they correspond, in varying degree, to the scheme for homonuclear diatomics.

Using these symbols, the molecules we are discussing have the configurations

$$NO[N(K)O(K)(z\sigma)^2(y\sigma)^2(x\sigma)^2(w\pi)^4(v\pi)^1]$$

and

$$SO[S(K)(L)O(K)(z\sigma)^2(y\sigma)^2(x\sigma)^2(w\pi)^4(v\pi)^2].$$

To relate these configurations to the binding energy, a more detailed consideration of the constituent AO's is necessary. In nitric oxide, for example, there is a significant difference (about 60 kcal) in the energy of the AO's involved (Fig. 5–29), so that the combination of the p AO's to form σ and π bonding MO's is not as effective in NO as it is in N_2 or O_2. Detailed calculations confirm this premise, and indicate that the bond strength should be considerably less than the apparent bond order of 2.5, as indeed it is found to be experimentally.

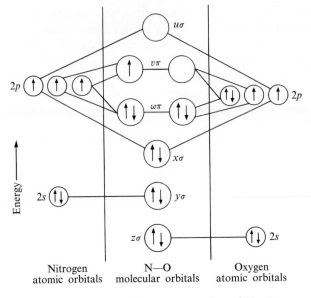

Fig. 5–29. Electronic configuration of N—O.

Another point of interest in connection with NO concerns the electronic charge distribution. For the electrons in the σ MO's and the $w\pi$ MO's the electronic charge is cylindrically symmetrical about the molecular axis, but for the $v\pi$ electron the charge does not have this symmetry if the standard p_x, p_y AO's are used. The difficulty is easily overcome, however, by using linear combinations of the real AO's to give AO's of cylindrical symmetry. The imaginary AO's, $p_x + ip_y$ and $p_x - ip_y$, are suitable. The total charge distribution then has the required symmetry. These considerations apply, of course, whenever there is a single electron in a $w\pi$ or $v\pi$ MO, such as B_2^+, O_2^+, etc.

The VB treatment requires similar adjustments when applied to heteronuclear diatomic molecules. In NO the pairing of p_x and p_y electrons from the nitrogen and oxygen atoms produces a double bond. This leaves an odd electron, so we could conceive of resonance between the structures as

I. $: \overset{\displaystyle .}{N} \!=\! \overset{\displaystyle ..}{O} :$

and

II. $\overset{\displaystyle ..}{^-N} \!=\! \overset{\displaystyle .}{\underset{\displaystyle ..}{O}}{}^+,$

which are equivalent to a double plus a three-electron bond, i.e.,

$: N \overset{...}{=\!=} O : \;\; .$

An interesting point in regard to NO is that while structure I is polarized slightly because of the higher charge on the oxygen nucleus, the negative charge on the oxygen is canceled by structure II. This provides an explanation for the very small dipole moment of NO.

The situation with HCl and the other hydrogen halides should be obvious. The principal pairing is of the hydrogen $1s$ and chlorine $3p_x$ electrons to give a structure I written

$$\text{I.} \qquad \text{H—Cl :} \quad .$$

The $3s$, $3p_y$ and $3p_z$ electrons of Cl, although in the valence shell, take little part in the bonding and may be considered lone pairs. [But see Section 5–3(a).] To make the VB treatment complete, however, we must take into account alternative resonance structures. For HCl these would be the ionic structures

$$\text{II.} \qquad \text{H}^+ \qquad : \text{Cl} : {}^-$$

and

$$\text{III.} \qquad \text{H} : {}^- \qquad \text{Cl} : {}^+.$$

That is, the VB wave function would be composed of three terms:

$$\Psi = [C_1\psi_{\text{H}}(1)\psi_{\text{Cl}}(2) + C_2\psi_{\text{H}}(2)\psi_{\text{Cl}}(1)]_{\text{I}}$$
$$+[C_3\psi_{\text{Cl}}(1)\psi_{\text{Cl}}(2)]_{\text{II}} + [C_4\psi_{\text{H}}(1)\psi_{\text{H}}(2)]_{\text{III}},$$

in complete analogy with the VB treatment of H_2.

With HCl, however, the high ionization energy of Cl and the low electron affinity of H make structure III much less favorable relative to I and II. In other words, the inclusion of the wave function corresponding to structure III in the overall wave function lowers the calculated energy by an insignificant amount. Conversely, the high electron affinity of chlorine makes the remaining ionic structure II relatively more important than the analogous ionic structure in the case of H_2. Thus, the inclusion of the ionic wave function II brings about a proportionately greater lowering of the calculated energy in the HCl treatment relative to H_2.

Strictly speaking, it is not just the ionization energy and electron affinity which determine the importance of the ionic contribution. A more accurate treatment would also take into account the Coulomb interaction energy of the ions. This would be inversely proportional to the internuclear separation of the ions and in the series of hydrogen halides would be largest for HF and smallest for HI. Such an argument offers an explanation for the greater importance of the ionic configuration in HF than HCl despite the fact that $E(\text{F}) < E(\text{Cl})$.

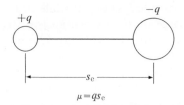

FIG. 5–30. Schematic illustration of a polar diatomic
molecule with dipole moment $\mu = qs_e$.

The question of estimating the degree to which the ionic configuration contributes to the overall bonding or, in other words, the polarity of the bond, is one which has received considerable attention. All approaches to the problem are largely empirical in nature and based on estimates of the ionic resonance energies or on dipole moments.

The electric dipole moment, or more commonly just the dipole moment, is the experimental measure of the polarity of a molecule generally and, in the case of diatomics, of the bond. It can be defined in terms of the product of the excess charge on one atom times the internuclear separation (Fig. 5–30). Since the molecule as a whole must be electrically neutral, there will be charges of equal magnitude but opposite sign on the two atoms. Mathematically we define the dipole moment μ as

$$\mu = qs_e, \tag{5-13}$$

where q is the excess charge and s_e is the equilibrium internuclear distance. Since the charge q is usually of the order of the charge on the electron, 4.8×10^{-10} esu, while s_e is of the order of 1 A, a convenient measure of the dipole moment is the Debye ($D = 10^{-10}$ esu A). The classical method of determining μ usually makes use of the relation between the dipole moment and the dielectric constant. The most precise values of μ are, at present, being obtained from intensity measurements on the rotational spectrum in the microwave region.

If a bond is 100% ionic in character, there will be charges of $\pm e$ on the atoms, while a completely covalent structure will be associated with a zero dipole moment. We may therefore employ the ratio of the observed dipole moment μ over the calculated dipole moment for a completely ionic structure, es_e, as a measure of the percent ionic character. That is,

$$\% \text{ ionic character} = (\mu/es_e) \times 100. \tag{5-14}$$

If we write the VB wave function as $\Psi = \psi_{cov} + \lambda'\psi_{ionic}$, then the weights of the covalent and ionic parts are in the ratio of $1 : (\lambda')^2$, and

$$\% \text{ ionic character} = \frac{100(\lambda')^2}{1 + (\lambda')^2}. \tag{5-15}$$

TABLE 5–9

PERCENTAGE IONIC CHARACTER IN THE HYDROGEN HALIDES

	s_e	es_e	μ	$\%$	λ'
HF	0.92 A	4.42 D	1.98 D	45	0.90
HCl	1.28	6.07	1.03	17	0.45
HBr	1.43	6.82	0.79	12	0.36
HI	1.62	7.74	0.38	5	0.23

Equations (5–14) and (5–15) may thus be used together to estimate λ'. These calculations have been carried out for the hydrogen halides, with the results listed in Table 5–9. Looking at the table, we see that for this series the bond in HF has the most ionic character and that in HI the least. Calculations involving the λ of the MO treatment show the same trend. It should be mentioned, however, that some doubt has been cast on the use of dipole moments as a measure of the ionic character of a bond. This arises because of hybridization and will be mentioned again in Section 5–3(c).

An alternative and much-used method for estimating the ionic character of a bond is based on an empirical calculation of the ionic resonance energy, i.e., the amount by which the overall binding energy is lowered when the ionic wave function is included in the overall function. This will be the difference between the actual dissociation energy, say $D(\text{H—Cl})$, and the energy of the purely covalent structure $E_{cov}(\text{H—Cl})$. Since the latter cannot be calculated by direct theoretical means, we make the postulate that $E_{cov}(\text{H—Cl})$ is the geometric mean of $D(\text{H—H})$ and $D(\text{Cl—Cl})$. The ionic resonance energy, $\Delta'(\text{H—Cl})$, is then given by

$$\Delta'(\text{H—Cl}) = D(\text{H—Cl}) - \left(D(\text{H—H})D(\text{Cl—Cl})\right)^{1/2}. \qquad (5\text{–}16)$$

It will be seen in Table 5–10 that the trend with regard to ionic character agrees with the dipole moment calculations.

TABLE 5–10

IONIC RESONANCE ENERGIES FOR HYDROGEN HALIDES
(in kcal/mole)

	HF	HCl	HBr	HI
Bond energy	134.6	103.2	87.5	71.4
$[D(\text{H—H}) D(\text{X—X})]^{1/2}$	61.8	72.7	69.3	61.4
Δ'	72.8	30.5	18.2	10.0

Pauling developed this aspect further, and proposed that the ionic character of the bond, as expressed in the ionic resonance energy, should be related to a char-

TABLE 5–11

ELECTRONEGATIVITY VALUES OF SOME ELEMENTS, ACCORDING TO PAULING

H 2.1			
C 2.5	N 3.0	O 3.5	F 4.0
Si 1.8	P 2.1	S 2.5	Cl 3.0
Ge 1.8	As 2.0	Se 2.4	Br 2.8
			I 2.5

acteristic quantity associated with the bonding atoms. He found, in fact, that

$$\Delta(A\!-\!B) = \big(x(A) - x(B)\big)^2 \text{ ev,} \qquad (5\text{–}17)$$

where $x(A)$ and $x(B)$, $\big(x(A) > x(B)\big)$ are the electronegativities of atoms A and B, and $\Delta(A\!-\!B)$ is derived from the arithmetic mean of the bond dissociation energies through the equation

$$\Delta(A\!-\!B) = D(A\!-\!B) - \tfrac{1}{2}[D(A\!-\!A) + D(B\!-\!B)]. \qquad (5\text{–}18)$$

It has since been found, however, that Δ' (using the geometric mean) is more suitable than Δ, and the electronegativity scale has been modified accordingly. With Δ' expressed in kcal, then, the current scale of electronegativities is derived from the relation

$$\Delta'(A\!-\!B) = 30[x(A) - x(B)]^2 \text{ kcal.} \qquad (5\text{–}19)$$

An interesting and important property of the electronegativities as expressed in Table 5–11 is that the difference $x(A) - x(B)$ is almost equal to the dipole

TABLE 5–12

COMPARISON OF DIPOLE MOMENT μ WITH $[x(X) - x(H)]$ FOR THE HYDROGEN HALIDES

	H—F	H—Cl	H—Br	H—I
μ	1.98 D	1.03 D	0.79 D	0.38 D
$[x(X) - x(H)]$	1.9	0.9	0.7	0.4

TABLE 5–13

COMPARISON OF MULLIKEN AND PAULING ELECTRONEGATIVITY SCALES

Atom	Ionization energy	Electron affinity	Sum/125	x
F	401.6	83.5	3.9	4.0
Cl	299.9	88.2	3.1	3.0
Br	272.9	81.6	2.8	2.8
I	241.0	74.6	2.5	2.5
H	313.4	17.2	2.6	2.1

moment of the bond A—B (Table 5–12). We could therefore combine Eqs. (5–14) and (5–19) and express the percent ionic character, as previously defined, in terms of electronegativity difference. This expression would, however, contain s_e as a parameter. As an alternative, several attempts have been made on a purely empirical basis to derive an equation for percent ionic character in terms of $x(A) - x(B)$ only. The most successful of these is

$$\% \text{ ionic character } = 16(x(A) - x(B)) + 3.5(x(A) - x(B))^2. \quad (5\text{--}20)$$

Mention should also be made of an alternative (and in some respects superior) definition of electronegativity, due to Mulliken, which is

$$x(A) = \tfrac{1}{2}[I(A) + E(A)], \quad (5\text{--}21)$$

where $I(A)$ and $E(A)$ are the ionization energy and electron affinity, respectively, of atom A. Fortunately, as can be seen in Table 5–13, the two electronegativity scales are equivalent if a proportionality factor is taken into account. In principle, Mulliken's definition is more precise than Pauling's because it is based directly on observable quantities. It may, furthermore, be extended to deal with changes in electronegativity arising from hybridization. In practice, one is severely hampered by the lack of accurate electron affinity data, so that the Pauling method is generally more useful than the Mulliken method.

5–3. POLYATOMIC MOLECULES

In beginning a discussion of the theoretical aspects of bonding in polyatomic molecules, it is appropriate to review the empirical facts presented in Sections 4–4 and 5–1.

One of the most striking features of bonding, to which much of the evidence points, is that in most cases the chemical bond is very localized. From the point of view of both the binding energy and the length of the bond we are forced to conclude that the bonding process is primarily a function of the two atoms being joined, and that adjacent atoms, even if attached to one of the bonded atoms, have only a secondary effect. There are certainly exceptions to the general rule, but these exceptions can in almost all cases be related to some special feature of the molecule involved.

We must also accept the fact that, in addition to being localized, the covalent bond is very directional in character. A good example of this is the pyramidal configuration of NH_3, which certainly has no counterpart in ionic bonding. Furthermore, similar structures are observed for compounds such as $NHCl_2$ and NF_3, so that the directional characteristics must be associated with the nitrogen atom. That the bond is dependent to a great extent on the properties of the individual atoms is also indicated by the validity of the covalent radius approximation. In the subsequent discussion we shall find that the concepts of localized bonds and directed valence are very closely linked.

(a) Localized orbitals and the overlap criterion

In terms of MO theory, a localized bond leads us directly to localized MO's. In other words, even in very complicated molecules we may still, to a good approximation, consider the bonding MO's to be bicentric and similar to those existing in diatomic molecules. For H_2O then, we would picture two separate O—H bonding MO's relatively independent of each other. Such a view is supported by the small difference in the O—H bond properties in the O—H radical ($s_e = 0.97$ A, $D(O—H) = 101.5$ kcal), and H_2O ($s_e = 0.96$ A, $D(HO—H) = 119.7$ kcal). It would appear, then, that one of the principles on which our theory will rest is the possibility of forming localized MO's.

Applying the LCAO method to H_2O, we would employ two of the oxygen p-orbitals, say the p_x and the p_y AO's, in combination with the hydrogen $1s$ orbitals. Two σ MO's are thus formed, which we might designate

$$[H_A(1s) + \lambda O(2p_x)] \qquad \text{and} \qquad [H_B(1s) + \lambda O(2p_y)].$$

In an abbreviated notation similar to that employed for diatomic molecules, the electronic configuration of H_2O would then be

$$H_2O\{O(1s)^2(2s)^2(2p_z)^2[O(2p) + H(1s), \sigma]^4\}.$$

We expect that, as in the case of diatomics, the bond is strongest if the overlap of the s and p AO's is as large as possible, a condition that is fulfilled if the hydrogen nuclei are located on the x- and y-axes to give an $\angle HOH$ of $90°$. Similarly, in NH_3, we picture the three half-filled p-orbitals of nitrogen combining with the hydrogen $1s$ AO's to give a pyramidal configuration. Thus the application of the overlap criterion to localized MO's forms the basis of a theory of directed valence.

In point of fact our theory must still overcome some problems, because the observed angle in H_2O is 104.5°. It has been proposed that this deviation is the result of Coulomb repulsion between the H atoms, but calculations have shown that 14° is too large a difference to be explained in this way.

Similar discrepancies are observed in NH_3 ($\angle HNH = 107°$) and PH_3 ($\angle HPH = 97°$). Fortunately, we need not restrict ourselves to p-orbitals, and the 90° angle attendant on their use. As we shall see in Sections 5–3(b) and 5–3(c), the apparent deviations in angle are readily explained qualitatively if we modify the AO's through hybridization.

In VB language, the localized bond means that the pairing of electrons from two different atoms to form a bond is independent of any other pairing that may take place in the rest of the molecule. Formally this is known as the approximation of perfect pairing. As in MO theory, maximum overlap leads to maximum energy and results in directed valence.

We therefore find that, from a qualitative point of view at least, the approach to bonding in polyatomic molecules is much the same for the VB and MO approximations. In both cases bonds or bonding orbitals are formed through the pairing of electrons with opposed spins such that a localized buildup of charge occurs between the bonded atoms. The restriction that only singly occupied AO's may be used in forming these bonds explains the characteristic valences associated with atoms, and at the same time reveals the theoretical basis of the Lewis octet rule. In both VB and MO theories, the criterion of maximum overlap plays the significant role of providing an explanation for directed valence. We can in fact regard these features common to both theories as forming a set of rules or principles by means of which we can explain many of the questions posed in our empirical study of Section 5–1.

(b) Hybridization

In describing the hydrogenlike p-orbitals in Section 3–4(b), we pointed out that the most general wave functions corresponding to $l = 1$ were the linear combinations of p_x, p_y, and p_z expressed in Eq. (3–50). This situation arises because of the degeneracy of the $l = 1$ energy level. It is not necessary, however, for orbitals to have precisely the same energy before linear combinations can be formed. We may form linear combinations of two or more s-, p-, d-, or f-orbitals as long as the energies are not too different.

The hypothetical process of forming these orbitals is termed hybridization, and the orbitals themselves are known as hybrid orbitals or simply hybrids. As we shall see shortly, hybrid orbitals play a large part in the theory of chemical bonding generally and in directed valence in particular; hence when the electrons of an atom occupy hybrid orbitals, the atom is said to be in the valence state.

The valence state is not a true atomic state, and would not be assumed by an isolated atom because of the different energies of the orbitals used to form the hybrid orbitals. It is sometimes described as a state assumed by the atom during the process of bonding, but even this is not completely correct, because at this point it is MO's and not AO's with which we are concerned. We must simply regard the hybrid orbital as a better AO to use in the LCAO method for describing a localized MO in some polyatomic molecules. Insofar as we may associate an energy with an imaginary state, the energy of atoms in the valence state is always somewhat higher than that of atoms with the ground-state configuration. On the other hand, this outlay of energy is more than compensated for by the extra binding energy resulting from the use of hybrid orbitals (Fig. 5–31).

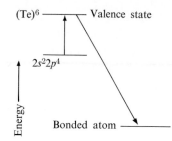

FIG. 5–31. Energy relationship between ground and valence states of the oxygen atom.

Consider, for example, neon with the electronic configuration $Ne[1s^2 2s^2 2p^6]$. Reference to Fig. 3–15 reveals that the $2s$ and $2p$ orbitals are relatively close together and far above the $1s$ energy. There exists therefore the possibility of forming hybrid orbitals with the $2s$ and $2p$ orbitals. One particularly important set is that of the *tetrahedral or sp^3 hybrids:*

$$Te_1 = \tfrac{1}{2}(s + p_x + p_y + p_z), \qquad Te_2 = \tfrac{1}{2}(s + p_x - p_y - p_z),$$

$$\text{(5–22)}$$

$$Te_3 = \tfrac{1}{2}(s - p_x + p_y - p_z), \qquad Te_4 = \tfrac{1}{2}(s - p_x - p_y + p_z).$$

As Fig. 5–32 shows, these orbitals differ significantly from the parent orbitals in several respects. Most important for our purposes is the fact that they are directed tetrahedrally and directed very strongly, because one lobe is far larger than the other. Since all four of the orbitals have the same shape, they are termed *equivalent orbitals.*

There are indications that hybridization may play a part in determining the crystal structures of neon and the other rare gases. Thus helium, without an accessible p-orbital for the formation of sp^3 hybrids, appears to crystallize in a hexagonal close-packed structure, while the remainder of the rare gases (the structure of radon is unknown) assume the cubic close-packed structure in the solid state (see Chapter 7).

The role played by hybrid orbitals in covalent bonding is a complicated and controversial one. If we accept the premise of the localized MO, then to account

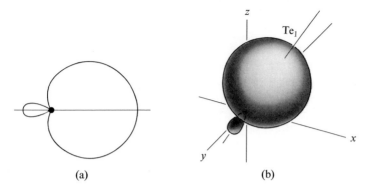

Fig. 5–32. (a) Planar section through generating axis of an sp^3 or tetrahedral hybrid orbital. (b) Sketch of the tetrahedral hybrid Te_1, showing the orientation relative to the cartesian axes. There are four equivalent orbitals of this type directed toward the corners of a regular tetrahedron.

for the observed geometry of molecules we must use hybrid orbitals in formulating the MO's by the LCAO method. It is difficult to see, for example, how the three equivalent bonds of BCl_3, or the equivalent tetrahedrally directed bonds of CH_4, could be explained in terms other than those of hybrid orbitals. This theory does not explain, however, why the molecules adopt this geometry.

From a theoretical point of view, a number of advantages accrue from the use of hybrid AO's in forming MO's. Probably the most important are the strongly directional properties of the hybrid orbitals. As Fig. 5–32 shows, nearly all of an sp^3 hybrid orbital extends in a single lobe in one direction from the nucleus, hence we would expect greater overlap and a correspondingly stronger bond. In addition, hybrid AO's obviously would better satisfy the requirements of electron correlation. The three pairs of electrons in the bonding MO's of BCl_3 are as far from one another as possible in the trigonal planar configuration. In this regard Linnett's Configurations of Most Probability are significant (see below).

Similar considerations will apply to repulsive effects between the nonbonding electrons of the constituent atoms, e.g., the $2p$ electrons of the chlorine atoms in BCl_3, and between the nuclei of these atoms. Note that all of these effects are concerned with the molecule as a whole, and the removal of an atom may change the situation significantly. The methyl radical, for example, is known to be planar, or very nearly so. The different successive bond dissociation energies of CH_4 further attest to this fact.

In H_2O, the use of hybrid orbitals in bonding should not only give a stronger bond (Fig. 5–31) but, in addition, predicts an $\angle HOH$ of 109°28′, the tetrahedral angle. This is much closer to the observed angle of 104°27′ than the 90° expected when pure p-orbitals are used in bonding. Therefore, a better approximation to the electronic configuration of H_2O would be (Fig. 5–33)

$$H_2O\{O(1s)^2(Te)^4[O(Te) + H(1s), \sigma]^4\}.$$

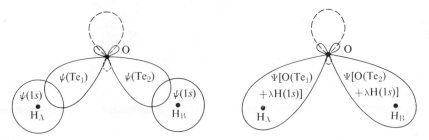

FIG. 5–33. (a) Overlap of H(1s) and O(Te) AO's.   (b) Localized σ-bonding MO's formed by the overlap.

Furthermore, hybridization offers a simple expedient for the explanation of the remaining 5° deviation, because we need not be restricted to pure sp^3 hybridization. We may "mix" varying degrees of s- and p-orbitals to produce hybrid orbitals with the desired angular relationship.   Thus we speak of the oxygen-bonding orbitals as having somewhat more p-character than pure tetrahedral orbitals, so that the ∠HOH closes up from 109°28′ to 104°27′.

If, however, the hybrid orbitals are formulated in this way, they are no longer equivalent.   The orbitals occupied by the lone pairs have correspondingly more s-character and are separated by a larger angle than the bonding orbitals.   This arrangement is probably the result of polarization or a pulling out of the bonding orbital by the hydrogen nucleus.   The lone pairs would therefore be closer to the nucleus than the bonding pairs, and repulsive effects would tend to open up the lone-pair–lone-pair angle slightly.   This is in fact an illustration of what appears to be a general principle, i.e., the repulsion effects between electron pairs in a valency shell give angles which decrease in the order: lone-pair–lone-pair > lone-pair–bond-pair > bond-pair–bond-pair.   We shall find this an extremely useful rule in predicting angular deviations from equivalent orbital configurations.

It is interesting that we may arrive at the same conclusions regarding the structure of the water molecule by starting from a somewhat different point of view, based on the most probable relative positions of the six oxygen valence electrons at any given instant.   In practice we calculate these positions by setting up a composite wave function for all six electrons, squaring the wave function to obtain ψ^2 (the probability distribution function) and treating ψ^2 to find for which values of the spatial coordinates of the electrons it is a maximum.

For oxygen in the ground state, Linnett has shown that the most probable simultaneous positions of the electrons, or the *Configuration of Most Probability* (CMP), is as shown in Fig. 5–34.   Four of the electrons are paired, with an angle between the pairs ∠POP = 133°, while the single electrons are separated by an angle ∠SOS = 103°.   It is these two single electrons which would pair with hydrogen 1s electrons in forming the H_2O molecule, so that an ∠HOH of about 103° would be expected.   The agreement is a striking illustration of how much the electronic configuration of oxygen alone determines the molecular structure.

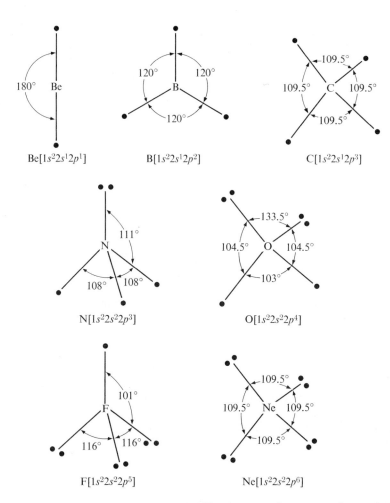

Fig. 5–34. Configurations of most probability for ground or appropriate excited states of second-row elements.

In principle the CMP describes the electron-density distribution as it is affected by spin correlation; i.e., the interaction of the electron spins according to the Pauli principle. Thus the tendency of electrons with the same spin to keep apart causes the valence electrons of neon to separate to the corners of a tetrahedron (Fig. 5–34), while in oxygen, where two of the electrons are unpaired, the angles are changed slightly from the tetrahedral angle. We may then regard hybrid orbitals as illustrating the effects of electron correlation more clearly than do the standard s- and p-orbitals.

In addition to the tetrahedral hybrids which we have been considering, there are two other important kinds of equivalent hybrid orbitals which can be formed from *s*- and *p*-orbitals. These are the *digonal* or *sp-hybrids*,

$$D_1 = \frac{1}{\sqrt{2}} (s + p_x),$$

$$D_2 = \frac{1}{\sqrt{2}} (s - p_x),$$

(5–23)

and the *trigonal* or *sp*^{2} *hybrids*,

$$T_1 = \frac{1}{\sqrt{3}} (s + \sqrt{2}\, p_x),$$

$$T_2 = \frac{1}{\sqrt{3}} s + \frac{1}{\sqrt{6}} p_x + \frac{1}{\sqrt{2}} p_y,$$

$$T_3 = \frac{1}{\sqrt{3}} s - \frac{1}{\sqrt{6}} p_x - \frac{1}{\sqrt{2}} p_y.$$

(5–24)

Both of these types of hybrid orbitals are much the same in shape as the tetrahedral hybrids, with most of the orbital concentrated in one lobe; but they are oriented differently. The digonal hybrids D_1 and D_2 point in opposite directions along the *x*-axis, while the three trigonal hybrids all lie in the *xy*-plane, with T_1 pointing along the *x*-axis, and the other two forming an angle of 120° with the *x*-axis.

The above cannot be considered a comprehensive discussion of hybridization, but we have covered the important principles involved. In the following section, these principles will be applied to the atoms of the first eight-membered period, with illustrations and a closer examination of some of the details.

(c) Directed valency in the second period

Having explained the structure of water in terms of our theory of localized bonds, we must now see if it may be extended to the structures of the molecules in Table 5–14. The angles are all suggestive of a basic tetrahedral electronic con-

TABLE 5–14

STRUCTURE OF H_2O AND RELATED MOLECULES

Molecule		$\angle$XOX, degrees	s(O—X), angstroms
OH_2	Water	104.5	0.96
OF_2	Oxygen difluoride	103.2	1.42
OCl_2	Oxygen dichloride	111	1.70
$O(CH_3)_2$	Dimethyl ether	111	1.42

TABLE 5–15

STRUCTURE OF NH_3 AND RELATED MOLECULES

Molecule		$\angle$XNX, degrees	s(N—X), angstroms
NH_3	Ammonia	107.3	1.01
NF_3	Nitrogen trifluoride	102.1	1.37
$N(CH_3)_3$	Trimethylamine	108	1.47
NH_4^+	Ammonium ion	109.5	1.03
$ON(CH_3)_3$	Trimethylamine oxide	114	1.49

figuration for oxygen with two lone-pair and two bond-pair sp^3 hybrids, the bonds being formed by overlap of these hybrids with H ($1s$) orbitals, or in other cases (the halogens, etc.), with $2p$ AO's. The deviations from the tetrahedral angle are systematic, and may be explained on the basis of the size and electronegativity of the atom concerned. Thus it is reasonable to expect a smaller angle in OF_2 than in OH_2, because the electronegativity of fluorine is nearly twice that of hydrogen, and the bonding electrons are pulled farther from the oxygen nucleus. On the other hand, atoms of Cl and of the methyl group are considerably larger than those of hydrogen, so that it is not surprising that the angle in these cases is larger than the tetrahedral angle. Presumably, the trend would continue in OBr_2, whose structure is unknown. Iodine forms no analogous oxide.

Turning to simple compounds of nitrogen, we see from Table 5–15 that these also are based on a tetrahedral electronic configuration for the nitrogen atom (Fig. 5–35). There is in NH_3 (in contrast to water) only a single lone pair, so the bonding pairs tend to spread out somewhat more, to give the larger angle of 107.3°. (Compare the CMP in Fig. 5–34.) On the other hand, in NF_3 the high electronegativity of F has reduced the angle by a slightly larger amount than in the corresponding oxygen compound. This is probably due to the somewhat longer bond in NF_3, which would lessen the effect of bond-pair repulsion in

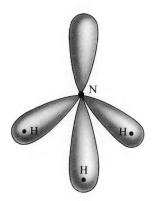

FIG. 5–35. Tetrahedral electronic configuration of NH_3. The upper lobe is a lone pair, while the lower three lobes are localized σ MO's of the type [H($1s$) + N(Te), σ].

TABLE 5–16

STRUCTURE OF CH_4 AND RELATED MOLECULES

Molecule	$s(C—X)$, angstroms	$s(C—H)$, angstroms	$\angle HCH$, degrees	$\angle XCX$, degrees
CH_4		1.09	109.5	
CF_4	1.32			109.5
CCl_4	1.77			109.5
CBr_4	1.94			109.5
CI_4	2.15			109.5
$CHCl_3$	1.77	1.07		110.4
CH_2Cl_2	1.77	1.07	112	112
CH_3Cl	1.78	1.11	111	

opening the angle. The same argument would account for the proportionately smaller increase in going from NH_3 to $N(CH_3)_3$. The ammonium ion, NH_4^+, is isoelectronic with NH_3, but all of the valence electrons are present as bonding pairs. As a consequence, the structure has full tetrahedral symmetry. Note that when the lone pair becomes a bond pair, the $\angle HNH$ is increased.

The N—O bond in $(CH_3)_3NO$ is an example of a *coordinate or dative bond*, so named because both of the bonding electrons come from the one atom. By virtue of the indistinguishability of electrons, we might expect this to be no different from a normal electron-pair bond, and such is found to be the case experimentally. For example, the N—O distance in trimethylamine oxide (1.44 A) is very nearly the same as that in hydroxylamine $H_2N—OH$ (1.46 A) and nitrous acid HO—NO (1.46 A). Because of its lone pair, ammonia often acts as an electron donor or Lewis base in forming bonds of this type. This is, in fact, the major reason for the participation of NH_3 in the formation of so many complex ions. One of the best known is the silver ammine complex $[H_3N—Ag—NH_3]^+$, but there are many more formed, particularly with the transition metals (Chapter 6).

There is little need to present evidence for the tetrahedral carbon atom, since this postulate has long formed the basis of structural organic chemistry. For reference purposes we have listed in Table 5–16 the structures of methane and a few of the many halogen-substituted compounds.

On the other hand, it is less easily seen how or why carbon is tetravalent. With a ground-state configuration of $C[1s^2 2s^2 2p^1 2p^1]$ we might expect carbon to be divalent, but there are in fact few compounds where this is so. Tetravalence is possible, however, in the excited state $C[1s^2 2s^1 2p^1 2p^1 2p^1]$ where there are four unpaired electrons. Furthermore, on the basis of our previous agrument, it is not surprising that four equivalent tetrahedral orbitals take part in the bonding. Energy is required to excite the $2s$ electron to the $2p$ orbital (about 96 kcal) but this is more than compensated for by the additional binding energy (Fig. 5–36).

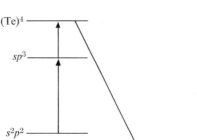

FIG. 5–36. Energy relationship between the ground
(s^2p^2) and valence $(Te)^4$ states of the carbon atom.

A similar situation arises in the case of boron, which in the ground state has the configuration $B[1s^2 2s^2 2p^1]$. The trigonal planar configuration adopted by simple boron compounds (Table 5–17) is readily explained if bonding occurs through trigonal sp^2 hybrids of the excited state $B[1s^2 2s^1 2p^1 2p^1]$. Even the mixed methylhalogen compounds are planar, although the interbond angles are modified.

TABLE 5–17

STRUCTURE OF BF_3 AND RELATED MOLECULES

Molecule	$s(B—X)$, angstroms	$s(B—C)$, angstroms	$\angle XBX$, degrees	$\angle CBC$, degrees
BF_3	1.30		120	
BCl_3	1.76		120	
BBr_3	1.87		120	
$B(CH_3)_3$		1.56		120
$B(CH_3)_2F$	1.29	1.55		117
$B(CH_3)F_2$	1.30	1.60	118	
$B(OH)_3$	1.36		120	

Unlike oxygen, nitrogen, and carbon, boron seems to violate the octet rule and be satisfied with a sextet of valence electrons, but this is not always the case. On the contrary, the very strong tendency of boron compounds, such as those of Table 5–17, to act as electron acceptors or Lewis acids plays a major role in the chemistry of boron; BF_3, for example, is the ideal complement for ammonia and its lone pair, and these two compounds readily react to form $F_3B—NH_3$. The planar BF_3 configuration is, of course, distorted by the B—N bond so that the structure of $F_3B—NH_3$ may be visualized as approximately that of two tetrahedra linked at a corner. In other cases ($NaBF_4$, KBF_4, $RbBF_4$), the octet is completed by formation of the BF_4^- ion, with complete tetrahedral symmetry.

This deficiency also leads to the unusual structures of the boron hydrides or boranes. The lowest of the series, BH_3, exists only in the form of the tetrahedral

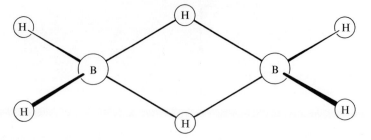

FIG. 5–37. Structure of B_2H_6. The bridge hydrogens lie in a plane perpendicular to that formed by the outer hydrogens.

BH_4^- ion ($NaBH_4$, KBH_4, $RbBH_4$), or in compounds such as trimethylamine borine $(CH_3)_3NBH_3$; attempts to prepare BH_3 itself produce only diborane, B_2H_6. At first sight this appears to be analogous to ethane, but there are two valence electrons too few for bonding according to the structure H_3B—BH_3. Instead, it is found experimentally that diborane has the rather unusual structure shown in Fig. 5–37, in which the borons are bonded together by *hydrogen bridges*. The length of the outer B—H bonds is 1.187 A, about that expected for a single bond. On the other hand, the distance between a boron atom and one of the bridging hydrogens is 1.334 A, considerably larger than the single-bond length. There is, in fact, a series of volatile boron hydrides ranging up to decaborane, $B_{10}H_{14}$, and all are bonded through the hydrogen bridge. The theoretical aspects of the bonding will be discussed briefly in Section 5–3(e); for further details the student is referred to the review by Lipscomb (*J. Chem. Phys.*, **22**:985, 1954).

Although beryllium is in Group II with the alkaline earths, it differs from them significantly in its chemical properties, and forms a number of compounds which exhibit tetrahedrally directed valency, through covalent bonding, in solids. By extrapolation of the discussion of carbon and boron, we expect bonding to occur through digonal hybrids of the excited state $Be[1s^2 2s 2p]$. No beryllium compounds are known where this occurs, but it is observed in the analogous compounds of Group IIB, such as ZnI_2, $CaCl_2$, $HgCl_2$. The structure of $BeCl_2$ in the solid phase is not molecular, but consists rather of infinite chains $(BeCl_2)_n$ in which the Cl atoms are approximately tetrahedrally located about the Be atoms. Again we note a tendency to complete the octet of electrons.

We have ignored fluorine up to this point because directed valence is not of great importance in this case. There is, however, no reason why hybrid orbitals cannot take part in bonding in diatomic molecules. Indeed, considerations of energy and other factors suggest that this is the case in some of the hydrogen halides. It has been shown, for example, that because of the larger size of the chlorine atom, a dipole moment of about 1.0 debye in the direction H^-—Cl^+ would be expected if pure *p*-orbitals were used in bonding.

If, on the other hand, an sp^3 hybrid orbital is used, then the lone pairs of Cl which are protruding away from the hydrogen cancel this and give rise to a dipole

H$^+$—Cl$^-$, more in agreement with experiment. The orbitals in HCl are
therefore probably as depicted in Fig.
5–38. By similar reasoning, a substantial part of the dipole moment of H$_2$O
can be explained through the presence
of lone pairs. We must, as a result, regard with some suspicion the estimates
of ionic character which are based on
dipole moment.

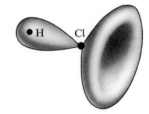

FIG. 5–38. Charge distribution for HCl
molecule, assuming that a hybrid AO is
used in forming the σ-bond.

Two remaining points should be
mentioned before we move on to more
complicated molecules. First, it should be clear that the phenomena of hybridization and localized orbitals are closely linked. The hybrid orbitals are so strongly
directed that they overlap significantly only one AO of the bonded atom, so that
a description in terms of localized MO's is possible.

The second point concerns the interpretation of the lone pairs in terms of bonding
power. In this regard, it is significant that in our localized MO description these
lone pairs are effectively unshared; hence they must be regarded as nonbonding
electrons. In fact, none of the hydride configurations we have discussed in
Section 5–3(c) contain any real antibonding electrons. The antibonding MO's are
available, as they must be if the general principles of MO theory are to be adhered
to, but in all these cases they are unoccupied because of their relatively high energy.
Indeed, as Mulliken has pointed out, this type of closed-shell configuration, in
which an additional electron must go into an orbital of distinctly higher energy,
is common to the majority of polyatomic molecules.

(d) Multiple bonding and delocalized orbitals

The principles of multiple bonding as discussed in relation to diatomic molecules
may, for the most part, be extended to cover polyatomic molecules as well. These
principles have special significance in the study of polyatomic molecules, however,
because in certain cases their existence forces us to discard the localized MO
concept which we have found so convenient. In light of the unique bonding
properties of carbon, and the considerable attention which these properties have
received theoretically, it is convenient to begin our discussion with examples of
some simple organic molecules.

Consider, therefore, the series methane, ethane, ethylene, and acetylene, for
which one may write the Lewis formulas:

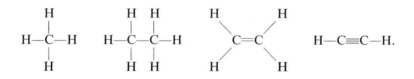

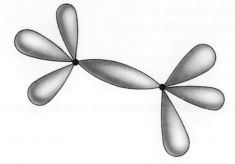

FIG. 5–39. Localized MO's (bonds) in ethane. There is a hydrogen nucleus (proton) embedded in each of the three σ-orbitals protruding from the ends.

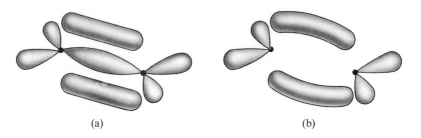

(a)   (b)

FIG. 5–40. Localized MO's in ethylene: (a) σ-π configuration; (b) "banana" MO description.

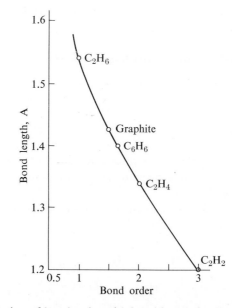

FIG. 5–41. Correlation of bond order with bond length for C—C bonds.

Such a description is qualitatively consistent with our more sophisticated theory, but the introduction of hybrid orbitals provides far more insight into the structural details.

In VB terms, each of these molecules admits of a fairly simple description in terms of electron pairing. As already discussed, we picture the carbon atom as hybridized tetrahedrally in CH_4, so that four σ-bonds are formed by pairing of these $C(sp^3)$ electrons with $H(1s)$ electrons. In ethane the carbon atom is again hybridized tetrahedrally, but in this case two of the $C(sp^3)$ electrons (one from each carbon) are paired to form a single bond between the carbons. The remaining six $C(sp^3)$ electrons pair with $H(1s)$ electrons to form σC—H bonds, as in methane, in accord with the observed $\angle HCH$ of 109.3° (Fig. 5–39). In ethylene the situation is obviously different, for the $\angle HCH$ has opened out to 120°, strongly suggestive of trigonal hybridization. Here the pairings are between $H(1s)$ and $C(sp^2)$ electrons in forming the C—H bonds, and two $C(sp^2)$ electrons in forming the C—C bond. In addition to this, the $C(p_z)$ electrons in orbitals perpendicular to the plane of hybridization couple to form a π bond [Fig. 5–40(a)].

There are, therefore, four bonding electrons, and we regard the C—C bond in ethylene as being double, in agreement with experiment (Fig. 5–41). Note also that the p_z orbitals exhibit maximum overlap when they point in the same direction; hence the CH_2 groups are coplanar and work has to be done to rotate one group relative to the other. Thus rotation about the central bond, as observed in ethane, is strongly hindered in ethylene. (Actually the rotation in ethane is not completely free. It is hindered somewhat by the repulsion of the σC—H MO's, so that the staggered configuration of Fig. 5–39 is preferred).

Continuing the process, the structure of acetylene follows immediately if we propose a digonally hybridized carbon atom. The C—C triple bond is made up of a σ-bond and two π-bonds, formed by the pairing of $C(sp)$ electrons, $C(p_y)$ electrons, and $C(p_z)$ electrons. The C—H bonds are σ-type, formed by pairing of $H(1s)$ and $C(sp)$ electrons; therefore the molecule is linear.

If localized MO's are employed, the electronic structures of CH_4, C_2H_6, C_2H_4, and C_2H_2 as derived from MO theory are much the same as in the VB case. Thus the σ-bonded structure of CH_4 would be written

$$CH_4\{C(K)[C(Te) + H(1s), \sigma]_{C-H}^8\}, \qquad (5\text{–}25)$$

with two electrons occupying each of the four equivalent σ-bonding MO's.

Similarly, in ethane there are six equivalent σ-bonding MO's formed by the overlap of $C(Te)$ and $H(1s)$ AO's, plus a σ-bonding MO localized between the carbon atoms. The structure, illustrated in Fig. 5–39, would be written:

$$C_2H_6\{C(K)(K)[C(Te) + H(1s), \sigma]_{C-H}^{12}[C(Te) + C(Te), \sigma]_{C-C}^2\}.$$

In ethylene the σ-bonding MO's are similar to the above, but they are now formed from trigonal or sp^2 hybrids. In addition there is a π MO localized in the

TABLE 5–18

STRUCTURES OF SOME SIMPLE ORGANIC MOLECULES

Molecule		$s(C—C)$, angstroms	$s(C—H)$, angstroms	$\angle HCH$, degrees
Ethane	C_2H_6	1.54	1.11	109.3
Ethylene	C_2H_4	1.34	1.07	120
Acetylene	C_2H_2	1.20	1.06	
Benzene	C_6H_6	1.40	1.08	

regions of the carbon nuclei, as shown in Fig. 5–40(a). Symbolically we write the electronic configuration of C_2H_4 as:

$$C_2H_4\{C(K)(K)[C(Tr) + H(1s), \sigma]^8_{C—H}[C(Tr) + C(Tr), \sigma]^2_{C—C}$$
$$[C(p_z) + C(p_z), \pi]^2_{C—C}\}.$$

In acetylene the carbon atom is digonally hybridized to give a linear σ-bonded structure. This leaves four electrons, which occupy two equivalent π-type MO's similar to those in the nitrogen molecule. The configuration is therefore:

$$C_2H_2\{C(K)(K)[C(D) + H(1s), \sigma]^4_{C—H}[C(D) + C(D), \sigma]^2_{C—C}$$
$$[C(p_z) + C(p_y), \pi]^2_{C—C}[C(p_z) + C(p_z), \pi]^2_{C—C}\}.$$

While experimental data on the C—H bond dissociation energies in these molecules are not completely reliable, there is little doubt that the bond energy increases in the order ethane < ethylene < acetylene (Table 5–18). This is in complete accord with the MO theoretical prediction that σ-bonds formed by the overlap of $H(1s)$ with digonal hybrids should be the strongest, while those formed with sp^2 hybrids should be weaker, and the sp^3 bonds the weakest of all.

The description given above of C—C multiple bonds in terms of σ and π MO's (hereinafter called the σ-π configuration) is not unique, because we may formulate an alternative configuration using sp^3 AO's in every case. Thus in ethylene we may picture the carbon atom as tetrahedrally hybridized and oriented so that two of the hybrid orbitals overlap at an angle with similar orbitals protruding from the other carbon atom. The resulting MO's are completely equivalent, and because of their bent shape are known as banana orbitals [Fig. 5–40(b)]. In acetylene, the alternative to the σ-π description is made up of three of these banana orbitals distributed symmetrically about the bonding axis.

It might be thought that because of their strong directional characteristics these hybrid orbitals would form stronger bonds than those resulting from p-orbital overlap; but it must be remembered that the axes of the hybrid orbitals are not collinear in this case. As a result of the angle at which they overlap one another,

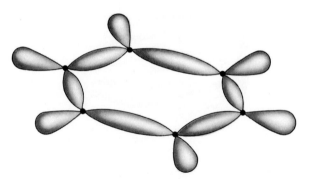

FIG. 5–42. Benzene: σ MO's.

the bond strength is reduced, so that the actual calculations tend to favor the σ-π configuration. We need not, however, be overly concerned as to which of these descriptions is the correct one, since they are in fact nearly equivalent. It can be shown through a relatively simple transformation that the σ-π MO's of ethylene are equivalent to a pair of MO's which are nearly identical to the banana MO's.

In dealing with molecules which contain more than one multiple bond, the distinction between the VB and MO approaches becomes more marked. Benzene is the classical example of delocalized bonds or orbitals, and so we shall begin by discussing its structure. From the regular hexagonal configuration of benzene, it seems fairly clear that the carbon atoms are trigonally hybridized, and utilize the hybrid orbitals in forming σ-bonds between themselves and the hydrogen atoms in the plane of the hexagon. This σ-bonded skeleton is shown in Fig. 5–42. The problem now arises in describing the participation of the six singly occupied carbon p_z AO's in the bonding. In VB terminology we may couple alternate pairs according to the Kekulé scheme I, but clearly the other Kekulé structure II has equal merit, so that the resulting structure must be a superposition of the two. In other words, the VB approach visualizes resonance between the two equivalent Kekulé structures:

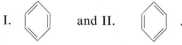

I.   and II.

On the basis of I and II we might expect each of the C—C bonds to partake of half a π-bond and have a bond order of 1.5, but experimentally it is in fact some-what closer to 2. This additional stabilization always accompanies the resonance phenomenon and is expressed quantitatively in the *resonance energy*, which is about 30 kcal for the whole benzene molecule. [See Section 4–4(c).]

When we fashion the MO's for benzene, it is obviously convenient to start with trigonally hybridized carbon, as in the VB approach, and form MO's of the type

$$[C(Tr) + C(Tr), \sigma]_{C-C},$$

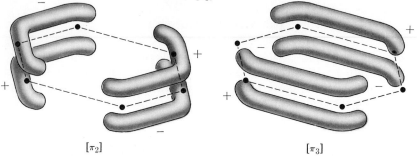

FIG. 5–43. Schematic illustration of the bonding delocalized ("streamer") π MO's of benzene.

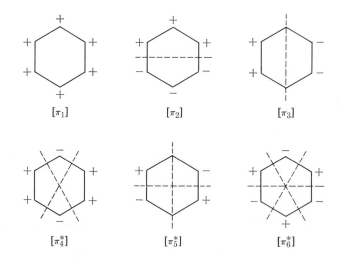

FIG. 5–44. Nodal planes (dashed lines) in the six π MO's of benzene.

which are localized in the region of the two carbon atoms involved. There will be six of these σ-orbitals, and they will be occupied by 12 electrons in all. In addition there will be six orbitals of the type

$$[C(Tr) + H(1s), \sigma]_{C-H},$$

which are localized between pairs of carbon and hydrogen atoms and take up 12 electrons. If we consider the carbon K-shell to be nonbonding, this will leave six electrons to be allotted, presumably to π-type MO's, since there remain the carbon p_z orbitals oriented perpendicular to the plane of hybridization.

It is no longer logical to take the p_z AO's in pairs, as in ethylene or acetylene, because they obviously overlap equally with each of their neighbors. We are forced, in fact, to accept a set of *delocalized orbitals* formed from linear combinations of the $C(p_z)$ orbitals such that all of the AO's contribute to each of the π MO's. Since six p_z AO's are involved, six MO's will be formed, three of which are bonding and three antibonding; only the three of lowest energy will be occupied by the six electrons. If we letter the carbon atoms A, B, C, D, E, F, around the ring, then the π-orbitals will be of the form:

$$[\pi_1]_{C-C} = [C_A(p_z) + C_B(p_z) + C_C(p_z) + C_D(p_z) + C_E(p_z) + C_F(p_z), \pi]_{C-C};$$

$$[\pi_2]_{C-C} = [C_A(p_z) - C_B(p_z) - 2C_C(p_z) - C_D(p_z) + C_E(p_z) + 2C_F(p_z), \pi]_{C-C};$$

$$[\pi_3]_{C-C} = [C_A(p_z) + C_B(p_z) - C_D(p_z) - C_E(p_z), \pi]_{C-C};$$

$$[\pi_4^*]_{C-C} = [C_A(p_z) + C_B(p_z) - 2C_C(p_z) + C_D(p_z) + C_E(p_z) - 2C_F(p_z), \pi]_{C-C};$$

$$[\pi_5^*]_{C-C} = [C_A(p_z) - C_B(p_z) + C_D(p_z) - C_E(p_z), \pi]_{C-C};$$

$$[\pi_6^*]_{C-C} = [C_A(p_z) - C_B(p_z) + C_C(p_z) - C_D(p_z) + C_E(p_z) - C_F(p_z), \pi]_{C-C}.$$

The energies of these orbitals increase in the order

$$[\pi_1] < [\pi_2] = [\pi_3] < [\pi_4^*] = [\pi_5^*] < [\pi_6^*],$$

with the first three MO's bonding and the latter three antibonding. The shapes of the bonding orbitals are illustrated in the three parts of Fig. 5–43.

It is interesting to note that in benzene as well as in the hydrogen atom there is a relationship between the nodes in the wave functions and the energy of the orbital. Referring to Fig. (5–44), we see that $[\pi_1]$ has no nodal plane, i.e., plane in which $[\pi_1] = 0$, perpendicular to the plane of the molecule. The degenerate MO's $[\pi_2]$ and $[\pi_3]$ have one each, while the other pair of degenerate MO's $[\pi_4^*]$ and $[\pi_5^*]$ have two each. The highest-energy MO has three nodal planes perpendicular to the plane of the molecule. It would appear then that the energy of a MO increases with the number of nodes.

There are a number of interesting ramifications of these delocalized orbitals in benzene. Since all six electrons are active in the binding of each pair of carbon atoms, we arrive immediately at the conclusion that all six bonds must be equal and the structure a regular hexagon, in agreement with experiment. Comparing this MO approach with the VB approach, we find that the greater freedom allowed the electrons in delocalized MO's results in a lowering of the energy relative to simple localized MO's between alternate pairs. Thus we have come to use the term *delocalization energy*, and refer to the electrons in such MO's as *mobile electrons*. The mobility of the electrons gives rise, in fact, to interesting magnetic effects due to their circulation about the delocalized MO. Furthermore, their presence explains the manner in which the effect of a substitution on one carbon atom is transmitted to the others. In other words, the delocalized MO forms the basis for a theory of chemical reactivity.

It should be emphasized that delocalized MO's are not restricted to cases such as that of benzene, where we are forced to adopt them. On the contrary, delocalized MO's may be formulated for any molecule, and this is, in fact, the more common procedure. In many simple molecules, however, we find that these delocalized MO's are mathematically equivalent to other MO's which are almost completely localized among the nuclei concerned. As pointed out previously, such a phenomenon is in keeping with the experimental observation that certain bond properties are practically invariant from molecule to molecule. Localized MO's are therefore easier to visualize and handle than delocalized MO's, because they are more closely allied conceptually to our empirical ideas of chemical bonding. The localized MO description is usually valid for the ground states of molecules containing no more than one multiple bond, but it breaks down for conjugated bond systems and excited states.

The benzene molecule which we have just discussed is an example of the former exception (conjugated bond systems), and the latter situation may be illustrated by considering the specific case of methane. We know from the electronic spectrum of CH_4 that it is possible to excite a single electron, yet it is difficult to reconcile such a phenomenon with the localized MO description in which the eight outer-shell electrons occupy four completely equivalent σ-orbitals (Eq. (5–25)). Because of this equivalence, it is impossible to assign the excited electron to any particular localized MO; in fact, we must conclude that the excitation exists partially in each bond.

In other words, the localized MO's are inadequate, and we must formulate delocalized MO's for this application. Thus the nonlocalized MO's, in addition to being more accurate, are of more general validity. It is beyond the scope of this text to describe in detail the mathematical procedures which are used in formulating delocalized MO's; suffice it to say that they are based largely on group theory as applied to symmetry, and provide yet another example of the importance of symmetry in the study of molecular structure. As in the case of atomic orbitals, the scheme of molecular orbitals is correlated with experiment by means of electronic spectra.

When we apply the above ideas to polyatomic inorganic molecules, it is convenient to begin with some simple compounds closely allied to those already discussed. Thus in hydrazine, H_2NNH_2, we visualize a tetrahedral nitrogen atom and localized MO's bonding together the two nitrogen atoms, and bonding the hydrogen atoms to the nitrogen atoms. The structure is in fact very much like that of ethane, with a C—H MO replaced by a lone pair on each nitrogen.

The similarity is even more marked in the ions $N_2H_5^+$ and $N_2H_6^{2+}$, in which the lone pairs are converted into localized N—H MO's. (Compare NH_3 and NH_4^+.) These descriptions are in accord with the available experimental data. In difluorodiazine, FNNF, the observed $\angle NNF$ of $115°$ suggests a trigonally hybridized nitrogen and the MO configuration

$$N_2F_2\{N(Tr)^2(Tr)^2[N(Tr) + N(Tr), \sigma]_{N-N}^2[N(Tr) + F(p_x), \sigma]_{N-F}^4$$

$$[N(p_z) + N(p_z), \pi]_{N-N}^2\}.$$

In addition, there are three lone pairs on each fluorine which, like the nitrogen lone pairs $(Tr)^2$, are essentially unshared and may be considered nonbonding. The N—N bond is of the σ-π type, and the molecule should be planar and exist in the two forms

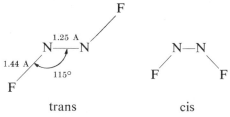

trans   cis

This is in complete accord with experimental observation.

Hydrogen peroxide, H_2O_2, forms an interesting contrast to N_2F_2, since there are two lone pairs on the tetrahedrally hybridized oxygen atom. The molecule is therefore not planar, and the relative orientation of the two O—H bonds will be determined primarily by the repulsion between the lone pairs on opposing oxygen atoms. Theoretically, it has been shown that the repulsive energy will be a minimum when the plane of the two lone-pair orbitals on one oxygen is perpendicular to the analogous plane on the other oxygen, a condition which would correspond to an azimuthal angle of about $90°$. The angle is known to be $93.6°$ in the crystal and seems to be about the same in the gas phase.

Turning to some molecules in which the bonding is more complicated, let us look first at the structures of some familiar triatomic molecules. Carbon dioxide (Table 5–19) is a special case, which has received considerable attention theoretically. In setting up the initial model, we shall assume that all the $1s$-electrons may be treated as unshared and nonbonding, and that the oxygen $2s$-electrons may also be so considered. Since CO_2 is linear, it is reasonable to propose digonal hybridization of the carbon atom and the formation of localized σ bonding MO's between the central carbon atoms and the two oxygens. Using the subscripts A and B for

TABLE 5-19

STRUCTURES OF SOME CARBON-OXYGEN COMPOUNDS

Molecule	$s(C{-}O)$, angstroms	Comments
CO	1.13	
CO^+	1.12	
CO_2	1.16	Linear
CO_3^{2-}	1.31	Trig. planar; cryst. $CaCO_3$
HCO_2^-	1.26	Planar; $\angle OCO = 126°$; Cryst. $Ba[HCO_2]$
H_2CO	1.23	Planar; $\angle HCH = 126°$; $s(C{-}H) = 1.06\ A$
COS	1.16	Linear; $s(C{-}S) = 1.56\ A$
COSe	1.16	Linear; $s(C{-}Se) = 1.71\ A$
H_3COH	1.43	$\angle COH = 107°$

the two oxygens, we shall write these MO's as $[\sigma]_{C-O_A}$ and $[\sigma]_{C-O_B}$. The remaining eight valence electrons may now be allotted as follows: two lone pairs $O_A(2p_y)^2$ and $O_B(2p_z)^2$, one on each oxygen atom; two electrons in a π-orbital localized between C and O_A of the form $[\pi_z]_{C-O_A} = [O_A(2p_z) + C(2p_z), \pi]_{C-O_A}$; two electrons in a similar orbital localized between C and O_B $[\pi_y]_{C-O_B} = [O_B(2p_y) + C(2p_y), \pi]_{C-O_B}$. The complete configuration may therefore be written

$$CO_2\{O_A(K)(2s)^2(2p_y)^2 O_B(K)(2s)^2(2p_z)^2 C(K)[\sigma]_{C-O_A}^2[\sigma]_{C-O_B}^2[\pi_z]_{C-O_A}^2[\pi_y]_{C-O_B}^2\}.$$

$$(5\text{-}26)$$

Unfortunately, this fairly straightforward configuration is not compatible with experiment. The C—O bond length of 1.16 A in CO_2 is considerably shorter than that expected for a normal σ-π double bond (about 1.24 A). It is not difficult to see the shortcoming of our initial model, for we have neglected the equally valid configuration

$$CO_2\{O_A(K)(2s)^2(2p_z)^2 O_B(K)(2s)^2(2p_y)^2 C(K)[\sigma]_{C-O_A}^2[\sigma]_{C-O_B}^2[\pi_y]_{C-O_A}^2[\pi_z]_{C-O_B}^2\},$$

$$(5\text{-}27)$$

in which the roles of the p_y and p_z orbitals are interchanged. We might speak of resonance between these two structures, but this is simply another way of saying that the localized MO approximation is inadequate. We must take account of the full symmetry of CO_2 and formulate delocalized π MO's. Since there are six p AO's involved, there is a pair of degenerate, strongly bonding, streamer-type

MO's extending over all the nuclei, and formulated

$$[\pi_z]^2_{O-C-O} = [O_A(p_z) + C(p_z) + O_B(p_z), \pi]_{O-C-O}$$

and

$$[\pi_y]^2_{O-C-O} = [O_A(p_y) + C(p_y) + O_B(p_y), \pi]_{O-C-O}.$$

Next in order of energy is another pair of degenerate MO's, written

$$[\pi_y]_{O-O} = [O_A(p_y) - O_B(p_y), \pi]_{O-O}$$

and

$$[\pi_z]_{O-O} = [O_A(p_z) - O_B(p_z), \pi]_{O-O}.$$

They do not involve the $C(p_y)$ or $C(p_z)$ AO's; hence they are localized in the region of the oxygens, and might be considered the counterparts of the oxygen lone pairs in Eqs. (5–26) and (5–27). Like the lone pairs, they may be considered O—C—O nonbonding. (Rigorously speaking, they are slightly O—O antibonding, but because of the relatively large O—O separation the effect is negligible). This completes the description of the occupied MO's in CO_2, but there are, of course, two more π-orbitals which may be formulated from the six AO's with which we started. These orbitals are of the form

$$[\pi_y^*]_{O-C-O} = [O_A(p_y) - C(p_y) + O_B(p_y), \pi]_{O-C-O}$$

and, since they have relatively high energy, will be strongly antibonding. The complete MO configuration of CO_2 is

$$CO_2\{O_A(K)(2s)^2 O_B(K)(2s)^2 C(K)[\sigma]^2_{C-O_A}[\sigma]^2_{C-O_B}$$
$$[\pi_y]^2_{O-C-O}[\pi_z]^2_{O-C-O}[\pi_y]^2_{O-O}[\pi_z]^2_{O-O}\}. \qquad (5\text{–}28)$$

The shapes of the bonding π-orbitals are illustrated in Fig. 5–45. As in the case of benzene, the greater freedom allowed to the electrons in the delocalized

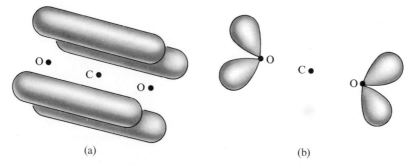

(a)   (b)

Fig. 5–45. Delocalized π MO's in CO_2. (a) The two bonding π MO's, $[\pi_y]_{O-C-O}$ and $[\pi_z]_{O-C-O}$. (b) The nonbonding MO $[\pi_z]_{O-O}$.

orbitals leads to stronger bonds than might be expected from Eq. (5–26). In fact, on the basis of the bond-length, bond-order curves, the order of the C—O bonds is closer to 2.5 than 2.0. The bond strength would also be influenced if the oxygen 2s electrons took part in the bonding through sp hybridization. Since this would have no effect on the linearity of the molecule, the extent to which sp hybridization occurs could only be assessed through accurate calculations of the bond energy, and this has not been done. Similar consideration would apply in the case of many of the polyatomic molecules discussed in this chapter.

The above discussion also leads to an explanation for the similarity of the bond lengths in CO_2 and CO, since the latter is usually regarded as having a triple bond. The MO configuration may be written in the usual way, as

$$CO[(K)(K)(z\sigma)^2(y\sigma)^2(x\sigma)^2(v\pi)^4], \qquad (5\text{–}29)$$

where $(z\sigma)^2$ is a nonbonding $O(2s)^2$ lone pair, and $(y\sigma)^2$ a $C(D)^2$ lone pair. The bonding σ MO will be a combination of a carbon digonal hybrid with an oxygen $2p_x$ AO, while the π MO's will be of the usual type formed by the combination of the p_y and p_z AO's.

The digonal lone pair on the carbon atom is important because it counterbalances the normal polarity of the bonding MO's, a polarity arising from the higher nuclear charge of oxygen, and explains the very small dipole moment of CO. It can be seen, in addition, that the lone pair is responsible for the electron donor properties of CO in, for example, H_3B—CO, and in many complex ions. Another unusual feature of CO is that the removal of an electron to produce CO^+ has very little effect on the length of the bond. This circumstance would indicate that the electron is removed from a lone pair, and could be explained by altering the sequence of the MO's in Eq. (5–29) to make the $C(D)^2$ that of highest energy.

Carbon dioxide and carbon monoxide also provide an interesting contrast between the VB and MO methods. In the case of CO_2, the VB approach explains the greater than double bond by proposing resonance among the structures

$$O{=}C{=}O \qquad {}^-O{-}C{\equiv}O^+ \qquad {}^+O{\equiv}C{-}O^-.$$

For C—O, one must consider resonance among three structures of approximately equal weight:

$$C{=}O \qquad {}^-C{\equiv}O^+ \qquad {}^+C{-}O^-.$$

The latter two of these, having opposite polarity, offer an explanation for the small dipole moment of CO.

Returning to triatomic molecules, we recall that CO_2, like N_2 and NO^+, has a configuration made up of a firmly bound closed shell of electrons. Isoelectronic triatomic molecules, such as NO_2^+, N_3^-, NNO, and CS_2, would be expected to have the same type of configuration, in which an additional electron would have to go into a strongly antibonding π MO. In agreement with this, all of these

TABLE 5-20

STRUCTURES OF SOME NITROGEN COMPOUNDS

Molecule	$s(N—O)$, angstroms	$s(N—N)$, angstroms	Comments
NO	1.15		
NO^+	1.06		
ONO^+	1.15		Linear; cryst. N_2O_5
NO_2	1.19		$\angle ONO = 134°$
NO_2^-	1.24		$\angle ONO = 115°$; cryst. $NaNO_2$
NO_3^-	1.24		Trig. planar; cryst. N_2O_5
NNO	1.19	1.13	Linear
O_2NNO_2	1.17	1.64	Planar; cryst; $\angle ONO = 108°$
H_2NOH	1.46		Hydroxylamine; $\angle HON = 103°$; $\angle HNO = 105°$; $\angle HNH = 107°$
N_2		1.10	
N_2^+		1.12	
N_2F_2		1.25	Planar; $s(N—F) = 1.44$ A; $\angle NNF = 115°$
N_2H_4		1.47	$s(N—H) = 1.04$ A;
		1.47	$\angle HNH = \angle HNN = 108°$

molecules are observed to be linear. In fact, consideration of the scheme of MO's shows that any molecule of the type AB_2 (in which $B \neq H$), which has 16 electrons or less in the valence shell, should be linear. At the same time, the closed-shell analogy between CO_2 or NO_2^+ and NO^+ is not complete, because the linear triatomic molecules have an alternative to accepting an electron in a loosely bound, strongly antibonding MO; they may change their shape.

Thus, in forming NO from NO^+, an electron is added to the antibonding MO so that the bond strength is reduced, and the bond length increases from 1.06 A in NO^+ to 1.15 A in NO. If, however, an electron is added to NO_2^+ to form NO_2, then the latter assumes a triangular shape ($\angle ONO = 134°$), and the NO bond length increases by only 0.04 A (Table 5-20). A further decrease in angle to 115° accompanies the addition of another electron in NO_2^-, and the bond length increases to 1.24 A. Walsh, Mulliken, and others have correlated this decrease in angle with a very marked decrease in the energy of the π antibonding MO to explain why the angular structure is preferred. On the other hand, the $[\pi_y]$ bonding MO is lost in the reshaping process, so that the bonding in nonlinear triatomic molecules results from σ-bonds plus a single delocalized π MO (Fig. 5-46).

While still a matter for discussion, it now seems fairly certain that the unpaired electron in NO_2 occupies what is essentially a nonbonding s or sp^2 AO localized in the nitrogen atom. This would explain the tendency of NO_2 to dimerize readily through an N—N bond. The structure of the dimer, N_2O_4, is more than a little unusual because, although the N—N bond is extremely weak $[D(O_2N—NO_2) =$

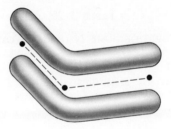

FIG. 5-46. Bonding $(p_z + p_z + p_z)$ π MO in ozone.

13.9 kcal], the molecular is planar. There must, therefore, be some interaction between the π MO's of the monomers, but the N—N bond obviously cannot be of the usual type.

Mention should also be made of the molecules I_3^-, $BrICl^-$, and $ClICl^-$, which are linear despite the 22 electrons in the valence shell. Obviously the MO scheme for these molecules is quite different from that in CO_2. This is not unexpected, for we have already observed that the antibonding MO's in NO_2^+ change to nonbonding MO's in NO_2^- as more electrons are added. A further change takes place in the halogen complex ions because d-orbitals become involved. This will be discussed further in Section 5–3(e); note, however, that triatomic molecules with 22 electrons in the valence shell are relatively rare.

Despite the complexity of the extra atom, the MO treatment of nonhydride AB_3-type molecules is quite straightforward, and much like that of triatomic molecules. The ion NO_3^- forms a convenient starting point. The MO's of interest are: (1) lone-pair $(2s)$ orbitals on each of the oxygens, each doubly occupied; (2) three localized σ-type N—O bonding MO's of the form $[\sigma]_{N-O_A} = [N(Tr) + O_A(2p_x), \sigma]$, each doubly occupied; (3) three doubly occupied orbitals which are approximately $O(2p_y)$ lone pairs; (4) four delocalized π MO's compounded from the $2p_z$ AO's of the four atoms. In order of increasing energy these are:

$$[\pi_1]_{N-O} = [N(p_z) + O_A(p_z) + O_B(p_z) + O_C(p_z), \pi]_{N-O},$$

$$[\pi_2]_{O-O} = [O_B(p_z) - O_C(p_z), \pi]_{O-O},$$

$$[\pi_3]_{O-O-O} = [O_A(p_z) - O_B(p_z) - O_C(p_z), \pi]_{O-O-O},$$

$$[\pi_4^*]_{N-O} = [O_A(p_z) + O_B(p_z) + O_C(p_z) - N(p_z), \pi]_{N-O}.$$

The first of these, $[\pi_1]_{N-O}$, is strongly N—O bonding, while $[\pi_2]_{O-O}$ and $[\pi_3]_{O-O-O}$ are degenerate and N—O nonbonding. In NO_3^-, the antibonding π MO, $[\pi_4^*]_{N-O}$ is unoccupied, so that the complete configuration may be written:

$$NO_3^- \{ O_A(K)(2s)^2 O_B(K)(2s)^2 O_C(K)(2s)^2 O_A(2p_y)^2 O_B(2p_y)^2 O_C(2p_y)^2$$

$$[\sigma]_{N-O_A}^2 [\sigma]_{N-O_B}^2 [\sigma]_{N-O_C}^2 [\pi_1]_{N-O}^2 [\pi_2]_{O-O}^2 [\pi_3]_{O-O-O}^2 \}.$$

A close analogy can be drawn between NO_3^- and NO_2^+. Both structures are of the closed-shell type, containing only strongly bound electrons. In the triatomic case, we saw that when another electron is added the molecule assumes a bent configuration, in which the energy of the antibonding MO is reduced. The corresponding phenomenon is observed in the tetratomic case, where molecules with 24 valence electrons or less, such as NO_3^-, CO_3^{2-}, SO_3, and BO_3^{3-}, are found to be planar. By changing from a planar to a pyramidal configuration, the molecule is able to lower significantly the energy of the antibonding MO which must accept the electron. It is interesting to observe that the MO configurations of NO_2^- and NO_3^- are very similar, as we would expect because of the identical bond lengths in the two molecules.

In considering tetrahedral pentatomic molecules such as SO_4^{2-}, it is tempting to carry the reasoning one step further and propose a configuration in which the only bonding MO's would be four of the σ-type localized between the sulfur and each oxygen. This would give a logical sequence of two, one, and zero π-bonding MO's in linear triatomic, planar tetratomic, and tetrahedral pentatomic molecules, respectively. Unfortunately, such a procedure only reveals the dangers of extrapolation, because the model it provides is incorrect.

That this is so is clearly illustrated by the bond lengths in these molecules which are closer to the normal double than single bond lengths: SO_4^{2-}, s_e(S—O) = 1.44 A; PO_4^{3-}, s_e(P—O) = 1.54 A; ClO_4^-, s_e(Cl—O) = 1.50 A. In this regard, it is also significant that no tetrahedral oxides are formed by elements of the first eight-membered period. A recent theoretical investigation by Cruickshank has shown that π-bonding MO's are probably formed by combination of the oxygen $2p_y$ and $2p_z$ AO's and the $d_{x^2-y^2}$ and d_{z^2} AO's of the central atom.

(e) Structure of more complex molecules

From the point of view of structure and bonding, several new features arise in a discussion of elements of the third and higher periods. Perhaps the most characteristic are multiple valency and the great variety of rather complex configurations which are observed. Thus, phosphorus forms two mononuclear fluorides PF_3 and PF_5 (in addition to PF_6^-), while nitrogen forms only one (NF_3). The halogens form a rather bewildering array of compounds ranging from the linear ICl_2^- to IF_5, IF_7, or I_8^{2-}.

Many of these characteristics are attributable to the ability of elements of the third and higher periods to make use of d-orbitals in bonding. We shall, however, restrict the present discussion to those elements which only make use of d-orbitals of the same principle quantum number as the highest s- and p-orbital; this excludes the transition elements, which will be discussed in the next chapter. The remaining elements will be discussed according to their grouping in the periodic table, with emphasis on the common characteristics of the members and any trends associated with the group. Furthermore, little attempt will be made to describe the bonding in detail; the discussion will center around a qualitative semi-empirical procedure which will enable us to predict approximate configurations only. There is little

TABLE 5–21

HYBRID ORBITAL CONFIGURATIONS

Number of orbitals	Arrangement	Hybrids
2	Linear	sp
3	Trigonal planar	sp^2
4	Tetrahedral	sp^3
5	Trigonal bipyramidal	$sp^3 d_{z^2}$
6	Octahedral	$sp^3 d_\gamma^2$
7	Pentagonal bipyramidal	$sp^3 d_\gamma^2 d_\epsilon$

doubt that from a rigorous theoretical point of view the approach will be found wanting in many respects, but this is true, to a greater or lesser extent, of any theoretical method of dealing with molecular structure.

As Fig. 3–9 shows, only four of the d-orbitals are equivalent in shape; the fifth, d_{z^2}, is quite different from the others. More important from the point of view of bonding is the distinction in terms of orientation. Thus the d_{z^2} and $d_{x^2-y^2}$ orbitals which are directed along the axes will be designated d_γ orbitals (or alternatively e_g orbitals), while the remaining three orbitals whose maxima are directed between the axes will be designated d_ϵ orbitals (alternatively t_{2g} orbitals).

Since we are restricting the discussion to bonding which involves s-, p- and d-orbitals of the same principal quantum number, the d-orbitals will always be of higher energy, and will be used only in addition to the single s- and three p-orbitals. The present discussion is, therefore, a continuation of our previous one of digonal, trigonal and tetrahedral hybrids, and begins with hybrids involving five orbitals. Reference to Table 5–21 will help to make this clear. Linnett and Mellish have shown theoretically that if only one d-orbital is used in bonding, then this should be a d_{z^2} orbital, and that the most probable configuration will have the five hybrid orbitals directed toward the corners of a trigonal bipyramid. Similarly, if two d-orbitals are employed, these will be the two d_γ-orbitals, and the most probable configuration will be one of six equivalent hybrids ($sp^3 d_\gamma^2$) directed toward the corners of a regular octahedron.

The only other set of hybrids which we need consider are the $sp^3 d_\gamma^2 d_\epsilon^1$, which have their maxima at the corners of a pentagonal bipyramid. Which d_ϵ orbital is used is of no consequence, since the choice simply affects the spatial orientation of the molecule as a whole.

To illustrate the qualitative but very useful approach which we shall use, let us look first at the series of second-period hydrides which are isoelectronic with neon. The structures of these were discussed previously, and the pertinent information is summarized in Table 5–22. Although the valency ranges from four

TABLE 5–22

CONFIGURATIONS BASED ON sp^3 (TETRAHEDRAL) HYBRIDIZATION

Number of bond pairs	Number of lone pairs	Shape	Example
4	0	Tetrahedral	H_4C
3	1	Trigonal pyramid	H_3N
2	2	Bent	H_2O
1	3		HF*
0	4		Ne†

* Exact degree of hybridization unknown; see Section 5–3(b).
† See Section 5–3(c).

with carbon to zero for neon, there are in every case four pairs of electrons distributed about the central atom in what is essentially a tetrahedral electronic configuration. Thus, knowing the total number of electrons and the number of lone pairs, we are able to predict the molecular structure.

Furthermore, recalling our previously discovered rule that the angles decrease in the order lone-pair–lone-pair > lone-pair–bond-pair > bond-pair–bond-pair, we may make a respectable guess at the angles involved. Note the steady decrease from 109.5° in CH_4 to 107.3° in NH_3 to 104.5° in H_2O, as the number of lone pairs increases. While somewhat more complicated because of the higher coordination, the trigonal bipyramidal, the octahedral, and the pentagonal bipyramidal electronic configurations may be treated in a quite analogous manner to explain the structures of the great majority of inorganic molecules and ions. Table 5–23, adapted from Gillespie and Nyholm, summarizes the arrangements. These will receive more detailed attention as we consider each group of the periodic table individually.

Almost all of the compounds of the alkali metals and the alkaline earths are ionic in nature. The structures of those halides of beryllium and of the alkaline earths which do exist in the gas phase are unknown, but they probably are linear and based on sp hybridization of the metal atom. This is observed for compounds of the B subgroup elements such as ZnI_2 and $CdCl_2$. To a limited extent this is also true of mercury (HgI_2, $HgCl_2$), but in most respects the chemistry of mercury differs rather markedly from that of the other members of the group. Notable in this respect are the mercurous compounds which have no analogs in the rest of the group. Comparatively little is known of the structures of these compounds, but it has been shown that the mercury is not truly monovalent in the cases investigated. The halides, for example, exist as linear dimers of the type Cl—Hg—Hg—Cl, in accord with the expected digonal hybridization of the Hg atom.

TABLE 5–23

CONFIGURATIONS BASED ON HYBRIDS INVOLVING d-ORBITALS

Hybrids	Number of bond pairs	Number of lone pairs	Shape	Example
$sp^3d_{z^2}$	5	0	Trigonal bipyramid	PCl_5
	4	1	Irregular tetrahedron	$TeCl_4$
	3	2	T-shape	ClF_3
	2	3	Linear	ICl_2^-
$sp^3d_\gamma^2$	6	0	Octahedral	SF_6
	5	1	Square pyramidal	IF_5
	4	2	Square planar	ICl_4^-
$sp^3d_\gamma^2d_\epsilon$	7	0	Pentagonal bipyramidal	IF_7

From the point of view of structural chemistry, boron bears little resemblence to its congeners (i.e., those of the same group) aluminum, gallium, indium and thallium. They do not, for example, form series of hydrides like those of boron. Furthermore, trigonal planar configurations are rare; those of GaI_3 and $(CH_3)_3In$ seem to be the only ones for which the structure has been confirmed. Almost all of the trivalent halides exist as dimers with a bridge structure, based on tetrahedral coordination, which is typified by Al_2Cl_6, shown in Fig. 5–47. One lone pair on each of the bridging chlorines is donated to make an approximately tetrahedral configuration about the aluminum possible. This is sometimes indicated

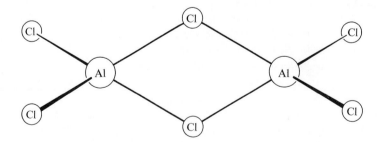

FIG. 5–47. Tetrahedral coordination of aluminum in the bridge-type structure of Al_2Cl_6.

by writing the structural formula as

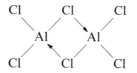

but it should not be taken to indicate that the four bridging bonds are not identical. Dialkyl compounds similar to $(CH_3)_2AlCl$, formed by gallium and indium, have a similar bridge structure, with the outer halides replaced by alkyl groups. On the other hand, the bridging in the dimer of the trimethyl compound

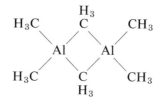

is obviously of a different type. Like B_2H_6 and the other boron hydrides, the compound is electron-deficient, and the bonding must be explained in terms of delocalized three-center (Al—C—Al) MO's. Apart from boron, all of the members of the group also form ions, such as AlF_6^{3-}; since there are six pairs of bonding electrons, the structure is a regular octahedron (Fig. 5–7).

One rather interesting feature of the boron group is that with increasing atomic number there is a tendency to form compounds in which monovalency is exhibited. It is observed in the case of gallium (GaCl) and indium (InCl, InF, etc.), but is particularly marked for thallium where the thallous (TlF, TlCl, etc.) state is the more common one. The bonding takes place, of course, through the ground-state s^2p configuration. Similarly, the thallous ion Tl^+ is found in ionic lattices where the inert pair of s-electrons is an important factor in determining the crystal structure.

The general remarks concerning the boron group apply for the most part to the carbon group of elements as well. Thus carbon differs markedly from the remainder of the group in a number of respects, but most notably in the vast array of carbon-hydrogen compounds it forms. It is in fact quite generally true that the first members (i.e., second period) of the periodic groups have properties which set them apart from the remainder of the group. In many ways they resemble the third-period elements of the next group (e.g., Li and Mg, Be and Al, B and Si), a fact formally expressed in the *diagonal relationship*. Silicon, for example, resembles boron in its oxygen chemistry. These compounds will be discussed in Chapter 7. Molecules based on a tetrahedral configuration are formed by all members of the group (CH_4, SiH_4, GeH_4, $SnCl_4$) but again the heavier members of the series exhibit a stable lower valence, in this case two. This results from the ground-state configuration. The molecules ($SnCl_2$, $PbCl_2$, etc.) are not linear, but the exact angle is unknown. Silicon, germanium, tin, and lead also form ions, such as SiF_6^{2-} or $PbCl_6^{2-}$, which are octahedral in shape.

Nitrogen and its congeners, phosphorous, arsenic, antimony, and bismuth display considerably more variety in their structural chemistry than do the boron and carbon groups. The ground-state electronic configuration for all of these elements is s^2p^3, or in box form

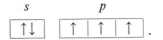

Hence we expect trivalency with pyramidal structures based on essentially tetrahedral hybridization. Many examples of this type of molecule (PBr_3, AsF_3, SbH_3, $BiCl_3$, etc.) are to be found, all similar to NH_3 in structure. They have some electron-donor properties, but are much weaker in this respect than nitrogen. The oxides of the type Cl_3PO and $(CH_3)_3AsO$ might be explained this way, but it seems likely that the d-orbitals also play some part in the bonding (see below). Significant is the decreasing tendency, with higher atomic number, to form "onium" ions analogous to NH_4^+. Thus, tetrahedral PH_4^+ ion is observed in crystals of phosphonium chloride, bromide and iodide, but only the organometallic analogs $(C_6H_5)_4As^+$ and $(CH_3)_4As^+$ are known in the case of arsenic, and no tetrahedral molecules of antimony or bismuth have been found.

In addition to their trivalent state, all of the members of the group except nitrogen may assume a pentavalent state by promotion of one of the s-electrons to a d-orbital. The valence state is the $sp^3d_{z^2}$ or

This state is common only with phosphorous, arsenic and antimony, however. Bismuth, in keeping with the trend observed in other periods, favors the lower valency state and rarely if ever exhibits pentavalency. This implies a greater stability of the inert pair, so that bismuth and antimony are found as the trivalent ions Bi^{3+} and Sb^{3+} in a number of salts. They are, therefore, more metallic in character than the other members of the group.

There are many examples of pentavalent compounds of phosphorous, arsenic, and antimony, but the most common are the halides, such as PCl_5, AsF_5, etc. Since there are five electron pairs, all bonding, situated about the central atom, the configuration assumed in every case is the trigonal bipyramid (Fig. 5–9). Pentavalent antimony forms an interesting series of trimethyl compounds of the type $(CH_3)_3SbX_2$ (X = Cl, Br, I), of similar structure, in which the halogens are

trans to the plane of the carbons

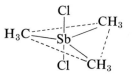

In the pentavalent state, phosphorous, arsenic, and antimony also form ions of the type PCl_6^-, AsF_6^-, and SbF_6^-, which have an octahedral shape [Fig. 5–7(c)]. More interesting, however, are the ions $SbCl_5^{2-}$ and SbF_5^{2-}, which exhibit a square-pyramidal configuration [Fig. 5–7(b)]. This structure is also based on octahedral $sp^3d_\gamma^2$ hybridization, but in this case there is a lone pair at one corner of the octahedron. Hence four of the halogens are coplanar with the Sb, and one lies vertically above, opposite the lone pair. It may be illustrated in this way:

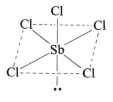

The oxides and sulfides of phosphorous, arsenic, and antimony display some very interesting and unique structures. Characteristic are the trioxide and pentoxide of phosphorous, which in the vapor exist as the dimers P_4O_6 and P_4O_{10}. As seen in Fig. 5–48, they have very similar cagelike structures in which there is a basically tetrahedral coordination about the phosphorous atoms. In phosphorous oxide, P_4O_6, one of the corners of each tetrahedron is occupied by a lone pair, while in P_4O_{10} (phosphoric oxide), an oxygen is bonded at these points. In the mixed oxide-sulfide, the outer oxygens (shaded in Fig. 5–48) are replaced by sulfur atoms.

In all three cases, the dimensions of the cage are about the same, but it is significant that the length of the P—O (and P—S) bonds outside the cage is abnormally short. Compare the observed $s(P—O) = 1.39$ A with the accepted lengths of 1.8 A, 1.5 A, and 1.4 A for single, double, and triple P—O bonds respectively. The bond is obviously not formed by simple lone-pair donation, nor is it an ordinary double bond. Similar trioxides have been observed for arsenic and antimony in crystals, but the structures of the pentoxides, which are unstable in the gas phase, are unknown.

The sulfides of these elements are even more varied than the oxides. Both P_4S_{10} and As_4S_6 have been investigated, and have structures of the same type as the corresponding oxides. The sulfide P_4S_3 also has a cage structure (Fig. 5–48) and, like the oxides, may be thought of as a derivative of the P_4 molecule. Similar is the cradlelike structure of As_4S_4 (Fig. 5–48). All of the angles are about 100°,

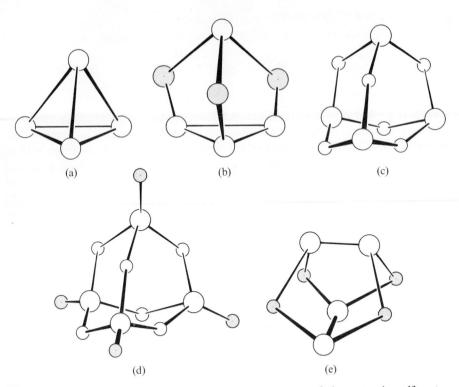

(a)   (b)   (c)

(d)   (e)

FIG. 5–48. Oxides and sulfides of the phosphorous group of elements; the sulfur atoms are shaded. (a) P_4, (b) P_4S_3, (c) P_4O_6, (d) $P_4S_4O_6$, and P_4O_{10} if the sulfur atoms are replaced by oxygens; (e) As_4S_4.

and the bond lengths approximately the same as those expected for single bonds. Nitrogen forms a similar compound, but there is some question as to the exact structure.

Oxygen excepted, the chalkogens may assume a divalent, tetravalent, or sexavalent state, depending on the number of d-orbitals used. The electronic configurations of these valence states are

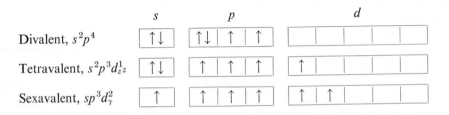

As with oxygen, the divalent compounds are bent because of the presence of two lone pairs; but the angles are, on the whole, much smaller than in oxygen. In the

hydrides H_2S and H_2Se, for example, the angles are 93° and 91° respectively. A similar phenomenon occurs with the hydrides of the nitrogen group (PH_3, 94°; AsH_3, 92°; SbH_3, 91°). The explanation probably lies in the lower electronegativity of the central atom relative to hydrogen, which would tend to polarize the bonding orbitals (as in NF_3) and allow them to come closer together.

Compounds such as SeF_4 and $TeCl_4$, where the chalcogenides exhibit a tetra-valency, have a single lone pair plus four bond pairs situated about the central atom; hence the structure is based on a trigonal bipyramid. In such a case there are two alternative structures (a) and (b), which differ in the location of the lone pair. These structures are:

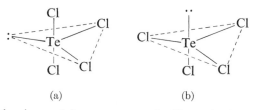

(a)   (b)

The lone-pair–bond-pair repulsions are most significant in determining the structure. In (a) there are two bond pairs at about 90° to the lone pair and two more at about 120°, but in (b) there are three bond pairs at about 90° to the lone pair; hence repulsive effects would favor (a). This is confirmed by experiment. Since the tellurium atom is not collinear with the two chlorines, the structure is usually described as a distorted tetrahedron.

In the sexavalent state, with twelve bonding pairs to be located, an octahedral configuration is both expected and observed. The fluorides SF_6, SeF_6, and TeF_6 are examples. Surprising, however, is the regular octahedral coordination in the ions $SeCl_6^{2-}$, $TeCl_6^{2-}$, and $PoBr_6^{2-}$. If this configuration is correct (and there seems to be a great deal of evidence in favor of these structures), then one would expect the extra electrons to be involved in π-bonding. However, it is significant that $s(\text{Te—Cl})$ in $TeCl_6^{2-}$ is much larger (2.51 A) than in $TeCl_4$ (2.33 A). On the basis of the arguments used here one would expect for these ions a distorted octa-hedral structure based on a pentagonal bipyramid, but this does not seem to be the case.

The halogens are monovalent in the ground state, but by using up to three d-orbitals in bonding they exhibit, in addition, valences of three, five, and seven. The electronic configurations corresponding to these valence states are:

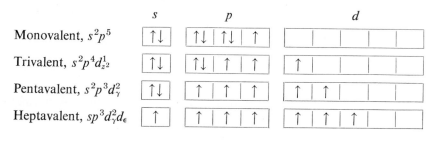

Examples of bonding in all states are known, although the higher valence states are most commonly observed in interhalogen compounds of fluorine and the heavier halogens.

The monovalent state is, of course, the most common one, and numerous examples have already been given. It is observed in the interhalogen compounds such as ClF, ICl, etc., and also in the ions ICl_2^- and I_3^-. These latter are of interest because their linear configuration is, at first sight, unusual. It is, however, in complete accord with our present argument. There are three lone pairs in addition to the two bond pairs, and of the three possible configurations based on the trigonal bipyramid, (c) is obviously the one favored by repulsive interaction. In

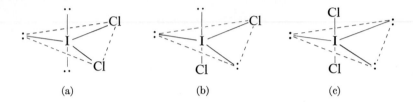

the trivalent compounds such as ClF_3 and BrF_3, there will also be five electron pairs situated about the central atom; but in this case, there are two lone pairs. It is not possible on the basis of our qualitative type of argument to choose between the three alternatives

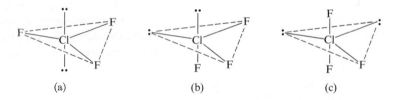

but the T-shape of (c) is observed experimentally. Because of repulsive effects, the $\angle FClF$ is reduced to 87.5°, but the structure is planar.

In the ICl_4^- ion, iodine is trivalent, with six pairs of electrons distributed about it in an octahedral configuration. Again there is a choice of structures, this time between

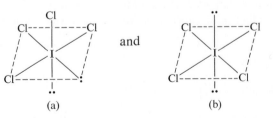

but (b) is favored over (a) because of the lone-pair repulsions. Accordingly, ICl_4^- assumes a square planar structure (Fig. 5–7).

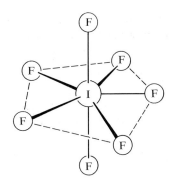

FIG. 5–49. Pentagonal bipyramidal configuration of IF_7.

Pentavalence is observed in BrF_5 and IF_5, where again there are six electron pairs to be considered. Since only one of these is a lone pair, there is no alternative, and a square pyramidal structure is observed (Fig. 5–7). The only interhalogen compound in which heptavalence is displayed is IF_7. In keeping with our scheme, IF_7 assumes a pentagonal bipyramidal configuration (Fig. 5–49), with seven bonding pairs of electrons situated about the iodine atom.

To bring this account up to date, it is necessary that we add a further paragraph on one of the most recent developments in inorganic chemistry: the preparation of compounds of the "inert" gases. Apart from the ionic compound previously mentioned, xenon has been shown to form at least three fluorides: XeF_2, XeF_4, and XeF_6. These are isoelectronic with IF_2^-, IF_4^-, and IF_6^-, and the difluoride and tetrafluoride are known to have the expected linear and square planar structures. Similar compounds of radon have also been prepared, despite the difficulties in handling resulting from the radioactivity of this element. Krypton does not seem to be chemically active; presumaby the $4d$ orbitals are at an energy level too high to permit bonding.

BIBLIOGRAPHY

A

CARTMELL, E., and G. W. A. FOWLES, *Valency and Molecular Structure*. London: Butterworth, 1961.

COULSON, C. A., *Valence*. New York: Oxford, 1961.

DAY, M.C., and J. SELBIN, *Theoretical Inorganic Chemistry*. New York: Reinhold, 1962.

EMELEUS, H. J., and J. S. ANDERSON, *Modern Aspects of Inorganic Chemistry*. London: Routledge and Kegan Paul, 1960.

GILLESPIE, R. J., and R. S. NYHOLM, "Inorganic Stereochemistry," *Quart. Rev.* **XI**, 273 (1957).

HEITLER, W., *Elementary Wave Mechanics*. New York: Oxford, 1956.

HESLOP, R. B., and P. L. ROBINSON, *Inorganic Chemistry*. Amsterdam: Elsevier, 1960.

KETELAAR, J. A. A., *Chemical Constitution*. Amsterdam: Elsevier, 1958.

LINNETT, J. W., *Wave Mechanics and Valency*. London: Methuen, 1960.

MULLIKEN, R. S., "Bonding Power of Electrons and Theory of Valence," *Chem. Rev.* **9**, 347 (1931).

PAULING, L., *The Nature of the Chemical Bond*. Ithaca, New York: Cornell, 1960.

RYSCHKEWITSCH, G. E., *Chemical Bonding and the Structure of Molecules*. New York: Reinhold, 1963.

WHEATLEY, P. J., *Molecular Structure*. New York: Oxford, 1959.

B

DAUDEL, R., R. LEFEBVRE, and C. MOSER, *Quantum Chemistry*. New York: Interscience, 1959.

FANO, U., and L. FANO, *Basic Physics of Atoms and Molecules*. New York: Wiley, 1959.

KAUZMANN, W., *Quantum Chemistry*. New York: Academic Press, 1957.

MULLIKEN, R. S., "Electronic Structure of Polyatomic Molecules and Valence," *Phys. Rev.* **40**, 55 (1932). (This paper and the one mentioned above are of a general nature, but others dealing with specific molecules may be found in the journals of this period; particularly *Phys. Rev.* and *J. Chem. Phys.*)

PAULING, L., and E. B. WILSON, *Introduction to Quantum Mechanics*. New York: McGraw-Hill, 1935.

POPLE, J. A., "The Molecular Orbital and Equivalent Orbital Approach to Molecular Structure," *Quart. Rev.* **XI**, 273 (1957).

RICE, F. O., and E. TELLER, *The Structure of Matter*. New York: Science Editions, Wiley, 1961.

SLATER, J. C., *Quantum Theory of Molecules and Solids, Volume I, Electronic Structure of Molecules*. New York: McGraw-Hill, 1963.

STREITWISER, A., *Molecular Orbital Theory for Organic Chemists*. New York: Wiley, 1961.

SUTTON, L. F., *Tables of Interatomic Distances and Configuration in Molecules and Ions*. London: Chemical Society, 1958.

VAN VLECK, J. H., and A. SHERMAN, "The Quantum Theory of Valence," *Rev. Mod. Phys.* **167** (1935).

WALSH, A. D., "The Electronic Orbitals, Shapes, and Spectra of Polyatomic Molecules," *J. Chem. Soc.* (1953), pp. 2260–2331.

WELLS, A. F., *Structural Inorganic Chemistry*. New York: Oxford, 1961.

PROBLEMS

5-1. List the symmetry elements possessed by the following molecules: (a) HOCl, bent, (b) N_2O_4, planar, (c) PCl_3, pyramidal, (d) NH_4^+, tetrahedral, (e) SF_6, octahedral, (f) C_6H_{12}, chair form.

5-2. Why is geometrical isomerism impossible in the case of tetrahedral $SiCl_2H_2$?

5-3. Why does Table 5-5 not include covalent radii for He, Ne and Ar?

5-4. Discuss the correlation between the covalent radii of Table 5-5 and the theoretical curves of Fig. 3-18.

5-5. (a) Prepare a table summarizing the MO configurations, bond orders, dissociation energies, and bond lengths for the homonuclear diatomic molecules of the elements of the first eight-membered period. (b) Plot a graph of homonuclear diatomic bond dissociation energies with the periodic group as the abscissa. Connect on the graph the values for the elements of a given period and discuss the periodic series in relation to the MO electronic configurations.

5-6. State which of N_2 and NO you would expect to have the larger ionization energy, and give your reasons.

5-7. Write the MO configurations for the following heteronuclear diatomic molecules: (a) LiH, (b) CN, (c) SO, (d) ClF, (e) HI.

5-8. (a) Use the values of Δ' given in Table 5-10 to calculate $[x(A) - x(B)]$ for the hydrogen halides, and compare your values with those obtained from Table 5-11. (b) Check the relation of Eq. (5-20), between percent ionic character and electronegativity, using the data of Table 5-9 and Table 5-11.

5-9. State, with reasons, which of the following triatomic molecules you would expect to be bent and which linear: (a) CS_2, (b) ClO_2, (c) C_3, (d) CSTe, (e) OCl_2, (f) $CdCl_2$, (g) $SnCl_2$, (h) ONCl, (i) CN_2^{2-}, (j) S_3^{2-}.

5-10. State, with reasons, which of the following tetratomic molecules you would expect to be planar and which pyramidal: (a) BO_3^{3-}, (b) PCl_3, (c) BrO_3^-, (d) AsH_3, (e) OH_3^+, (f) SeO_3^{2-}, (g) SbF_3.

5-11. Use the methods of Section 5-3(e) to predict the shapes of the following molecules and ions: (a) BrF_3, (b) TeF_6, (c) $F_5S_2F_5$, (d) $BiCl_6^{3-}$, (e) $SbCl_5$, (f) $Pb(CH_3)_4$, (g) $Tl(CH_3)_2^+$, (h) $IBrCl^-$, (i) $TlCl_5H_2O^{2-}$.

5-12. (a) Employ the data of Table 5-20 to establish a bond-length, bond-order relation for the N—N bond (see Fig. 5-28). (b) Use the curve from (a) to obtain the order of the bond in linear N_3^- ($s_e = 1.12$ A), and discuss the result in relation to the electronic configuration.

5-13. Hydrogen azide HN_3 and diazomethane CH_2N_2 have the following structures (distances in A):

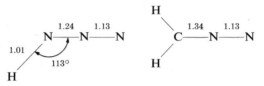

Describe the electronic configurations of these two molecules in both VB and MO terms.

5-14. Discuss (in both VB and MO terms) the reasons why a molecule such as LiNe is unstable relative to dissociation into its component atoms.

5–15. Discuss the electronic configurations and bonding in the following structures (distances in A): (a) carbon suboxide, C_3O_2,

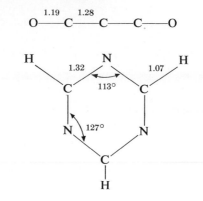

$$O \overset{1.19}{—\!\!\!—} C —\!\!\!— C \overset{1.28}{—\!\!\!—} C —\!\!\!— O$$

(b) triazine, $C_3H_3N_3$,

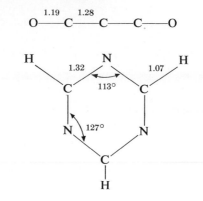

(c) borazole, $B_3H_6N_3$,

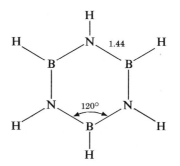

(d) orthoboric acid, H_3BO_3,

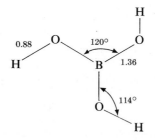

(e) octasulfur, S_8, puckered ring, $s(S—S) = 2.07$ A, $\angle SSS = 105°$.

5–16. Show that the overall charge distribution for the electrons occupying the π MO's in B_2 is cylindrically symmetrical about the bond axis. Use the hydrogen wave functions of Table 3–2.

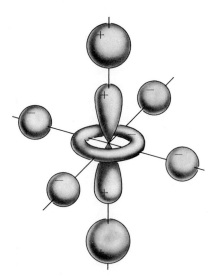

CHAPTER SIX

Transition Metal Complexes

6–1. INTRODUCTION

As our factual knowledge of chemistry grows, the definition of a complex ion becomes more difficult. The elementary definition of a complex ion as a charged group of atoms is equally valid when we apply it to simple ions such as SO_4^{2-} and NH_4^+, or to more involved ions of the type $Cu(NH_3)_4^{2+}$ and $PtCl_3(C_2H_4)^+$. Nevertheless, most chemists reserve the term "complex ion" almost solely for reference to ions of the latter type.

The hydration or aquation of ions also introduces a problem. The above definition clearly includes ions such as $Cu(H_2O)_4^{2+}$ and even $Na(H_2O)_n^+$, but one does not usually consider a hydrated sodium ion to be a complex ion. Furthermore, it is difficult to extend this definition to neutral complexes without including all polyatomic molecules.

Because of their distinctive electronic structures, the transition metals enter into the formation of a great many complex ions. As a consequence, the complexes are very important in both the crystal and solution chemistry of the transition metals. The ions are characterized by a structure which comprises a central metallic cation, to which are bonded a number of ions or molecules referred to as *ligands*. There is a large variety of ligands involved, however, and coupled with a variable oxidation number for the metallic cation, they lead to a bewildering array of complexes. We need not, furthermore, restrict ourselves to discrete neutral or ionic complexes, for essentially the same interactions are present in extended crystalline arrays. It is unlikely, for example, that there is much difference between the octahedral environment of Co^{2+} in crystalline $CoCl_2$ [$CdCl_2$ structure; Section 7–5(a)] and that in the $CoCl_6^{4-}$ ion. In fact, the pale-blue color of both $CoCl_2$ and $Li_4(CoCl_6)$ suggests that the environment of the Co^{2+} ion is very similar in the two compounds.

A major part of current research interest in inorganic chemistry centers on coordination chemistry, or the study of complexes, particularly those of the transition elements. The theoretical considerations required to interpret the bonding in these compounds are basically no different from those discussed in Chapter 5, except that the presence of partly filled d-orbitals has important consequences.

6–2. STEREOCHEMISTRY OF TRANSITION METAL COMPLEXES

While coordination numbers from two to eight have been reported, most transition metal complexes exhibit two-, four- or six-fold coordination, with structures based on those shown in Fig. 6–1. (See also Section 5–1). The octahedral structure (d), in regular and distorted forms, characterizes most of the complexes which are six-coordinated. The square planar shape (b) has been identified in complexes of Pt(II), Pd(II), Ni(II), Ag(II), Cu(II) and Au(III), in which the coordination number is four. The assignment of a tetrahedral structure (c) is experimentally more difficult than the others, but, in general, is largely limited to the complexes of nontransition elements. The two-coordinated complexes of Cu(I), Ag(I) and Au(I) all have a linear structure (a).

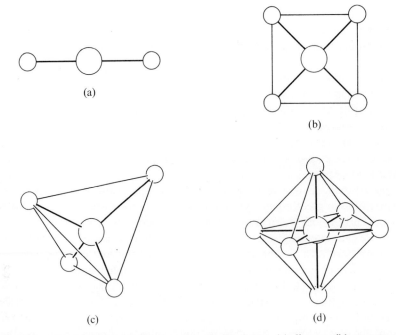

(a)

(b)

(c)

(d)

FIG. 6–1. Some common shapes of complex ions: (a) linear, (b) square planar, (c) tetrahedral, and (d) octahedral.

TABLE 6–1

SOME COMMON LIGANDS*

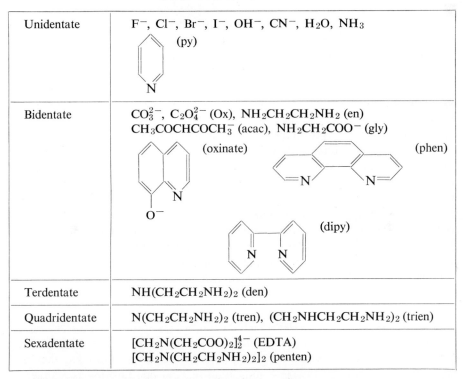

Unidentate	F^-, Cl^-, Br^-, I^-, OH^-, CN^-, H_2O, NH_3 (py)
Bidentate	CO_3^{2-}, $C_2O_4^{2-}$ (Ox), $NH_2CH_2CH_2NH_2$ (en) $CH_3COCHCOCH_3^-$ (acac), $NH_2CH_2COO^-$ (gly) (oxinate) (phen) (dipy)
Terdentate	$NH(CH_2CH_2NH_2)_2$ (den)
Quadridentate	$N(CH_2CH_2NH_2)_2$ (tren), $(CH_2NHCH_2CH_2NH_2)_2$ (trien)
Sexadentate	$[CH_2N(CH_2COO)_2]_2^{4-}$ (EDTA) $[CH_2N(CH_2CH_2NH_2)_2]_2$ (penten)

* Abbreviations used in formulas are given in parentheses.

A ligand will usually, but not necessarily, have at least one electron pair in an orbital of σ-symmetry which is not already directly involved in bonding. This allows the ligand to form a coordinate bond with the metal ion; hence the term *coordination compound*. A ligand capable of forming *one* such bond is referred to as a *unidentate ligand*, examples of which are H_2O, F^-, NH_3, CN^-, etc. When the ligand has *two* positions available for bonding, it is *bidentate*. Two bonds from different parts of the bidentate ligand to the central ion form a ring which includes the metal; the resulting compound is known as a *chelate* (Greek, *khele—claw*).

Ligands with coordinating positions up to six in number are known; for example, versene (ethylenediamine tetraacetate ion), which has revolutionized solution analytical chemistry. Some of the more common ligands are listed in Table 6–1. Multidentate ligands, i.e., those forming chelates, have provided more useful information about complexes, because chelates are generally more stable with regard to dissociation than complexes with unidentate ligands only. (However, see Chapter 9.)

(a) Geometrical isomerism

The phenomenon of isomerism, i.e., the occurrence of species having the same empirical formula but with different physical and chemical properties, has had an important role in the development of inorganic stereochemistry. The maximum number and type of isomers which can be synthesized can provide chemical evidence as to the structure of the complex. This information is particularly valuable as an adjunct to one of the more definitive diffraction techniques.

We distinguish two kinds of isomerism: geometric and structural. *Geometrical isomers* differ only in the spatial arrangement of the ligands around the central atom, but *structural isomers* may either have different ligands coordinated to the metal atom, or ligands coordinated through different atoms of the ligand.

Of the two types, data concerning geometrical isomerism provide the most information regarding structure. *Position isomerism* such as *cis* and *trans* can be found in both octahedral (Fig. 6–2) and square planar (Fig. 6–3) complexes, but not in tetrahedral ones. The prefix "trans" refers to two ligands across from one another, i.e., a straight line connecting them goes through the center of the complex; while "cis" implies adjacent positions. All ligands in a tetrahedral complex are cis to all others; hence the absence of this particular type of isomerism. Cis and trans isomers of octahedral complexes can exist for the compounds of general formulas MA_2B_4 and MA_3B_3 (unidentate ligands).

Still other positional isomers are possible with three or more ligands. In general, bidentate ligands occupy cis positions only, a fact which can often be used to great advantage in the synthesis or identification of cis and trans isomers.

The convention used to illustrate octahedral complexes in Fig. 6–2 has been chosen for convenience of representation. Some other ways of drawing the trans compound are shown in Fig. 6–4, indicating that no one position is unique; in

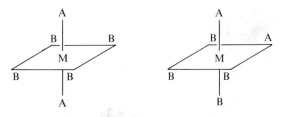

FIG. 6–2.   Trans and cis isomers of octahedral complexes of formula MA_2B_4.

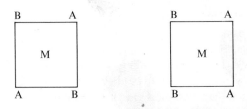

FIG. 6–3.   Trans and cis isomers of square planar complexes of formula MA_2B_2.

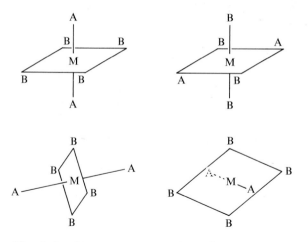

Fig. 6-4.   Alternate representations of trans-MA_2B_4.

fact, all six corners of a regular octahedron are identical. The existence of two and only two geometric isomers for compounds of the MA_2B_4 type is evidence for an octahedral six-coordinated complex. Other possible configurations, such as a planar hexagon or a trigonal prism, would have three geometric isomers.

The existence of two forms of the compound $PtCl_2(NH_3)_2$ led Werner, in 1893, to suggest the square structures for the isomers shown in Fig. 6-5. Other compounds of a similar type justified this assignment, which has been verified by X-ray analysis. The compounds $Pt(NO_2)_2(NH_3)_2$ and $PtCl_2(py)_2$ which can be isolated in two forms, and $PtBrCl(NH_3)(py)$ which has three geometric isomers, all have planar structures.

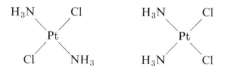

Fig. 6-5.   Trans and cis isomers of $PtCl_2(NH_3)_2$. (See also Fig. 5-8.)

An important aspect of the stereochemistry of complexes is *optical isomerism*, a special type of geometrical isomerism. Any molecule which lacks a plane of symmetry can exist in two nonequivalent forms which are mirror images of each other. The separated optical isomers, *diastereoisomers*, have the ability to rotate the plane of polarized light passed through them, but in equal and opposite senses for each of the two forms, *dextro* (right) and *laevo* (left). Diastereoisomers differ from one another as a left hand differs from a right hand; it is not possible by rotation of any sort to superimpose one on the other. The existence of diastereoisomers is often difficult to confirm, however, because an equilibrium mixture of the isomers may not be resolvable into the two forms. This is the case, for example, when the rate of conversion from one form to the other is rapid, so that equilibrium

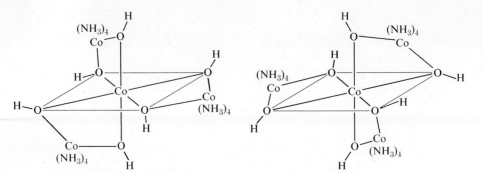

Fig. 6-6. Inorganic optical isomers isolated by Werner.

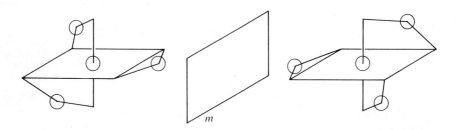

Fig. 6-7. Schematic drawing of chelated octahedral diastereoisomers.

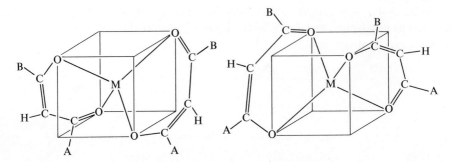

Fig. 6-8. Tetrahedral diastereoisomers (A = CH$_3$, B = C$_6$H$_5$, M = Be).

concentrations are maintained. The term *labile* (unstable with respect to decomposition or change) is often applied to describe isomers of this type.

On the other hand, complexes involving chelating ligands usually have a much lower rate of conversion. Thus Werner in 1914 succeeded in isolating the diastereoisomers of the compound whose structure is shown in Fig. 6-6. The schematic illustration of Fig. 6-7 shows clearly the left hand–right hand relationship of the two diastereoisomers. Because of their slower conversion rate, most of the complexes which have been resolved are chelates.

Tetrahedral complexes with four different ligands should also show optical activity, but again only chelates with unsymmetrical ligands have been resolved, because of the lability of those with unidentate ligands. One such example is illustrated in its two isomeric forms in Fig. 6–8. Square planar complexes also exhibit this phenomenon, but again only with specific unsymmetrical chelating ligands.

(b) Structural isomerism

Structural isomerism provided the basis on which Werner, in 1891, proposed the concept of primary and secondary valences in complexes. His idea was that *primary valences* are those required to satisfy the overall charge of the complex, i.e., the ionic association required for electroneutrality. *Secondary valences*, on the other hand, are those directly involving the central metal atom, i.e., those satisfied by coordination of ligands. Werner also suggested, in order to account for the various isomers found, that the secondary valences are directed in space.

The pair of isomeric compounds having the empirical formula $Co(NH_3)_5Br(SO_4)$ demonstrates this point particularly well. One of the compounds, when dissolved in water, gives an immediate precipitate with $BaCl_2$, but no precipitate forms on addition of $AgNO_3$. The second compound behaves in just the opposite way, giving an immediate positive test for bromide ion, but not for sulfate ion. These experiments can best be interpreted to mean that, in the first compound, bromide is coordinated to the cobalt, satisfying one of the secondary valences, while the sulfate ion is a separate entity in the crystal. Thus we would write its formula explicitly as $[CoBr(NH_3)_5]SO_4$, while the second compound would be $[Co(SO_4)(NH_3)_5]Br$. The compounds are described as *ionization isomers*.

A somewhat similar situation arises in *hydrate isomerism*. There are three compounds having the same formula: $Cr(H_2O)_6Cl_3$. On the basis of the chemistry discussed below they can be assigned the formulas

$$[Cr(H_2O)_6]Cl_3 \quad \text{(violet)},$$

$$[CrCl(H_2O)_5]Cl_2 \cdot H_2O \quad \text{(light green)},$$

$$[CrCl_2(H_2O)_4]Cl \cdot 2H_2O \quad \text{(dark green)}.$$

Experimental evidence for these formulas exists in the observation that: (1) All, two-thirds and one-third, respectively, of the chlorine content, i.e., that satisfying primary valences, is precipitated from solution on addition of excess $AgNO_3$. (2) Conductivity measurements indicate that four, three and two moles, respectively, of ions are formed in aqueous solution per mole of compound. (3) Drying the compounds over sulfuric acid results in the removal of zero, one and two moles of water, respectively. The water bound directly to the chromium ion by secondary valences is unaffected. Hence we again have examples of primary and secondary valences, as well as hydrate water molecules bound in the crystals in the second and third compounds.

An important but rare type of isomerism is *linkage isomerism*. It has been dem-onstrated unequivocally only with the ligand NO_2^-, although it could conceivably occur with other ligands. The nitrite ion can coordinate to the metal atom either through the lone pair of electrons on the nitrogen atom or through one of the lone pairs on the oxygen atoms. Hence there are the two possible configurations, shown in Fig. 6–9. The form coordinated through the nitrogen atom is generally the more stable of the two. Thus, the complex ion $Co(ONO)(NH_3)_5^{2+}$, which is red, rearranges readily to form the yellow complex $Co(NO_2)(NH_3)_5^{2+}$.

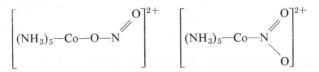

Fig. 6–9. Linkage isomerism.

Two other kinds of structural isomerism are illustrated by the occurrence of crystals having the same empirical formulas:

$$[Pt(NH_3)_4]PtCl_4 \quad \text{and} \quad PtCl_2(NH_3)_2$$

and

$$[Cr(NH_3)_6]Co(Ox)_3 \quad \text{and} \quad [Co(NH_3)_6]Cr(Ox)_3.$$

The first is called *polymerization isomerism*, and the second is called *coordination isomerism*.

6–3. NOMENCLATURE

Just as organic substances acquired common names before the present great complexity set in, so also has the pattern been repeated in inorganic chemistry. While such names as luteocobaltic chloride and praseocobaltic chloride (derived from the Grecian names for the colors of these compounds) served reasonably well at one time, the vast number of coordination compounds already known and the almost unlimited number yet to come make it mandatory that a systematic nomenclature be used. Even so, such systematic names are somewhat unwieldy; hence we must realize that while $Fe(CN)_6^{4-}$ is called hexacyanoferrate (II) ion, it will be more readily recognized by chemists as ferrocyanide. The following few paragraphs summarize the pertinent recommendations of the International Union of Pure and Applied Chemistry with regard to the naming of complexes.*

1. In naming complexes, the central atom (or atoms) is placed after the ligands; but in the formula, the order is reversed.

---

* "Nomenclature of Inorganic Chemistry," *J. Am. Chem. Soc.*, **82**, 5523 (1960).

2. The oxidation number of the central atom is indicated by a roman numeral in parentheses after the name of the complex.

3. In anionic complexes, the name of the central atom ends in -ate, but in neutral or cationic complexes, the name of the central atom is that of the element.

4. Ligands are cited in both formulas and names in the order: (a) simple anionic ligands: H^-, O^{2-}, OH^-, S^{2-}, I^-, Br^-, Cl^-, F^-, (b) other inorganic anions, (c) organic anions, (d) H_2O, NH_3, (e) other inorganic neutral ligands, (f) neutral organic ligands.

5. The names of anionic ligands end in -o, while neutral ligands simply use the name of the molecule. Exceptions to the latter rule are water and ammonia, which have the names aquo and ammine, respectively, as ligands.

6. The prefixes mono, di, tri, tetra, penta, hexa, hepta, octa, ennea, deca, hendeca, and dodeca (one to twelve respectively) are used to show the number of individual ligands of one kind, but mono is usually omitted as understood. With more complicated ligands, the prefixes bis, tris, and tetrakis (two to four) precede the name of the ligand, which is set off by parentheses.

7. A bridging group (one joining two or more metal atoms) is indicated by the symbol μ (mu) preceding its name. In the formula, bridging is shown by a structural formula.

Some inorganic ligands are listed in Table 6–2, giving the order in which they should appear in names and formulas according to Rule 4. A list of complexes is given in Table 6–3, to illustrate the rules set out above.

TABLE 6–2

INORGANIC LIGANDS

H^-	hydrido	$[NH]^{2-}$	imido
O^{2-}	oxo	$[NO_3]^-$	nitrato
$[OH]^-$	hydroxo	$[ONO]^-$	nitrito
S^{2-}	thio	$[NO_2]^-$	nitro
I^-	iodo	$[SO_4]^{2-}$	sulfato
Br^-	bromo	$[SO_3]^{2-}$	sulfito
Cl^-	chloro	$[HS]^-$	thiolo
F^-	fluoro	$[S_2O_3]^{2-}$	thiosulfato
$[CO_3]^{2-}$	carbonato	$[ClO_3]^-$	chlorato
$[CN]^-$	cyano	$[ClO_2]^-$	chlorito
$[OCN]^-$	cyanato	$[O_2]^-$	peroxo
$[C_2O_4]^{2-}$	oxalato	H_2O	aquo
$[SCN]^-$	thiocyanato	NH_3	ammine
$[NH_2]^-$	amido	CO	carbonyl
$[N_3]^-$	azido	NO	nitrosyl
$[NHOH]^-$	hydroxylamido		

TABLE 6–3

NAMES AND FORMULAS OF SOME COMPLEXES

Diamidotetraamminecobalt(III) ethanolate
$[Co(NH_2)_2(NH_3)_4]OC_2H_5$

Azidopentaamminecobalt(III) sulfate
$[Co(N_3)(NH_3)_5]SO_4$

Sodium bis(thiosulfato)argentate(I)
$Na_3[Ag(S_2O_3)_2]$

Ammonium tetrathiocyanatodiamminechromate(III)
$NH_4[Cr(SCN)_4(NH_3)_2]$

Potassium oxotetrafluorochromate(V)
$K[CrOF_4]$

Bis(dimethylglyoximato)nickel(II)
$[Ni(dmg)_2]$

Bis(acetylacetonato)copper(II)
$[Cu(acac)_2]$

Bis(8-quinolinolato)silver(II)
$[Ag(oxinate)_2]$

Dichlorobis(dimethylglyoxime)cobalt(II)
$[CoCl_2(dmgH)_2]$

Tetrapyridineplatinum(II) tetrachloroplatinate(II)
$[Pt(py)_4][PtCl_4]$

Tris(ethylenediamine)cobalt(III) sulfate
$[Coen_3]_2(SO_4)_3$

Potassium trichloromonoethyleneplatinate(II)
$K[PtCl_3(C_2H_4)]$

Hydroxopentaaquoaluminum(III) ion
$[Al(OH)(H_2O)_5]^{2+}$

Trichlorodiammine(dimethylamine)cobalt(III)
$\{CoCl_3(NH_3)_2[(CH_3)_2NH]\}$

Potassium hexacyanoferrate(III)
$K_3[Fe(CN)_6]$

Potassium pentacyanocarbonylferrate(II)
$K_3[Fe(CN)_5CO]$

Bis(cyclopentadienyl)iron(II)
(common name: ferrocene)
$[Fe(C_5H_5)_2]$

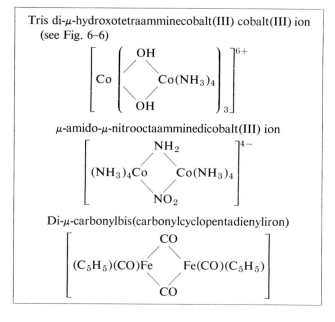

TABLE 6–3   (*Continued*)

NAMES AND FORMULAS OF SOME COMPLEXES

Tris di-μ-hydroxotetraamminecobalt(III) cobalt(III) ion (see Fig. 6–6)

$$\left[Co \left(\begin{array}{c} OH \\[1em] \diagdown \diagup \quad Co(NH_3)_4 \\[1em] OH \end{array} \right)_3 \right]^{6+}$$

μ-amido-μ-nitrooctaamminedicobalt(III) ion

$$\left[(NH_3)_4Co \begin{array}{c} NH_2 \\ \diagup \diagdown \\ \diagdown \diagup \\ NO_2 \end{array} Co(NH_3)_4 \right]^{4-}$$

Di-μ-carbonylbis(carbonylcyclopentadienyliron)

$$\left[(C_5H_5)(CO)Fe \begin{array}{c} CO \\ \diagup \diagdown \\ \diagdown \diagup \\ CO \end{array} Fe(CO)(C_5H_5) \right]$$

6–4. BONDING IN TRANSITION METAL COMPLEXES

Three different methods of treating the bonding in complexes have been developed during the last 30 years. The earliest of these, the *valence bond* approach (Pauling, 1931), considers bond formation through the various ways in which AO's, particularly hybridized orbitals, overlap, making use of resonance structures when appropriate. In some respects it is the most satisfying method, especially in its intuitive appeal. Until about 1950 it was, in fact, the only method which had been applied to the interpretation of chemical properties of complexes. Aside from some specific problems mentioned below, its principal drawback is that the theory is qualitative. In order to draw quantitative conclusions, it is sometimes necessary to include the participation of thousands of resonance structures.

Crystal-field theory (Bethe, 1929, and van Vleck, 1932) was developed originally to interpret certain anomalous magnetic effects in crystals. Essentially the same theory has been applied with surprising success to complexes, on the assumption that only electrostatic forces exist between the central metal ion and the ligand ions or dipolar molecules. Despite the fact that covalent bonding is completely neglected, the method gives a reasonably good quantitative interpretation of the magnetic and optical absorption properties of complexes.

On the other hand, it is possible to adopt the approach used previously for covalent bonding, and to treat complex ions from the *molecular-orbital* point of view. Orbitals of appropriate symmetry are formed according to the same rules and by the same procedures as those used in the simple molecules discussed in Chapter 5. In practice, however, the MO approach alone has not met with complete success, and developments in the field have led to a more flexible composite of the crystal-field and MO theories, known as *ligand-field* theory.

(a) Valence-bond theory

Excluding the extreme case of ionic bonding, the characteristic feature of six-coordinating molecules and complexes is the requirement that *d*-orbitals take part in the bonding. In valence-bond theory, as applied to complexes, we determine how these *d*-orbitals can be hybridized with other orbitals of the same atom to provide new orbitals directed according to the symmetry of the complex. Once the hybridization is decided, these orbitals are considered to overlap those of ligand orbitals, each occupied by a pair of electrons. The disposition of the *d*-electrons depends on the particular complex, and we can best illustrate it by an example.

Consider first an octahedral complex in which we use the locations of the six ligands to define a cartesian coordinate system, as illustrated in Fig. 6–10. We also choose the set of *d*-orbitals discussed in Chapter 5, and shown in Fig. 3–9. Comparison of these two diagrams shows that there are two *d*-orbitals: d_{z^2} and $d_{x^2-y^2}$, which are concentrated in the ligand directions, and hence are suitable for the formation of hybrid AO's, while the other three, d_{xy}, d_{xz}, and d_{yz} lie in the regions between the ligands. In treating transition metal complexes, it is assumed that the $(n-1)d$ AO's (n is the principal quantum number of the valence electrons of the metal atom) and the ns and np AO's are sufficiently close in energy for them

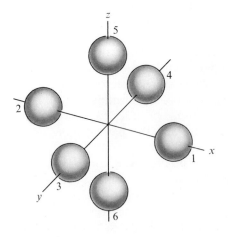

Fig. 6–10. Six ligands defining a cartesian coordinate system.

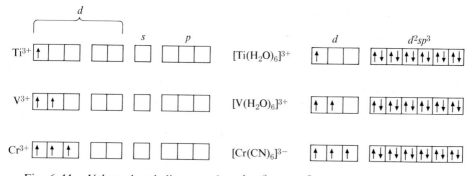

Fig. 6–11. Valence-bond diagrams for d^1, d^2, and d^3 octahedral complexes. The electronic configurations on the left are those of the free metal ions, while those on the right include the twelve electrons of the ligands.

to be hybridized. Thus, if the six orbitals

$$ns, np_x, np_y, np_z, (n - 1)d_{z^2},$$

and

$$(n - 1)d_{x^2-y^2}$$

are combined, six new orbitals are formed by hybridization, each pointing along the axes of the coordinate system, i.e., toward the six ligands. These are the same hybrid orbitals as those discussed in Section 5–3(e), except that in the case of transition metal atoms the d-orbitals and the s- and p-orbitals are from different shells. Since, in the present case, the orbitals have more similar energies, a stronger bond may be expected than when all of the orbitals are of the same shell.

Valence-bond diagrams are shown in Fig. 6–11 for complexes of Ti(III), V(III) and Cr(III), having one, two and three d-electrons, respectively. The electron configurations on the left are for the free ions, while those on the right include a pair of electrons from each ligand shared with the metal atom in coordinate bonds. These extra 12 electrons are shown in the diagrams as occupying the six hybridized metal AO's.

Hund's rule applies to the nonbonding d-electrons; hence they occupy separate orbitals with their spins parallel. For this reason, each of these complexes is paramagnetic, with a magnetic moment corresponding to the number of unpaired electrons.

Magnetic moments can be measured by comparing the weight of a substance suspended so that part of it is in a strong uniform magnetic field to the weight of a substance which is free of the magnetic field (Gouy balance). Those substances in which all electrons are paired are *diamagnetic* (repelled by a magnetic field), while those with unpaired electrons are *paramagnetic* (attracted into a magnetic field). Since in the latter case the paired electrons make a diamagnetic contribution to the total moment, the experimental moment must be corrected slightly to give the value due to the paramagnetism alone. The paramagnetic moment of a compound with n unpaired electrons is given by

$$\mu = \mu_0 \sqrt{n(n + 2)}.$$

Moments are usually expressed in terms of μ_0, the Bohr magneton, abbreviated BM. A complication can arise in that the orbital angular momentum of unpaired electrons can contribute to the overall magnetic moment. To a first approximation this effect can be neglected; however, Pauling has shown that valuable information about the environment of a metal ion can be deduced by a comparison of the experimental moment with that predicted for spin only.

When we come to consider a $3d^4$ complex, such as one containing Cr(II) or Mn(III), we must take account of two possible configurations of the d-electrons, as revealed by the magnetic moments. The complex, potassium hexacyanomanganate(III), $K_3[Mn(CN)_6]$, has a magnetic moment of 3.18 BM in the range expected for two unpaired electrons. Thus there is no difficulty in making the assignment shown in Fig. 6–12, with two of the four d-electrons in one of the nonbonding d-orbitals, with spins paired. This is the only assignment we can use if the $3d$ orbitals are to be used in forming d^2sp^3 hybrid orbitals.

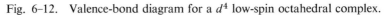

Fig. 6–12. Valence-bond diagram for a d^4 low-spin octahedral complex.

A problem arises, however, with the compound potassium tris(oxalato) manganate(III) trihydrate, $K_3[Mn(Ox)_3]\cdot3H_2O$. This complex has four unpaired electrons, as evidenced by a magnetic moment of 4.81 BM. There are essentially two approaches we can make to explain this fact according to the valence-bond method. The first is to say that the bonding is exclusively ionic, and hence the $3d$ orbitals are not required in bonding at all. Thus the four unpaired d-electrons can occupy the $3d$ orbitals, all of which are considered nonbonding. The second approach is to consider that the outer d-orbitals, $4d$, are used in forming the hybrid AO's, again leaving the $3d$ orbitals free to take four electrons with parallel spins. According to the first concept, we distinguish between covalent and ionic complexes, while in the second, the two cases are referred to as *inner* and *outer orbital complexes*. As we shall see in a later section, the approaches based on crystal-field or on MO theories give a more satisfactory interpretation of the magnetic properties than either of these.

However, independent of the interpretation of the bonding, these two octahedral compounds and other pairs like them, with d^4, d^5, d^6, and d^7 configurations, can be classified into *low-spin* (or *spin-paired*) and *high-spin* (or *spinfree*) *complexes* on the basis of their magnetic moments. Some examples of octahedral complexes are listed in Table 6–4, together with the magnetic moments and the number of unpaired electrons deduced therefrom.

The d^7 low-spin octahedral complexes pose a difficult problem for the valence-bond approach. In order that there be only one unpaired electron, as required

TABLE 6-4

MAGNETIC MOMENTS OF OCTAHEDRAL COMPLEXES

Low spin		μ, BM	n^*	High spin	μ, BM	n^*
d^4	$[Cr(dipy)_3]Br_2 \cdot 4H_2O$	3.27	2	$[Mn(acac)_3]$	4.95	4
d^4	$K_3[Mn(CN)_6] \cdot 3H_2O$	3.18	2	$K_3[Mn(Ox)_3] \cdot 3H_2O$	4.81	4
d^5	$K_4[Mn(CN)_6] \cdot 3H_2O$	1.80	1	$[Mn(py)_6]Br_2$	6.00	5
d^5	$[Fe(phen)_3](ClO_4)_3$	2.45	1	$(NH_4)_3[FeF_6]$	5.98	5
d^6	$[Fe(dipy)_3]SO_4$	0.00	0	$[Fe(NH_3)_6]Cl_2$	5.45	4
d^6	$[Co(NH_3)_6]Cl_3$	0.00	0	$K_3[CoF_6]$	4.26	4
d^7	$K_2Ca[Co(NO_2)_6]$	1.9	1	$[Co(NH_3)_6](ClO_4)_2$	5.04	3
d^7	$\{NiBr_3[(C_2H_5)_3P]\}$	1.82	1	$[Co(dipy)_3](ClO_4)_2$	4.86	3
d^8	(planar only)			$[Ni(NH_3)_6]Cl_2$	3.11	2
d^8				$K_3[CuF_6]$	2.83	2

* n = number of unpaired electrons.

by the experimental magnetic moment (see Table 6-4), there must be spin pairing in three of the d-orbitals. If the other two d-orbitals are used in bonding, the seventh d-electron must be promoted to a higher energy AO, such as one of the $4d$ orbitals. This seems reasonable, and is often cited as the reason that covalent Co(II) complexes are powerful reducing agents. However, this interpretation must be used again with Cu(II) square planar complexes, which are not good reducing agents, as discussed below.

Some of the transition metals characteristically adopt the lower coordination number of four in their complexes, for which the two configurations, tetrahedral and square planar, are found. This behavior is limited largely to those having d^7, d^8, and d^9 electron configurations. In general, the low-spin complexes are square planar, while the high-spin complexes are tetrahedral (or often tetragonally distorted octahedral). The square planar structure can be accounted for with four hybrid dsp^2 orbitals using the set $(n - 1)d_{x^2-y^2}$, ns, np_x, and np_y. All of the complexes of Pd(II) and Pt(II), which are $4d^8$ and $5d^8$, respectively, are diamagnetic (no unpaired electrons), and many have been unequivocally identified with the square planar structure. A number of the complexes of Ni(II), Cu(II), Ag(II), and Au(III) are of the same type, such as $K_2[Ni(CN)_4]$, $Ni(dmg)_2$, and $Cu(acac)_2$. The d^9 configuration poses the same problem here as the d^7 does in octahedral complexes, in that the odd electron must be put in an AO somewhat higher in energy than the d-orbitals. In these, however, the np_z orbital is available for this purpose.

The tetrahedral complexes have available all of the $(n - 1)d$ orbitals for the electrons not involved in bonding, so that such d^8 and d^9 complexes would have two and one unpaired electrons, respectively. In the latter case, of course, the

magnetic moment cannot be used as a criterion of the nature of the bonding, since
both the square planar and tetrahedral complexes would have one unpaired electron.
Figure 6–13 shows the orbital diagrams for the two complexes $Ni(CN)_4^{2-}$ and
$NiCl_4^{2-}$, which are square planar and tetrahedral, respectively.

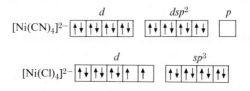

FIG. 6–13. Valence-bond diagrams for d^8 low and high spin complexes, showing
dsp^2 (square planar) and sp^3 (tetrahedral) hybridization.

(b) Crystal-field theory

For the purposes of crystal-field theory, we regard a complex ion as composed
of a central metal ion surrounded by negative ions or by the negative ends of
polar ligands. The bonding is assumed to be completely electrostatic, i.e., no
covalent bonding.

Just as we did in the previous section, we establish a coordinate system so that
each ligand is on one of the three axes of the cartesian coordinate system employed
in Fig. 3–9. We now consider the effect of bringing the ligands toward the metal
ion from infinite distance. There will be a net coulombic attraction, but repulsion
between electrons in the d-orbitals and the ligands will lead to a general increase in
energy of the orbitals. Those electrons which lie in the ligand directions will be
repelled more strongly, and therefore raised in energy more, than those lying
between the ligands. Thus the degeneracy of the five d-orbitals will be partially
removed, so that there will be a higher-energy, doubly degenerate pair of orbitals,
d_{z^2} and $d_{x^2-y^2}$, and a lower-energy, triply degenerate set, d_{xy}, d_{xz}, and d_{yz}, as
shown in Fig. 6–14. The former have been labeled the d_γ or e_g orbitals; the latter,
the d_ϵ or t_{2g} orbitals.

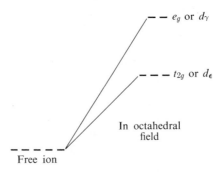

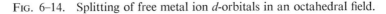

FIG. 6–14. Splitting of free metal ion d-orbitals in an octahedral field.

That the e_g orbitals are degenerate follows from the symmetry of the d_{xy}, d_{xz} and d_{yz} orbitals with respect to the symmetry of the octahedral field of the ligands. It is not so clear why the t_{2g} orbitals should be degenerate. The d_{z^2} orbital is a linear combination of two orbitals, $d_{z^2-x^2}$ and $d_{z^2-y^2}$, each of which is equivalent to $d_{x^2-y^2}$, but oriented differently. This combination is taken because, of the six d-orbitals found on solution of the Schrödinger equation, only five are independent. Since by symmetry the $d_{z^2-x^2}$ and $d_{z^2-y^2}$ orbitals are affected by octahedrally located ligands in the same way as the $d_{x^2-y^2}$ orbital, their sum is also; hence the t_{2g} orbitals are degenerate in an octahedral field.

The energy difference between the t_{2g} and the e_g orbitals, i.e., the *crystal-field splitting*, symbolized by Δ (or sometimes by $10\,Dq$, for involved reasons into which we shall not venture here), depends on the particular ligands as well as on the central metal ion. The equation derived from the electrostatic interaction is

$$\Delta = 5eqa^4/3s^5 \qquad \text{or} \qquad \Delta = 5e\mu a^4/s^6, \tag{6–1}$$

in which e is the charge on an electron, q (or μ as appropriate) is the charge (or dipole moment) of one ligand, a^4 is the average of the fourth power of the radius of the d-electrons, and s is the distance from the nucleus of the central ion to the nucleus of a coordinated atom of a ligand. Substitution of reasonable values for these parameters permits an order of magnitude calculation (usually somewhat low) for the energy difference. The quantity can usually be measured directly from the absorption spectrum of a complex.

In simple cases, at least, the frequency at the maximum of the first absorption band (lowest frequency) corresponds to the promotion of an electron from a t_{2g} to an e_g orbital, and gives Δ directly, usually quoted in cm^{-1}. For many transition metal complexes this absorption lies in the visible region of the spectrum and gives rise to the bright colors associated with transition metal compounds. As an example, the hydrated Ti(III) ion has a single broad absorption band in the visible region of the spectrum at 20,300 cm^{-1} (Fig. 6–15) which accounts for its

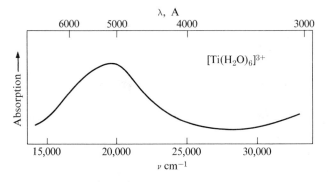

FIG. 6–15.   The absorption spectrum of Ti(H$_2$O)$_6^{3+}$.

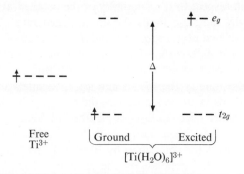

FIG. 6–16. Splitting of Ti^{3+} d-orbitals in an octahedral environment, showing the ground and excited
d-electron configuration for $Ti(H_2O)_6^{3+}$.

TABLE 6–5

CRYSTAL-FIELD SPLITTINGS (Δ in cm^{-1})

Metal ion		Ligand				
		Cl^-	H_2O	NH_3	en	CN^-
$3d^5$	Mn(II)		7,800		9,100	
$3d^7$	Co(II)		9,300	10,100	11,000	
$3d^8$	Ni(II)	7,300	8,500	10,800	11,600	
$3d^6$	Fe(II)		10,400			33,000*
$3d^3$	V(II)†		12,600			
$3d^9$	Cu(II)†		12,600	15,100	16,400	
$3d^5$	Fe(III)		13,700			
$3d^4$	Cr(II)		13,900			
$3d^3$	Cr(III)†	13,600	17,400	21,600	21,900	26,300
$3d^2$	V(III)†		17,700			
$3d^1$	Ti(III)†		20,300			
$3d^4$	Mn(III)		21,000			
$3d^6$	Co(III)		18,600	23,000	23,300	34,000
$4d^6$	Rh(III)		27,000	33,900	34,400	
$5d^6$	Ir(III)				41,200	

* Underlined splittings refer to low-spin complexes.
† Electron configuration is the same for weak and strong fields.

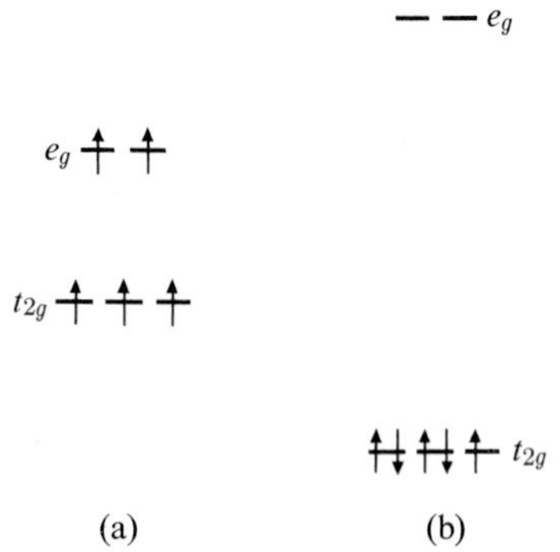

$$- - e_g$$

$$e_g \uparrow \uparrow$$

FIG. 6–17. (a) Weak crystal-field splitting, d^5 octahedral complex. (b) Strong crystal-field splitting, d^5 octahedral complex.

$$t_{2g} \uparrow \uparrow \uparrow$$

$$\uparrow\downarrow \uparrow\downarrow \uparrow \; t_{2g}$$

(a)   (b)

violet color. In Fig. 6–16, the splitting of the d-orbitals is represented schematically, showing the ground state and the first excited state for Ti(III).

The magnitude of Δ varies little through the first transition series (e.g., about 10,000 cm^{-1} for the divalent hydrates, about 20,000 cm^{-1} for the trivalent hydrates), but becomes considerably larger in the second and third transition series, as indicated by the data in Table 6–5. From such measurements as these, the effect of various ligands on the crystal-field splitting is given by the following *spectrochemical series:*

$$Br^- < Cl^- < F^- < OH^- < Ox^{2-} < H_2O < gly^-$$

$$\approx EDTA^{4-} < py \approx NH_3 < en < dipy < phen < NO_2^- \ll CN^-,$$

in which Δ increases, for any given metal ion, approximately as indicated. This series, however, cannot be explained solely on the basis of the electrostatic approach, since not only does ordinary covalent bonding play an important role in determining the order, but multiple bonding can also be a major factor.

The splitting of the d-orbitals by the electrostatic field of the ligands also provides a good interpretation for the magnetic properties of complexes. The important factor is the magnitude of Δ compared with the energy required to pair the d-electrons [Section 3–5(b)]. Consider a pair of octahedral complexes of the same metal ion having a d^5 configuration, but with different ligands far apart in the spectrochemical series. The ligands near the beginning of the series give rise only to a weak field, hence the splitting is small. In this case [Fig. 6–17(a)], the difference in energy of the e_g and t_{2g} orbitals is insufficient to restrict all of the d-electrons to the latter orbitals. Therefore each of the five d-electrons occupies a separate d-orbital, and the magnetic moment corresponds to that of five unpaired electrons.

Ligands which cause strong perturbations of the d-orbitals, and hence a large splitting, are in the latter part of the spectrochemical series. Complexes of this type with five d-electrons are also paramagnetic, but only to the extent which corresponds to one unpaired electron. The energy splitting is greater than that which can be gained by maintaining the free-ion configuration. Therefore the t_{2g} orbitals will be filled as far as possible, as shown in Fig. 6–17(b). These two

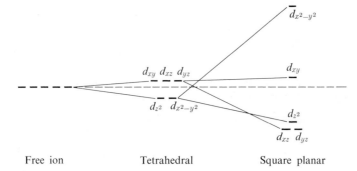

Fig. 6–18.   Splitting of d-orbitals in tetrahedral and square planar fields.

situations correspond to the ionic-covalent or inner-outer orbital classification of valence-bond theory.   In the case of the d^5 configuration, the complexes FeF_6^{3-}, $Fe(H_2O)_6^{3+}$, and $Fe(Ox)_3^{3-}$ are examples of weak field splitting, having magnetic moments of 5.7 to 6.0 BM.   The complexes $Fe(phen)_3^{3+}$ and $Fe(CN)_6^{3-}$, with magnetic moments of 2.45 and 2.40 BM, represent the strong field case.

Thus some point in the spectrochemical series of ligands corresponds, for a particular metal ion, to the change from a weak field to a strong field, with a corresponding change in paramagnetism of the complex (for d^4, d^5, d^6, and d^7) and in the arrangement of the d-electrons.   Different metal ions give rise to different splittings even with the same ligand, as reference to Table 6–5 will show.   Thus the aquo complexes of Co(III) and Fe(II), which are in fact isoelectronic (d^6), are diamagnetic and paramagnetic, respectively, consistent with a larger Δ in the former (18,600 cm^{-1}) than in the latter (10,400 cm^{-1}).

Crystal-field considerations show that the degeneracy of the d-orbitals is also removed in tetrahedral and square planar fields to give the pattern of orbital energies shown in Fig. 6–18.   The tetrahedral field causes splitting into an upper triplet and a lower doublet, but the effect is much smaller than for the octahedral case, and is generally too small to cause modification of the electron configuration. In a square planar field, the $d_{x^2-y^2}$ orbital, which is concentrated just in the ligand directions, is considerably raised in energy with strong field ligands.   Thus the complex ion $Ni(CN)_4^{2-}$ (d^8 configuration) is diamagnetic, i.e., all eight d-electrons are paired in the lowest four orbitals.   However, [Ni(NH$_3$)$_4$]SO$_3$ is paramagnetic, and presumably (although this is not yet verified) the complex is tetrahedral. Because of the greater splittings in d^7, d^8, and d^9 complexes of the second and third transition series, complexes of Pd(II), Pt(II) and Au(III) are invariably square planar and have low spin.

(c) Ligand-field theory

As the first step in applying ligand-field theory, we must formulate delocalized MO's with a symmetry appropriate to the complex being treated.   This will be done in the same manner as in Section 5–3(d), but in the present case it is instruc-

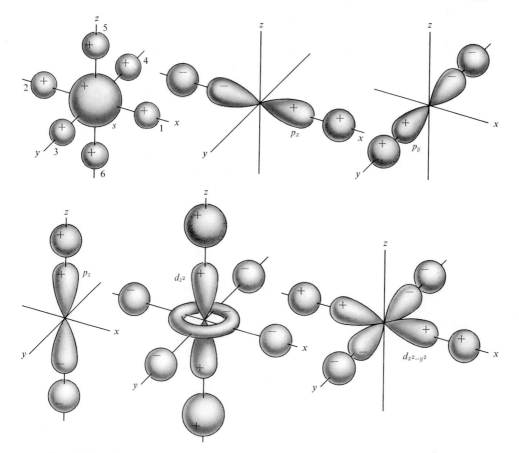

FIG. 6–19.   Symmetry combinations of ligand σ-orbitals and metal AO's used in forming MO's for an octahedral complex.

tive to see how symmetry can be utilized to obtain the correct combinations by the LCAO method.

Dealing first of all with an octahedral complex, we shall assume the presence of six ligands octahedrally coordinated about the metal atom and defining a set of cartesian axes (Fig. 6–10). We shall furthermore assume that each ligand has available an AO of σ-symmetry which may be used in forming MO's. These σ AO's (which we shall designate ϕ_1, ϕ_2, ϕ_3, ϕ_4, ϕ_5 and ϕ_6) might, for example, be the p-orbitals of halogen atoms or lone-pair hybrids of ammonia molecules (Fig. 5–35). The choice of a set of metal atom AO's suitable for use in achieving octahedral symmetry has already been discussed in Section 6–4(a). These were, we recall, the ns and the np_x, np_y and np_z orbitals, and the two $(n-1)$ d-orbitals of e_g symmetry, d_{z^2} and $d_{x^2-y^2}$ (Table 6–6). The problem now is to use these 12 AO's in the formulation of six bonding and six antibonding MO's.

TABLE 6-6

METAL ORBITALS USED IN LCAO-MO TREATMENT OF COMPLEXES

Structure of complex	With ligand σ-orbitals	With ligand π-orbitals
Square planar	$d_{x^2-y^2}, s, p_x, p_y$ $d_{x^2-y^2}, d_{z^2}, p_x, p_y$	p_x d_{xz}, d_{yz}
Tetrahedral	s, p_x, p_y, p_z $s, d_{xy}, d_{xz}, d_{yz}$	p_x, p_y, p_z All d-orbitals
Octahedral	$s, p_x, p_y, p_z, d_{x^2-y^2},$ d_{z^2}	p_x, p_y, p_z d_{xy}, d_{xz}, d_{yz}

With the metal AO's specified, this problem resolves itself into one of finding combinations of the ligand σ-orbitals which have the same symmetry as those of the central atom. Schematically, these combinations are shown in Fig. 6–19. The wave functions, listed in Table 6–7, are mathematical expressions of these combinations. Inspection will also reveal that the quantity α^2 is a parameter which measures the degree of mixing or overlap of the ligand orbitals with the metal orbitals. Pure covalent bonding corresponds to $\alpha^2 = \frac{1}{2}$, while complete

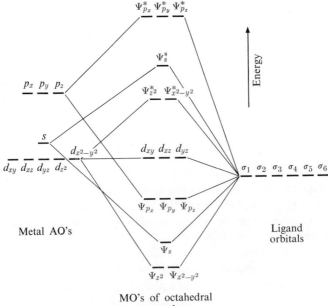

FIG. 6–20. Energy diagram of MO's for an octahedral complex.

TABLE 6–7

LCAO OCTAHEDRAL MOLECULAR ORBITALS

$$\Psi_{z^2} = \alpha d_{z^2} + \left(\frac{1 - \alpha^2}{12}\right)^{1/2} (2\phi_5 + 2\phi_6 - \phi_1 - \phi_2 - \phi_3 - \phi_4)$$

$$\Psi_{z^2}^* = (1 - \alpha^2)^{1/2} d_{z^2} - \left(\frac{\alpha^2}{12}\right)^{1/2} (2\phi_5 + 2\phi_6 - \phi_1 - \phi_2 - \phi_3 - \phi_4)$$

$$\Psi_{x^2-y^2} = \alpha d_{x^2-y^2} + \left(\frac{1 - \alpha^2}{4}\right)^{1/2} (\phi_1 + \phi_2 - \phi_3 - \phi_4)$$

$$\Psi_{x^2-y^2}^* = (1 - \alpha^2)^{1/2} d_{x^2-y^2} - \frac{\alpha}{2} (\phi_1 + \phi_2 - \phi_3 - \phi_4)$$

$$\Psi_s = \alpha s + \left(\frac{1 - \alpha^2}{6}\right)^{1/2} (\phi_1 + \phi_2 + \phi_3 + \phi_4 + \phi_5 + \phi_6)$$

$$\Psi_s^* = (1 - \alpha^2)^{1/2} s - \left(\frac{\alpha^2}{6}\right)^{1/2} (\phi_1 + \phi_2 + \phi_3 + \phi_4 + \phi_5 + \phi_6)$$

$$\Psi_{p_x} = \alpha p_x + \left(\frac{1 - \alpha^2}{2}\right)^{1/2} (\phi_1 - \phi_2)$$

$$\Psi_{p_x}^* = (1 - \alpha^2)^{1/2} p_x - \left(\frac{\alpha^2}{2}\right)^{1/2} (\phi_1 - \phi_2)$$

$$\Psi_{p_y} = \alpha p_y + \left(\frac{1 - \alpha^2}{2}\right)^{1/2} (\phi_3 - \phi_4)$$

$$\Psi_{p_y}^* = (1 - \alpha^2)^{1/2} p_y - \left(\frac{\alpha^2}{2}\right)^{1/2} (\phi_3 - \phi_4)$$

$$\Psi_{p_z} = \alpha p_z + \left(\frac{1 - \alpha^2}{2}\right)^{1/2} (\phi_5 - \phi_6)$$

$$\Psi_{p_z}^* = (1 - \alpha^2)^{1/2} p_z - \left(\frac{\alpha^2}{2}\right)^{1/2} (\phi_5 - \phi_6)$$

ionic bonding would be indicated by $\alpha^2 = 0$; that is, the orbitals remain purely ionic in character. (The remaining numerical factors are normalization constants.)

The energy level diagram for the ligand and metal atom AO's and the resulting σ MO's is shown in Fig. 6–20, from which we see that the t_{2g} orbitals are unaffected by σ-bonding, while the e_g orbitals (d_{z^2} and $d_{x^2-y^2}$), when combined with the ligand orbitals, give two degenerate bonding orbitals and two antibonding orbitals, also degenerate. The order of the lowest six orbitals is uncertain, and unimportant for our purpose. To complete the picture, the electrons must be placed in these orbitals in order of increasing energy, but with regard to Hund's rules for degenerate orbitals. There are always 12 electrons from the ligands (in an octa-hedral complex) which are paired in the lowest six MO's. Then the d-electrons are relegated to the next lowest lying orbitals (electrons are, of course, not dis-tinguishable, but this approach shows more clearly the analogy with the crystal-field treatment).

Thus we find essentially the same result as that found by crystal-field theory, namely that there are available for the d-electrons a lower set of three degenerate orbitals (t_{2g}), the d_{xy}, d_{xz}, and d_{yz} AO's, and an upper doubly degenerate set, the $\Psi_{z^2}^*$ and $\Psi_{x^2-y^2}^*$ orbitals. Thus the magnetic and optical properties of complexes are interpreted in exactly the same way as outlined earlier for crystal-field theory, except that now the optical transition is from an AO (to a first approximation a d-orbital) to an antibonding MO, rather than to another AO. The splitting of the t_{2g} and e_g orbitals, which in crystal-field theory is due to the electrostatic interaction with the ligands, now comes about through the antibonding character of the latter orbitals.

We now return to the problems of d^7 low-spin octahedral complexes, which pose a significant problem in valence-bond theory because the last d-electron has to be put into an energetic or excited AO, the $4d$ for a complex in the first transi-tion series. In the molecular-orbital or ligand-field theory, there is available another antibonding orbital (see Fig. 6–21) which can accommodate this extra electron. It is the neglect of this antibonding orbital which causes the trouble in valence-bond theory.

Similar conclusions can be reached about tetrahedral and square planar com-plexes, in that the results are in essential agreement with those of the electrostatic approach. For example, in a square planar configuration, the $d_{x^2-y^2}$ orbital combines with the ligand orbitals to give, aside from the bonding MO, an anti-bonding orbital lying at higher energy than any of the d-orbitals. Thus with a d^8 configuration, there are a total of 16 electrons (eight from the ligands) which occupy the lowest four bonding MO's and the four essentially atomic d-orbitals. For a square planar d^9 com-plex [such as one with Cu(II)], the last electron would occupy the antibonding orbital formed from the $d_{x^2-y^2}$ orbital.

Octahedral complexes with the con-figuration d^9, d^7 (low spin), and d^4 (high spin), having an odd number of electrons in the antibonding orbitals, $\Psi_{z^2}^*$ and $\Psi_{x^2-y^2}^*$, are subject to a further com-plication, first predicted on theoretical

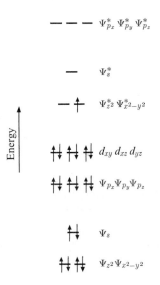

FIG. 6–21. Energy diagram of MO's for a d^7 low-spin octahedral complex.

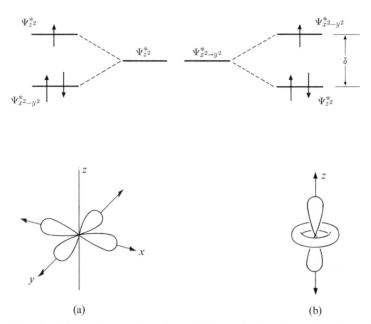

FIG. 6–22. Splitting of e_g antibonding MO's in distorted octahedral field (Jahn-Teller effect): (a) extension in x- and y-directions; (b) extension in z-direction.

grounds by Jahn and Teller (1937). Consider a d^9 complex which has three elec-trons in these antibonding MO's. Either of the configurations $(\Psi_{z^2}^*)^2(\Psi_{x^2-y^2}^*)^1$ or $(\Psi_{z^2}^*)^1(\Psi_{x^2-y^2}^*)^2$ is possible. The first implies that there is more antibonding in the z-direction than in the x- and y-directions, while the second implies the reverse. Since more antibonding character in a particular bond corresponds to a weaker and therefore longer bond, it follows that the first configuration would lead to a distortion of the octahedral shape by extension in the z-direction, while the second implies a similar distortion in the x- and y-directions. Energetically this means that the degeneracy of the $\Psi_{z^2}^*$ and $\Psi_{x^2-y^2}^*$ MO's will be removed, with the $\Psi_{z^2}^*$ MO having lower energy for lengthened bonds in the z-direction (Fig. 6–22), and the $\Psi_{x^2-y^2}^*$ becoming relatively the more stable for extended bonds in the x- and y-directions.

Although the theory is, at present, unable to predict which is the more stable configuration, the experimental data favor the former. In the compounds MnF_3, CuF_2, CrF_2, and Mn_3O_4, and in the ions MnF_6^{3-} and $Co(NO_2)_6^{4-}$, all of which have coordination number six for the metal atom, the environment of the metal atom is that of an octahedron so distorted that there are four near positions and two farther trans positions. Nevertheless, there are some examples, such as K_2CuF_4 and other crystalline alkali metal fluorides, wherein the distortion is in the opposite sense, i.e., a flattening of the octahedron. A similar effect might

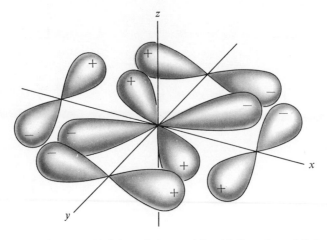

FIG. 6–23.   Combination of $d_{x^2-y^2}$ AO with ligand π-orbitals.

be expected when the t_{2g} orbitals are unsymmetrically occupied; but because these orbitals are often nearly nonbonding, there would be little effect on the metal-ligand distances.   Such distortion has so far not been detected experimentally.

According to the concepts of ligand-field theory, the formation of additional bonds between the metal atom and the ligand follows naturally when there are appropriate orbitals available.   Not only can the e_g metal orbitals form σ MO's with ligand orbitals, but there is also the possibility of π-bonding, for which the t_{2g} metal orbitals have the correct symmetry.   The way in which a d_{xy} orbital, for example, combines with p_x and p_y ligand orbitals (see Table 6–6), is shown in Fig. 6–23.   There result delocalized MO's, having π-character with respect to the xy plane.   As always, there will be two MO's formed, one bonding, the other antibonding, provided that the energies of the metal and ligand AO's do not differ too much in energy.

The effect on the ligand-field splitting is illustrated in Fig. 6–24.   On the left is shown the situation when the ligand π-orbitals are fully occupied; the t_{2g} orbital then assumes antibonding character and is raised in energy, decreasing the value of Δ over that which would occur without multiple bond formation.   On the right, the ligand orbitals are assumed to be unoccupied.   In this case, the d-electrons occupy a bonding t_{2g} orbital which is lower in energy than the original t_{2g} orbital, thus increasing Δ.   This argument, while qualitative in nature, does describe the situation in which ligand π-orbitals can act as electron acceptors, and accounts for the large ligand-field splittings observed with, for example, cyanide and orthophenanthroline as ligands.

The cyanide ion is a unique ligand, in that it usually produces a larger Δ than any other ligand.   This would be strange indeed if the cyanide ion formed only single bonds with metal atoms, because the lone-pair orbitals on the carbon atom are not expected to have unusual or even strong electron-donor properties.   Since the cyanide ion is isoelectronic with N_2, there will be (see Chapter 5) a pair of

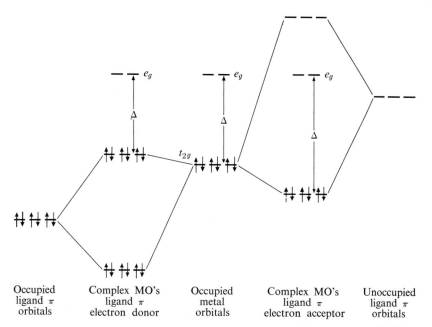

Fig. 6–24.   Energy levels for π-bonding, with donor and acceptor ligands.

degenerate, normally unoccupied, antibonding π-orbitals. These have just the right symmetry to combine with t_{2g} orbitals in an octahedral complex.

It is this strong electron-accepting property of the cyanide ion that places it at the head of the spectrochemical series. Also, the fact that in the formation of double bonds by the cyanide ion, electrons are withdrawn to some extent from the metal atom, thereby increasing its effective charge, permits the stabilization of low-valence complexes [such as Ni(0) and Ni(I), Co(I) and Pd(0)] having lower oxidation numbers than are ordinarily encountered.

A similar situation occurs with phosphine and arsine derivatives as ligands. These have d-orbitals which are relatively low-lying (compared with ammines), and which can act as electron acceptors. Enhanced stability of such complexes in part arises from the back-donation of electrons. That is, the formation of σ-bonds between the ligand and the metal atom, in which electrons are partially transferred to the metal atom, is aided by the reverse transfer of electrons in the formation of π-bonds.

The metal carbonyl compounds fall in the same class. These are neutral molecules having carbon monoxide ligands. The compounds $Ni(CO)_4$, $Fe(CO)_5$, and $Cr(CO)_6$ have in common the feature that the metal atom has and shares a total of 18 valence electrons, i.e., a d^{10} configuration. In fact, the elements Co and Mn, which have odd numbers of electrons, do not form simple carbonyls; however, the dimeric compounds $Co_2(CO)_8$ and $Mn_2(CO)_{10}$, conforming to the 18-electron rule, do exist. The electron-donor properties of carbon monoxide, involving the lone pair on the carbon atom, must be very small, particularly with zero-valence

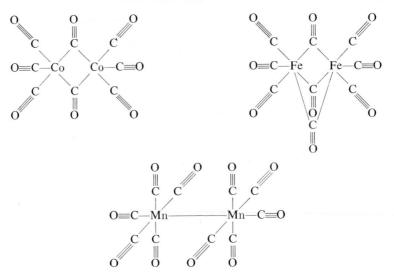

FIG. 6–25.   Structures of some binuclear carbonyls.

metal atoms as acceptors. Thus, in order to account for the formation of these neutral carbonyls, there must be appreciable double-bond formation involving the π-antibonding orbitals of the ligand. Carbon monoxide, since it is a neutral molecule, would be a better electron acceptor than the cyanide ion, hence would be able to stabilize low-valence metal atoms as well as or better than cyanide.

It is noteworthy that almost all compounds so far investigated which have carbonyl ligands are diamagnetic, and correspond in electron configuration (based on two electrons donated per ligand) to that of the next-higher inert gas. Thus, although cobalt can only form a dimeric neutral molecule with carbon monoxide, $HCo(CO)_4$ and $Co(CO)_3NO$ can be prepared, both of which are isoelectronic with $Ni(CO)_4$. Similarly, the compounds $H_2Fe(CO)_4$ and $Fe(CO)_2(NO)_2$ are well known, and have the same electron configuration. In the binuclear compounds $Co_2(CO)_8$, $Fe_2(CO)_9$, and $Mn_2(CO)_{10}$, there is direct bonding between the two metal atoms, although in the first two there are also bridging carbonyl ligands (see Fig. 6–25).

Metal atoms also form complexes which involve a rather different type of bonding with unsaturated hydrocarbon molecules. Structural information about these compounds, obtained for the most part during the last decade, shows that the double- or triple-bond axis of the ligand is perpendicular to the ligand-metal atom axis, that is, the ligand bonds "sideways" rather than "end on." In such a configuration, an occupied π-bonding orbital of the ligand can form a three-center MO with an empty e_g metal orbital, while an empty antibonding orbital of the ligand has the correct symmetry to combine with one of the occupied t_{2g} metal atom orbitals, as illustrated in Fig. 6–26.

Such compounds as $K[PtCl_3(C_2H_4)]$ [potassium trichloromonoethyleneplatinate(II)] and $Fe(CO)_3C_4H_6$ [tricarbonylbutadieneiron (0)] are representative of

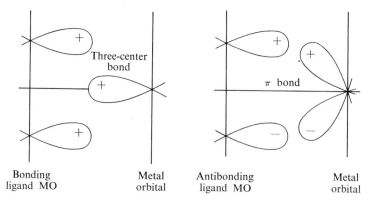

Bonding   Metal   Antibonding   Metal
ligand MO   orbital   ligand MO   orbital

FIG. 6–26.   Metal atom and olefin orbitals which lead to the formation of σ and π MO's.

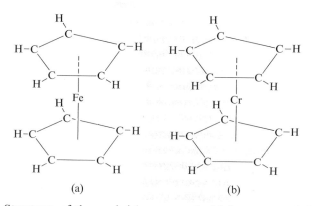

(a)   (b)

FIG. 6–27.   Structures of the sandwich compounds (a) ferrocene and (b) dibenzene-chromium.

the complexes formed with olefins. In the platinum compound, ethylene occupies one coordination position of the square planar complex, and the axis of the ethylene double bond is perpendicular to the coordination plane.

A more extensive series of metal-olefin coordination compounds is that in which cyclic aromatic hydrocarbons are ligands. Some of these [for example, $Fe(C_5H_5)_2$, biscyclopentadienyl iron, commonly known as ferrocene] are exceptionally stable compounds. The number of compounds in which a cyclopentadienyl group is a ligand runs into the hundreds, and includes most of the transition elements and even magnesium. Analogous compounds, much less diverse, have been prepared with both larger and smaller rings, such as $Cr(C_6H_6)_2$ and $[NiCl_2(C_4(CH_3)_4)_2]_4$. These, particularly those with two-ring systems, have been given the descriptive name *sandwich compounds*, which follows from their structure (see Fig. 6–27). The molecular-orbital pattern for compounds with five- or six-membered rings, in common with that for carbonyls, has nine stable molecular orbitals, which, when occupied, each by a pair of electrons, gives the inert-gas electronic structure.

BIBLIOGRAPHY

A

GRADDON, D. P., *An Introduction to Coordination Chemistry.* London: Pergamon, 1961.

GRIFFITH, J. S., and L. E. ORGEL, *Quart. Rev.*, **11**, 381 (1957).

JØRGENSEN, C. K., *Absorption Spectra and Chemical Bonding in Complexes.* London: Pergamon, 1962.

LEWIS, J., and R. G. WILKINS, *Modern Coordination Chemistry, Principles and Methods.* New York: Interscience, 1960.

LINNETT, J. W., *Wave Mechanics and Valency.* London: Methuen, 1960.

ORGEL, L. F., *An Introduction to Transition-Metal Chemistry, Ligand-Field Theory.* London: Methuen, 1960.

PAULING, L., *The Nature of the Chemical Bond.* Ithaca, New York: Cornell, 1960.

B

BASOLO, F., and R. G. PEARSON, *Mechanism of Inorganic Reactions.* New York: Wiley, 1958.

GRIFFITH, J. S., *Theory of Transition-Metal Ions.* New York: Cambridge, 1961.

MARTELL, A. E., and M. CALVIN, *Chemistry of the Metal Chelate Compounds.* New York: Prentice-Hall, 1962.

PROBLEMS

6–1. List the isomers and the kinds of isomerism which are possible for complexes having the following formulas:

(a) $Co(en)_2Cl_2^+$

(b) $Pt^{II}Pt^{IV}(en)_2(Cl)_6$ (two complex ions)

(c) $Co(NH_3)_5(H_2O)(NO_3)_3$

(d) $Cr(en)_3Cl_3$

(e) $CoCl_2(NH_3)_2en^+$

(f) $Co(den)_2^{3+}$

(g) $Co(trien)Cl_2^+$

(h) $Co(EDTA)^-$

6–2. Name the complexes in the previous question according to the IUPAC nomenclature rules.

6–3. Write the formulas of the following substances:

(a) dichloroaquotriamminecobalt(III) chloride

(b) diaquodiphenanthrolinecopper(II) ion

(c) nitritopentaamminecobalt(III) ion

(d) potassium octacyanotungstate(V) dihydrate

(e) bis(acetylacetonato)nickel(II)

(f) potassium bis(oxala o)diaquomanganate(II)

(g) tris(dipyridyl)chromium(II) bromide tetrahydrate

(h) μ-oxodecaamminedichromium(III) ion

6–4. Show the disposition, according to valence-bond theory, of electrons of octahedral complexes with one to ten d-electrons, and distinguish between inner and outer orbitals, as appropriate. Indicate in each case the number of unpaired electrons predicted.

6-5. Predict the number of unpaired electrons in each of the following complexes (a decision must first be made as to whether a given complex is low or high spin).

(a) $Fe(CN)_6^{3-}$ (b) $Co(phen)_3^{3+}$ (c) $Fe(CN)_6^{4-}$

(d) $Co(H_2O)_6^{2+}$ (e) $Au(CN)_4^-$ (f) $Cu(H_2O)_4^{2+}$

(g) $Zn(en)_3^{2+}$ (h) $Ir(NH_3)_6^{3+}$

6-6. A crystal field of pentagonal bipyramidal symmetry perturbs the d-orbitals so that they increase in energy in the order: (d_{xz}, d_{yz}), $(d_{xy}, d_{x^2-y^2})$, d_{z^2}, in which the parentheses enclose degenerate pairs of orbitals. Account for the fact that $Na_3(RhF_7)$ has a magnetic moment of about 1.7 BM.

6-7. Construct a molecular-orbital diagram similar to that of Fig. 6–20 for a square planar complex, and indicate the electron configuration for a d^8 low-spin complex. Note that the p_z, d_{xy}, d_{xz}, and d_{yz} AO's cannot form σ-bonds in the x- and y-directions, and that either but not both of the s and d_{z^2} orbitals can be used (see Table 6–6).

6-8. The ions Co^{2+} and Ni^{2+} are usually confirmed in qualitative analysis schemes through the use of the organic complexing agents α-nitroso-β naphthol and dimethylglyoxime respectively. The formulas of the neutral complexes are

$$Co[C_{10}H_6(NO)O]_3 \quad \text{and} \quad Ni[C_4H_6(NO)NOH]_2.$$

What structures would you expect them to have?

6-9. It has been suggested that multiple bonding must be of considerable importance in the carbonyl coordination compounds. What evidence can you cite in favor of this idea?

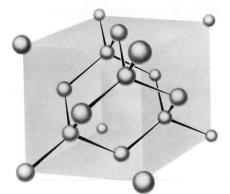

CHAPTER SEVEN

Crystal Chemistry

Up to this point our treatment of the solid state has been limited to the simple ionic crystals described in Chapter 2. We now propose to extend the discussion to crystalline solids generally, correlating their physical properties and structures with the types of interaction present.

7-1. THE CLASSIFICATION AND DESCRIPTION OF CRYSTALS

Any system of classification or method of describing crystals must, of course, reflect the interest of the individual. Our interest is in the internal structure of crystals; hence the external morphology and the properties such as density, color, hardness, etc., which may be most important to the mineralogist, shall concern us only insofar as they are related to the internal structure. Since our aim is to relate the internal structure of crystals to the properties of the constituent atoms, the discussion will largely center on bonding. However, for reasons which will be set out below, it is difficult to classify crystals solely on the basis of the type of bonding involved. As it does in the case of molecules, symmetry plays a role of fundamental importance, and it is with this factor that we shall begin the discussion.

(a) Symmetry and space lattices

The regular arrangement of atoms in crystals and the manifestations of this arrangement have been discussed in Section 2-1. In many respects, the simple ionic crystals of Chapter 2 are unique, but the basic elements employed in their description, the *space-point lattice* and the *unit cell*, are geometrical entities which may be used to describe any type of crystal.

234

In considering translational periodicity generally, it is convenient to begin with a discussion of the planar pattern of Fig. 7–1. It might be considered the two-dimensional analog of the periodic pattern of a crystal. As Fig. 7–2 shows, such a pattern may be resolved into two components, a unit of pattern and a plane-point lattice, which together make up a description of the crystal. The translational periodicity represented by the point lattice is readily specified in terms of the vectors **a** and **b** and the angle between them. The correct specification of the unit of pattern or unit cell is somewhat more complicated. To a large extent, the choice of unit cell is arbitrary and is determined by practical considerations.

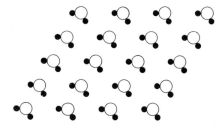

Fig. 7–1. Two-dimensional periodic pattern.

Note, to begin with, that Fig. 7–2(a) insufficiently describes the unit of pattern, because it gives no information regarding the orientation of the unit of pattern on the lattice point. A complete description requires reference axes, most conveniently the same ones used in specifying the point lattice, so that we may combine a description of the two components in one figure. Thus Fig. 7–3(a) may be chosen as a unit cell. Repetitions of this unit according to the translational periodicity, as represented by the point lattice, will reproduce the pattern of Fig. 7–1.

Although it indicates correctly that there is one unit of pattern per unit cell, Fig. 7–3(a) has several drawbacks as a unit cell. It does not, for example, reveal the environment of the "molecule" relative to others, and would not unless several unit cells were portrayed. Further, it is customary to designate the positions of the atoms in terms of coordinates referred to the unit-cell edges, and an obvious simplification results if one atom can be located at the origin.

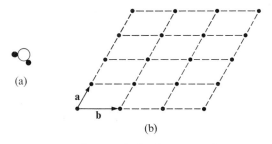

(a)

(b)

Fig. 7–2. Geometrical elements of pattern of Fig. 7–1: (a) unit of pattern, (b) planar point lattice.

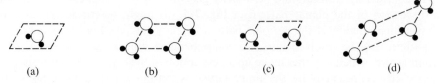

(a)   (b)   (c)   (d)

FIG. 7–3. Alternative unit cells for the pattern of Fig. 7–1. The preferred choice is (b), it being understood that parts of the unit of pattern falling outside of the dashed boundaries are not part of the geometric unit cell.

Both of these objections are overcome in the cell of Fig. 7–3(b), and this would be the most common choice of unit cell for the pattern of Fig. 7–1. Observe, however, that Fig. 7–3(b) actually portrays more than a single geometric unit cell, since the drawing includes parts of the pattern outside the dotted boundaries of the unit cell proper. This is the conventional practice, and is of great assistance in producing clarity in illustrations. Figure 7–3(c) and (d) show alternative choices of unit cell which, like Fig. 7–3(a), may be ruled out on practical grounds.

The extension of these concepts to three dimensions is fairly obvious, but rather more complicated. One of the simplest examples for discussion is the structure of cesium bromide, described in Chapter 2. We saw that the unit cell is cubic and that there is one Cs^+ and one Br^- ion per unit cell, located at the corner and at the center of the cube. Thus the CsBr structure (Fig. 7–4) may be described by saying that it is cubic (cell edge $a = 4.296$ A) with Cs^+ and Br^- ions at $(0, 0, 0)$ and $(\frac{1}{2}, \frac{1}{2}, \frac{1}{2})$, respectively; the coordinates refer to fractions of the cell edge. Alternatively, by a shift of origin, we may place Br^- ions at the corners of the cube $(0, 0, 0)$, and Cs^+ ions at the center $(\frac{1}{2}, \frac{1}{2}, \frac{1}{2})$. Since there is only one unit of pattern (one Cs^+ ion plus one Br^- ion) associated with each unit cell, the unit cell of CsBr is said to be *primitive*.

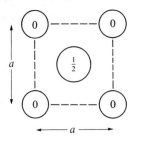

FIG. 7–4. Projection of CsBr structure on one of the cubic faces. A Cs^+ ion is located at the corner $(0, 0, 0)$, and a Br^- ion at the center $(\frac{1}{2}, \frac{1}{2}, \frac{1}{2})$ of the cubic unit cell.

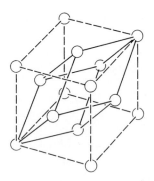

FIG. 7–5. Face-centered cubic structure of copper. The preferred nonprimitive cell is outlined with dashed lines and the primitive rhombohedral cell with solid lines.

TABLE 7–1

THE CRYSTAL SYSTEMS

System	Lattice type	Lattice symmetry	Description of coordinate system
Triclinic	P	None	$a \neq b \neq c$ $\alpha \neq \beta \neq \gamma$
Monoclinic	P, I	2-fold axis and/or mirror plane	$a \neq b \neq c$ $\alpha = \gamma = 90° \neq \beta$
Orthorhombic	P, I, C, F	3 2-fold axes and/or 3 mirror planes	$a \neq b \neq c$ $\alpha = \beta = \gamma = 90°$
Tetragonal	P, I	4-fold axis	$a = b \neq c$ $\alpha = \beta = \gamma = 90°$
Hexagonal	P, R P	3-fold axis* 6-fold axis	$a = b \neq c$ $\alpha = \beta = 90°$ $\gamma = 120°$
Cubic	P, I, F	4 3-fold axes	$a = b = c$ $\alpha = \beta = \gamma = 90°$

* Crystals with threefold symmetry are sometimes classified separately as belonging to the trigonal or rhombohedral system.

In some cases it is appropriate to employ a unit cell which contains more than one unit of pattern. The face-centered cubic structure of copper illustrates this very well. This unit cell, which is portrayed in Fig. 7–5, is said to be *nonprimitive* or *compound*, because there are four copper atoms associated with each unit cell. (Note again that the illustration actually shows more than one unit cell. Only one-eighth of each corner atom and one-half of the centering atoms actually belong to the unit cell.)

A primitive unit cell containing only one Cu atom may be chosen (as shown), but there are obvious disadvantages in doing so. The cube is a far more convenient frame of reference than a rhombohedron, but more important is the fact that the nonprimitive cell reveals more clearly the cubic symmetry possessed by the overall arrangement of the atoms. Similar considerations apply in the case of NaCl, but here the unit of pattern is made up of a Na^+ ion plus a Cl^- ion.

The only patterns of exactly repeated environments which are capable of indefinite extension in three dimensions are those in which successive pattern units lie on straight lines. Furthermore, since it is impossible to construct space-point lattices with fivefold or with greater than sixfold symmetry, the number of types of

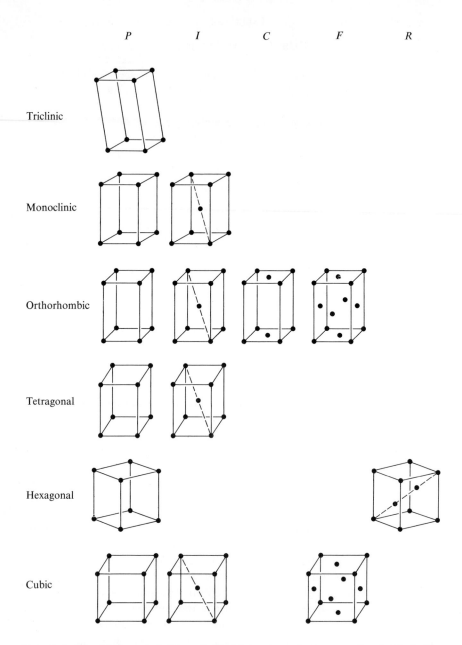

FIG. 7–6. The 14 Bravais lattices divided into six systems according to their macroscopic symmetry. The symbols at the top of the page denote: *P*, primitive, *I*, body-centered, *C*, centered (on one face), *F*, face-centered, and *R*, rhombohedral. The figures also represent the usual choice of unit cell for the systems.

lattice is severely limited. In fact, as pointed out by Bravais in 1848, there are only 14 different space lattices.

The unit cells associated with the different space lattices are illustrated in Fig. 7–6. In some cases, two or more lattice types share the same basic symmetry and coordinate system; hence they are customarily grouped into six *crystal systems*. This grouping is indicated in Fig. 7–6, and complete information regarding the lattice symmetries and dimensions is given in Table 7–1 and in Fig. 7–7. In the remainder of this chapter we shall discuss examples of most of the crystal systems.

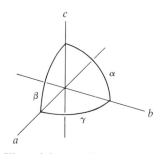

FIG. 7–7. The axial cross, illustrating the coordinates used in specifying unit cell and lattice dimensions.

(b) Classification according to bonding or structure type

When we recall the artificiality of the designation of four types of bonding, emphasized in Chapter 1, it is not surprising that we should run into difficulties when attempting a classification of crystals in terms of bond type. In isolated cases we may, with confidence, assume one type of bonding to predominate; but generally such examples are few in number.

Thus the discussion of Chapter 2 leaves little doubt that the bonding in crystals of the alkali halides is almost completely ionic. But, as we shall see shortly, in some other crystals of the same structure type (such as AgF, AgCl, and AgBr), additional interactions contribute significantly to the bonding. In more extreme cases (such as AgI), these interactions are sufficient to change the structure type.

More difficulties are introduced when complex ions are present in the structure. Thus in $NaNO_2$ crystals, as shown in Fig. 7–8, the structure is a body-centered one of Na^+ and NO_2^-. While coulombic interactions predominate in the interionic bonding, the forces between the nitrogen and oxygen atoms in the NO_2^- ion (intra-ionic) must be almost wholly covalent. On the other hand, the bonding within a complex ion need not be completely covalent. In BF_4^-, for example, the arguments of Chapter 5 would lead us to expect that ionic and covalent forces contribute more or less equally.

An additional comparison might be drawn between the two polymorphs or allotropes of carbon, graphite and diamond. In the latter case, each carbon atom is tetrahedrally bonded to four equivalent carbon atoms to give the structure shown

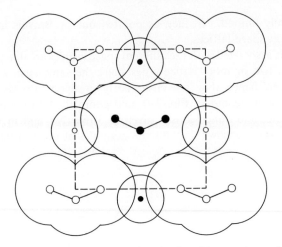

FIG. 7–8. Projection of the body-centered orthorhombic structure of $NaNO_2$ on the *bc* face. The small open circles designate nuclei in the $a = 0$ plane, and the shaded circles designate nuclei in the $a/2$ plane. The lighter outlines of the ionic and van der Waals radii illustrate the close-packed nature of the structure.

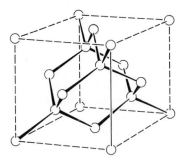

FIG. 7–9. Unit cell of the diamond structure (cubic).

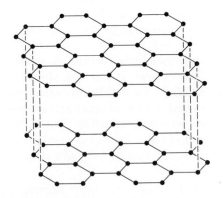

FIG. 7–10. Layer structure of graphite. Note that the hexagons of one layer are displaced relative to those of adjacent layers.

in Fig. 7–9. As pointed out in Chapter 1, this gives a strong hard crystal which has a high mp and which is electrically nonconducting: properties which are in marked contrast to those of graphite. The softness and electrical conductivity of graphite result from the layer structure shown in Fig. 7–10. The bonding in each individual layer is covalent, but the layers are held together by much weaker forces of the van der Waals type.

We see, then, that a classification according to bond type is by no means clear-cut. Nevertheless, the present state of development of the theory of bonding makes it convenient, if not imperative, that we carry out our discussion along these lines.

7–2. MOLECULAR CRYSTALS

The term "molecular crystal" is used to refer to those substances which, in the crystalline state, may be regarded as aggregates of discrete molecules. Properties which characterize this type of crystal and from which we may deduce the general nature of the bonding forces are: (1) optical absorption, which is essentially the same as that of the free molecules, (2) melting points that are usually quite low, and (3) efficient packing of the molecules in the crystal.

That the infrared absorption spectrum changes little from gas to solid indicates (as does the low melting point) that the intermolecular forces involved are weak. Furthermore, since the crystal structure is determined largely by the shape of the molecules, the forces must be predominantly nondirectional. A detailed discussion of the nature of these forces is beyond the scope of this text, but they are discussed briefly in Section 7–2(c). The term *van der Waals forces* is usually applied to the weak intermolecular forces which are involved.

(a) Close packing of spheres

In many crystalline structures in which nondirective forms of bonding play the dominant role, it is found that the structure assumed is simply a result of the most efficient packing of the units involved. Since these units are often atoms or approximately spherical molecules, it is of interest to study the most efficient means of packing hard spheres of equal size in three-dimensional arrays.

As shown in Fig. 7–11, a single layer of spheres packed in the closest possible manner arrange themselves so that their centers are at the corners of an equilateral triangle and each sphere is surrounded hexagonally by six others. Continuing with the building process, we may construct the second layer by placing spheres in the hollows on the top of the first layer. Note, however, that it is not possible to place second-layer spheres in all of the hollows of the first layer. The result of this is that there are two kinds of hollows in which we may place the spheres of the third layer. They may be placed so that each sphere of the third layer lies directly over a sphere of the first layer (so that the first and third layers are identical), or they may be situated over hollows in the first layer. In either case, once the first

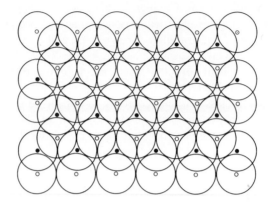

FIG. 7–11. Two layers of close-packed spheres. The small open circles show the positions of the centers of the spheres of the lower layer, and the shaded small circles show the centers of the upper layer. The interstitial sites may also be seen in this figure. The tetrahedral holes lie immediately above each sphere of the lower layer and immediately below each sphere of the upper layer. The octahedral holes are the unfilled hollows of the first layer.

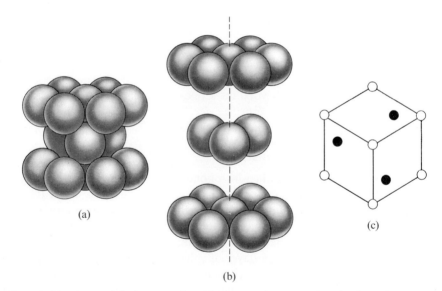

FIG. 7–12. Hexagonal close packing of spheres: (a) normal and (b) exploded views, showing the relative orientation of adjacent layers. The projection (c) illustrates the hexagonal symmetry and the unit cell (solid lines). The dark and light spheres are in adjacent layers.

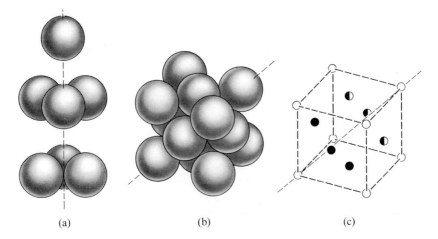

(a)   (b)   (c)

Fig. 7–13. Cubic close-packing: (a) Exploded view showing relative positions of spheres in the three-layer repeating unit (*xyz*). Figures (b) and (c) show the positions of the spheres in the resulting face-centered cubic structure. Open, half-shaded, and fully shaded atoms are in successive layers perpendicular to the body diagonal shown.

sphere has been placed, the remainder will automatically locate themselves in hollows of the same type.

Referring to Fig. 7–11, we see that the two possible types of close-packed structures of equivalent spheres may be described as having layer sequences *xyxyxy* . . . or *xyzxyz* . . . .   In both arrangements, any given sphere is surrounded by 12 equidistant nearest neighbors, six in the same plane and three in each adjacent layer, but the symmetry of coordination, and therefore the overall symmetry, is different in the two cases.   When there are only two layers in the repeat unit (*xyxyxy* . . .), then, as Fig. 7–12 shows, the resulting arrangement has hexagonal symmetry and is termed a *hexagonal-close-packed* (HCP) structure.   The axial ratio of the hexagonal unit cell for an HCP structure is $c/a = 1.633$.   When there are three layers in the repeat unit (*xyzxyz* . . .), an arrangement based on a face-centered cubic lattice is formed. This structure, known as *cubic-close-packed* (CCP), is illustrated in Fig. 7–13.

The HCP and CCP are the most common close-packed arrangements, and the only ones in which the environment of every sphere is identical.   There are, however, a great variety of close-packed structures in which this condition is not fulfilled.   If, for example, the arrangement of layers were *xyxzxyxz* . . . , then a close-packed arrangement results in which there are two types of nonequivalent spheres.   More complete discussions of close-packed structures, with more than three layers in the repeating unit, may be found in advanced texts.

A further point of interest regarding close-packed structures is the *interstitial sites*, or holes between the spheres.   In Fig. 7–11 and Fig. 7–14, we see two types of interstitial holes, one surrounded by six spheres and the other by four.   Of these, the *octahedral hole* is the larger, and may accommodate a sphere of radius 0.41 times that of the larger spheres without distorting the close-packed structure. The *tetrahedral hole* is smaller and will not accommodate spheres with a radius any larger than 0.23 times the close-packed ones. In the discussions to follow, we shall see that many crystal structures containing two types of atoms or ions may be regarded as close-packed structures of the larger atoms, with the smaller ones occupying interstitial holes.

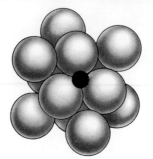

FIG. 7–14. Cubic close-packed structure with corner atom removed to show smaller atom occupying tetrahedral hole. The octahedral holes are at the center of the cube and midway along the edges.

(b) Simple molecular crystals

The simplest examples of crystals in which the bonding results from van der Waals forces are those provided by the solid inert gases. The molecular units are simply atoms, and in all cases for which the structures are definitely known (Ne, Ar, Kr, Xe), the atoms exhibit a cubic-close-packed arrangement. The structure of solid radon is unknown, but crystalline helium appears to be hexagonal-close-packed. With an appreciation of the close relationship between cubic and tetrahedral symmetry, we can now understand the suggestion of Linnett [Section 5–3(b)] that hybridization may play a role in determining these structures.

Modified close-packing arrangements are also observed for many diatomic molecules. Typical are the arrangements displayed by chlorine, bromine and iodine in the condensed state. Unlike the atoms of the inert gases, the molecules are not spheroids; hence there is a departure from cubic symmetry in the crystals. On the other hand, as Fig. 7–15 shows, the structure is closely related to the face-centered-cubic symmetry of CCP. Similar arrangements are found for N_2 and O_2, but both of these exhibit more than one crystalline modification, depending on the temperature. In some cases the higher temperature form has the cubic symmetry associated with spheroidal units, and there is evidence to indicate that this symmetry arises from free rotation of the molecules.

We see that in a crystal of the type just described there are two types of interatomic distances: that between an atom and its molecular partner and that between

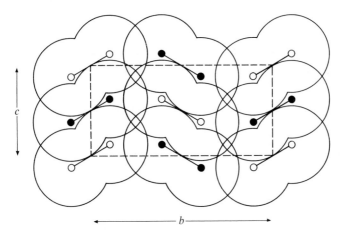

FIG. 7–15. Projection on the *bc* face of the face-centered orthorhombic structure of I_2, Cl_2, and Br_2. The shaded circles represent nuclei at $a/2$.

atoms not covalently bonded to one another. In iodine, for example, the internuclear distance in the molecule is 2.68 A, while the distance of closest approach of two nonbonded atoms is 4.54 A: considerably larger.

From an empirical point of view, this distance of closest approach is obviously very significant in determining the packing in molecular crystals, and it is conveniently tabulated as the *van der Waals radius*. In the present example, the van der Waals radius of iodine is found to be 4.54/2, or about 2.3 A. Like the other radii previously defined, the concept is purely an empirical one, and the experimentally derived radii are adjusted so that in the majority of cases their sum will give the distance of closest approach of two nonbonded atoms. The results of such labors are the van der Waals radii given in Table 7–2. In addition to their usefulness in structural problems involving molecular crystals, these radii find application in problems of steric hindrance in large molecules.

It is interesting to note that the van der Waals radii of Table 7–2 are very similar to the ionic radii quoted in Table 2–3. This similarity is a ramification of the fact that it is the same repulsive forces which govern the internuclear separation in both cases. As Fig. 2–22 shows, the repulsive forces act over a very small distance, and the strength of the attractive forces has little bearing on the internuclear separation. It is perhaps pertinent to point out that these repulsive forces are, at present, rather poorly defined theoretically.

Many interesting examples of molecular crystals may be found in the structures of the elements. Sulphur (in the plastic form) and selenium and tellurium have similar structures, composed of long spiral chains packed together with their axes parallel (Fig. 7–16). One observes here, however, a transition from the molecular crystal to the semimetallic, for the physical properties of selenium and tellurium indicate that the forces binding the chains are not simply van der Waals forces.

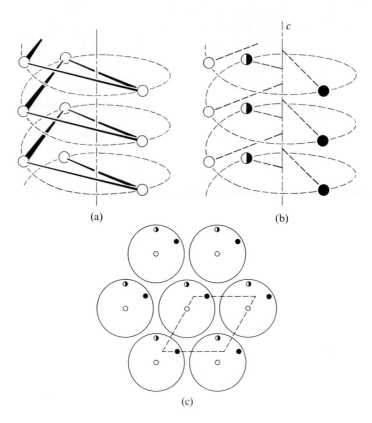

FIG. 7–16. Crystal structure of selenium, showing spiral chain of selenium atoms (a) ∠Se Se Se = 105°, and orientation of atoms about c-axis of hexagonal unit cell (b). Figure (c) is a projection on the rhombic face of the hexagonal unit cell. The van der Waals radii for the atoms at one level have been included to illustrate the packing.

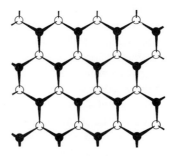

FIG. 7–17. Structure of one of the double layers of black phosphorous, or metallic arsenic, antimony, or bismuth.

TABLE 7–2

VAN DER WAALS RADII
(in angstroms)

		H 1.2
N 1.5	O 1.40	F 1.35
P 1.9	S 1.85	Cl 1.80
As 2.0	Se 2.00	Br 1.95
Sb 2.2	Te 2.20	I 2.15

Methyl group CH_3 and methylene CH_2: 2.0.

A similar transition may be seen in the layer structures of black phosphorous, and in the metallic forms of arsenic, antimony, and bismuth (Fig. 7–17). In black phosphorous, covalent bonding in the layer leads to bond lengths of 2.2 A, while the smallest separation of phosphorous atoms in adjacent layers is 3.87 A. The difference becomes less significant with the heavier elements so that in metallic bismuth the intra-layer and inter-layer distances are 3.10 A and 3.47 A respectively.

As intimated earlier, polymorphism is common among all types of crystals. Phosphorous, arsenic, and antimony are all dimorphic, and assume, in addition to the layer-type arrangements, less stable configurations (yellow P, As and Sb) which appear to be composed of close-packed tetrahedral P_4, As_4, or Sb_4 molecules, such as are found in the vapors of these substances. In addition to the monoclinic plastic form, sulfur has at least one other monoclinic modification, and an orthorhombic one as well. The latter, known as rhombic sulfur, has an extremely large and complicated unit cell made up of 16 S_8 molecules. These have the form of a puckered ring with $s(S{-}S) = 2.10$ A and $\angle SSS = 103°$ (Fig. 7–18).

Turning to larger, nonelemental molecules, we find that the fundamentals of close-packing are still observed, even in these more complex structures. Solid methane, for example, exhibits a cubic structure arising from some form of close-

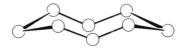

FIG. 7–18. Puckered ring of S_8, as found in rhombic sulfur.

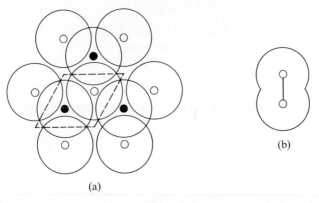

(b)

(a)

FIG. 7–19. Projection on the hexagonal face of the structure of ethane (and diborane). The C—C (B—B) axes are parallel to the c-axis of the cell. Since hydrogen atom positions are usually not obtainable from X-ray data, it is customary, in packing diagrams, to consider the CH_3 groups as spherical, so that C_2H_6 would appear as in (b). The shaded atoms are $c/2$ above the unshaded ones.

packing of the methane molecules. Crystals of ethane (and B_2H_6) and ethylene, as might be expected, have less symmetry; but Figs. 7–19 and 7–20 show clearly that they are essentially HCP and body-centered, respectively. As a form of close-packing, the latter is slightly less efficient than HCP or CCP, but is still commonly found.

Aromatic molecules display a form of packing which is characterized by that of benzene in Fig. 7–21. The planes of the molecules are almost parallel to one of the crystal axes, though nearly at right angles to one another. The arrange-

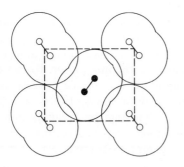

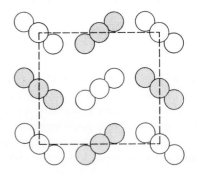

FIG. 7–20. Packing of ethylene molecules, as seen in a projection on one face of orthorhombic unit cell. The shaded atoms lie at the center of the cell and the unshaded ones lie at the corners.

FIG. 7–21. Crystal structure of benzene in projection on a plane perpendicular to the c-axis. The plane of the molecules is parallel to the c-axis, with the shaded molecules displaced by $c/2$.

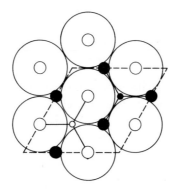

FIG. 7–22. Crystal structure of BCl_3 (and BI_3). The structure is essentially one in which the large halide atoms (large circles) are in an HCP array, with the boron atoms in octahedral holes. The shaded atoms are at $a/2$ and the remainder at $a = 0$. The van der Waals radii of the halide atoms of the lower layer have been drawn in to illustrate the packing.

ments in other aromatic crystals such as naphthalene, coronene, etc., are similar to this, with the planes of the molecules no longer necessarily parallel to a crystal axis. In boron trichloride (and boron tribromide), the larger halogen atoms form a hexagonal close-packed structure with the much smaller boron atoms in interstitial sites (Fig. 7–22). The structure of CO_2 crystals may also be regarded as typical of molecular crystals. As Fig. 7–23 shows, the structure of CO_2 crystals is similar to that of iodine but, although the centers of the molecules lie on face-centering positions, the axes of the molecules are no longer parallel to any of the crystallographic axes.

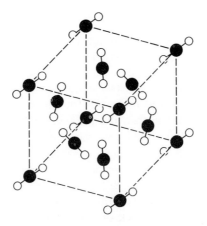

FIG. 7–23. Cubic unit cell of CO_2. The shaded carbon atoms lie exactly on an FCC lattice. The axes of the molecules are inclined at about 55° to each of the crystal axes.

(c) Intermolecular forces and hydrogen bonding

To achieve a better understanding of molecular crystals, we must inquire into the nature of the forces involved in binding the molecules together. In comparison with that of ionic crystals, the case of molecular crystals is considerably more complicated. The success of the Born-Mayer treatment confirms the fact that ionic crystals may be described quite accurately in terms of simple Coulomb inter-action of the ions, and that the van der Waals forces, and even repulsion from electron cloud overlap, are of only secondary importance.

In molecular crystals, on the other hand, it is these latter forces which are the major consideration. Their formal expression in the case of solids is very difficult, with the result that most of our knowledge of these interactions is derived from experimental work on the departure of gases from ideality.

For our purposes, the intermolecular forces present may be classified as (1) London dispersion forces, and (2) dipole-dipole interactions. Of these, only the *London dispersion forces* are operative in the absence of a permanent dipole moment; hence they are responsible for the bonding in the crystals of the inert gases and molecular crystals, where the symmetry of the molecule precludes a permanent dipole moment.

The London dispersion forces are quantum mechanical in origin, and difficult to describe in classical terms. However, one reasonably successful semiclassical approach interprets the bonding as arising from a synchronization of the outer electrons of the atoms or molecules involved. Thus, at any instant, the position of an electron in one molecule will be such as to impart to the molecule a dipole moment. This dipole will influence the motion of an electron in an adjacent molecule, in effect inducing a dipole, and the resultant interaction of the dipoles gives rise to weak bonding. For this reason the forces are often said to result from an induced dipole–induced dipole interaction.

London dispersion forces are nondirective, and the binding energy involved is proportional to α^2/s^6 where s is the internuclear separation and α the polarizabil-ity. As a result, the structures giving rise to the largest bonding energy are those in which s is as small as possible. They are, then, the close-packed ones typified by the examples of Section 7–2(b). One might conceive of a simpler structure for I_2, or the other nonspherical molecules, in which the axes of the molecules are arranged parallel to one another and parallel to the crystal axes. However, consideration reveals that this would give rise to layer structures of lower overall symmetry and crystal energy.

The problems involved in the theoretical treatment of the crystal or cohesion energy for molecular crystals are rather formidable, and very few calculations have been carried out. Apart from the general complexity of the interactions, a more serious problem arises because of lack of knowledge of the repulsion interaction. In the case of ionic crystals, the repulsion energy is but a small part of the total, so that errors introduced because of this deficiency are not significant. But, in molecular crystals, the contribution due to repulsion may be half the size of the attraction energy, and the errors correspondingly larger. It is possible, however, to make a qualitative comparison of theory and experiment if polarizability data are available.

As pointed out in Section 2–5, the electronic charge distribution of an atom or molecule in an electric field will be deformed in such a way that the centers of negative and positive charge will no longer be coincident. In other words, the electric field **E** induces a dipole moment in the atom or molecule. Quantitatively, this may be expressed by the relation

$$\mu_{\text{ind}} = \alpha \mathbf{E}.$$

The polarizability α is therefore a measure of the extent to which the molecule or ion interacts with the field. A close relationship clearly exists between the polarizability and the dielectric constant, and measurement of the latter is one experimental source of data on the polarizability. Alternatively, the polarizability may be obtained from the refractive index of the substance in question. Table 7–3

TABLE 7–3

POLARIZABILITIES* OF SOME ATOMS, IONS, AND MOLECULES
(α in cm$^3 \times 10^{-25}$)

He	2.0	O^{2-}	39
Ne	3.9	S^{2-}	102
Ar	16.2	Se^{2-}	105
Kr	24.6	Te^{2-}	140
Xe	39.9		
		Cl_2	46.1
Li^+	0.3		
Na^+	2.4	HF	24.6
K^+	10.0	HCl	26.3
Rb^+	15.0	HBr	36.1
Cs^+	24.0	HI	54.4
Be^{2+}	0.1	H_2	7.9
Mg^{2+}	1.0	N_2	17.6
Ca^{2+}	6.0	O_2	16.0
Sn^{2+}	9.0	CO	19.5
Ba^{2+}	16.9	CO_2	26.5
		SO_2	37.2
F^-	8.1	N_2O	30.0
Cl^-	29.8	H_2S	37.8
Br^-	42.4		
I^-	64.5		

* For nonisotropic molecules, the value listed is an average of the components of the polarizability tensor.

shows clearly the expected correlation between polarizability and the quantum number of the valence electrons.

Experimentally, the cohesion energy of a molecular crystal is defined as the enthalpy of the reaction

$$M \text{ (gas)} \xrightarrow{\Delta H} M \text{ (crystal)},$$

where M is the molecular unit in the solid. Caution must be exercised in applying this definition, since M may be different in polymorphs and, in addition, M need not be the stable form in the gas phase. In the simpler cases such as nitrogen there are no difficulties, since N_2 is the molecular unit in all polymorphs, as well as the stable form in the gas phase.

This does not mean, however, that the cohesion energy is the same for the different crystalline forms, since there will be an enthalpy associated with the transition from one form to another. Sulphur requires more careful consideration, since the molecular unit is S_8 in the rhombic form and infinite chains in the plastic form, and neither of these persist to any great extent in the gas phase, where S_2 seems to predominate.

In any event, there is insufficient thermochemical data in most cases to allow estimation of the cohesion energy as defined above. We have therefore listed, in Table 7–4, the mp, bp, and heats of vaporization and fusion for the crystals of interest. To a first approximation, the experimental cohesion energy is simply minus the sum of ΔH_{fus} and ΔH_{vap}. (This table should be compared with the corresponding data for ionic crystals in Tables 2–1 and 2–7.)

We can see that the experimental data of Table 7–4 are qualitatively in agreement with the remarks above concerning the dependence of the London dispersion forces on the polarizability. The situation is typified by the series of inert gases, or the halogens where the increased polarizability associated with the larger atoms leads to larger cohesion energies and higher melting and boiling points (Fig. 7–24). This case is in contrast to that of ionic crystals, where the inverse dependence on internuclear separations results in crystals of the heavier ions having lower melting and boiling points.

If the close-packed molecules possess a dipole moment, then we can expect that dipole-dipole interactions will take place, and that they will contribute to the cohesion energy. Although the size of the contribution varies with the magnitude of the dipole moment, Table 7–5 shows clearly that the binding energy arising from such interactions can be significant.

In comparing the properties of the series of halogen acids with the corresponding inert gases, we note that argon and HCl, for example, have comparable polarizabilities, but that the heat of vaporization, mp, and bp of the latter are all considerably higher. For HF the influence of the dipole interaction is even more important, producing a sharp break upward in the bp curve for the series. In fact, the bp seems anomalously high in relation to the increase in dipole moment, with the implication that some additional interaction is taking place. Similar

TABLE 7–4

PHYSICAL PROPERTIES OF CRYSTALS OF NONPOLAR MOLECULES

	mp, °K	bp, °K	ΔH_{fus}, kcal/mole	ΔH_{vap}, kcal/mole
He	3.5	4.2	0.005	0.02
Ne	24.5	27.3	0.08	0.43
Ar	83.9	87.3	0.28	1.56
Kr	116	119	0.39	2.16
Xe	161	165	0.55	3.02
Rn	202	211	0.69	3.92
F_2	55.2	85.2	0.37	1.51
Cl_2	172	239	1.53	4.88
Br_2	266	298	2.52	7.34
I_2	298*			14.88*
H_2	14.0	20.4	0.03	0.22
N_2	63.1	77.3	0.17	1.33
O_2	54.0	90.2	0.11	1.63
S_8	368*			3.01
BF_3	145*			5.7*
BCl_3	166	286		5.7
BBr_3	226	364		7.3
CO_2	195*			6.03*
SiF_4	177*			6.15
CH_4	90.7	112	0.23	1.96
SiH_4	89	161	0.16	2.9
GeH_4	107	185	0.20	3.36
SnH_4	123	221		4.4

* Sublimation.

trends are observed in the H_2O and NH_3 series, and are commonly ascribed to the effects of *hydrogen bonding*.

Further justification for saying that these are special cases is found in the crystal structures of HF, NH_3, and H_2O, particularly the latter. Thus, although in the majority of cases the presence of a dipole moment does not bring about any major departure from close-packed arrangements, the structure of water is the rather open, inefficiently packed one of Fig. 7–25. On the other hand, SO_2, with a comparable dipole moment, has a close-packed structure not unlike that of CO_2. The tetrahedral coordination of the oxygen atoms in H_2O, in combination with the inefficient packing, is strongly suggestive of directional forces.

Recalling from Section 5–3(b) the approximately tetrahedral configuration attributed to the bond orbitals and lone-pair orbitals of the oxygen atom, the

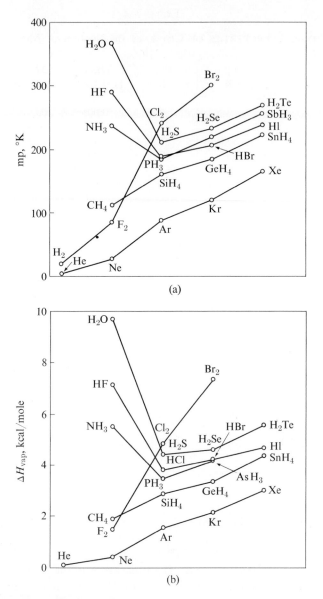

FIG. 7–24. Boiling points (a) and heats of vaporization (b) of some substances which form molecular crystals.

TABLE 7–5

PHYSICAL PROPERTIES OF SOME CRYSTALS OF POLAR MOLECULES

	μ, debye	mp, °K	bp, °K	ΔH_{fus}, kcal/mole	ΔH_{vap}, kcal/mole
HF	1.98	190	293	1.09	
HCl	1.08	158	188	0.48	3.86
HBr	0.79	186	206	0.56	4.21
HI	0.38	222	237	0.69	4.72
H_2O	1.84	273	373	1.44	9.72
H_2S	0.89	188	213	0.57	4.46
H_2Se		207	232	0.60	4.62
H_2Te		222	271	1.0	5.55
NH_3	1.45	195	240	1.35	5.58
PH_3		139	185	0.27	3.49
AsH_3		157	211	0.56	4.18
SbH_3		185	256		
SO_2	1.62	198	263	1.77	5.96
NO	0.16	110	121	0.55	3.29
N_2O	0.17	182	185	1.56	3.96
N_2H_4	1.84	275	387		10
H_2CO		155	254		5.85
HCOOH	1.2	282	373	3.03	5.32
CH_3COOH	1.86	290	391	2.8	5.83
CH_3OH	1.68	175	338	0.76	8.94
C_2H_5OH	1.70	159	352	1.2	9.22

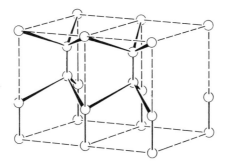

FIG. 7–25. Tetrahedral coordination in the oxygen skeleton of common ice (ice I). Two of the hexagonal unit cells are shown, but the hydrogen atoms have been omitted. These are statistically located on the lines joining the oxygen atoms (see text).

structure of ice can be explained, given that these directed lone pairs are capable of exerting an attraction for the protons of adjacent oxygens. Such an argument is reasonable on electrostatic grounds alone but, as pointed out below, the interaction is a complex one, and a completely satisfactory theory of hydrogen bonding has yet to be devised.

The exact positions of the hydrogen atoms in relation to the oxygens have been determined by neutron diffraction for D_2O ice, and the results show that they lie on, or at least very close to, the O—O bonds. More interesting is the fact that the diffraction pattern indicates that there is one-half of a hydrogen atom bonded to each oxygen! In other words, ice has a statistical structure in which the hydrogens are in motion, and are alternately bonded to one oxygen or the other. At any given instant, however, there are only two hydrogens covalently bonded to any given oxygen, so that we may still think of the structure as an aggregate of discrete water molecules. A disordered structure such as this is also suggested by the residual entropy of ice (Chapter 8); the disordered structure was in fact predicted by Pauling on this basis.

The ice structure is described, then, as a hydrogen-bonded aggregate of H_2O molecules. The hydrogen bond is schematically portrayed as

$$O^1—H----O^2,$$

where the dashed line indicates the hydrogen bond proper. We are led, however, to inquire in what way the hydrogen bond differs from the expected dipole-dipole interaction. The question is a controversial one, and is usually answered in terms of what effect the O^1H group has on the electron distribution of the more distant O^2. Pauling describes the hydrogen bond in terms of resonance among the three structures:

$$O^1—H \quad :O^2, \qquad {}^-O^1\colon H^+ \quad :O^2, \qquad O^1\colon H----O^2.$$

The first represents normal covalent bonding between O^1 and the hydrogen, while the second allows for ionic character in this bond. The third structure represents covalent bonding between O^2 and H, necessarily weak because of the large O^2—H distance. An alternative approach described by Coulson lists four contributions to the total bond energy: (1) electrostatic (dipole), (2) delocalization, (3) repulsive, and (4) dispersion.

Of these, only (2) is peculiar to the hydrogen bond, and refers to the delocalization of electrons away from the O^2 region to the O^1—H region. The relative importance of the different interactions as estimated theoretically is shown in Table 7–6. The experimental value represents half the heat of sublimation of ice, since there are two hydrogen bonds per molecule. While the theory obviously requires refinement, it is clear from Table 7–6 that all four effects are important.

The strengths of hydrogen bonds involving other atoms (Table 7–7) correlate fairly well with the atomic properties. Thus, the more electronegative fluorine forms F—H----F bonds in crystalline HF, which are stronger than the O—H----O bonds in ice; while the hydrogen bonds in solid NH_3 are correspondingly weaker.

TABLE 7–6

CONTRIBUTIONS TO THE ENERGY OF
THE HYDROGEN BOND IN ICE

Type of energy	kcal/mole
Electrostatic	6
Delocalization	8
Repulsive	−8
Dispersion	3
Calculated total	9
Experimental total	6.1

TABLE 7–7

ESTIMATED ENERGIES OF HYDROGEN BONDS
(in kcal/mole)

Bond	Energy
F—H----F	7
N—H----N	6
O—H----O	6
N—H----F	5
O—H----N	4.7
C—H----O	2.6
N—H----O	2.3

These differences are reflected in the crystal structures of HF and NH_3. The former is composed of zigzag chains of hydrogen-bonded fluorines (Fig. 7–26) but in crystalline NH_3 the arrangement is very nearly a cubic-close-packing of the NH_3 molecules. The strongest hydrogen bond known is that in the HF_2^- ion, where the proton lies midway between the fluorines. By means of thermochemical data and a calculated crystal energy, it has been estimated that dissociation into HF and F^- requires about 58 kcal/mole.

Hydrogen bonds are important in determining the crystal structures of many more substances than the few mentioned here. It is extremely common in crystals of organic molecules, the structure of solid methanol (Fig. 7–27) being typical. The question as to which atoms are capable of forming hydrogen bonds is again a controversial one. Probably the most commonly held view reserves these powers for nitrogen, oxygen, and fluorine; but this seems unnecessarily restrictive, since the problem of definition is really one of degree. Evidence points to the fact that the structure of crystalline HCl is very similar to that of HF, and it would not be incorrect to describe this as a result of Cl—H----Cl bonding.

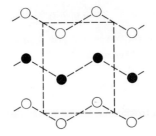

FIG. 7–26. Zigzag chains of fluorine atoms in crystalline HF. The hydrogen atoms are presumed to lie on the dashed lines joining the fluorine atoms. Projection is on the *bc* face of the orthorhombic cell, with the shaded atoms at $a/2$ and the remainder at $a = 0$.

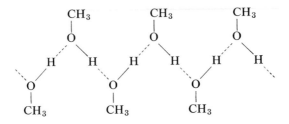

FIG. 7–27. Hydrogen bonded chains in solid methanol. All carbon and oxygen atoms lie in the same plane.

The present discussion only hints at the great mass of literature which is available concerning hydrogen bonding. (The excellent review by Pimentel and McClellan*, for example, lists over 2000 references.) In particular nothing has been said here of the role of hydrogen bonding in the liquid state.

7–3. METALS

A division of the elements into metals and nonmetals in a manner which conforms to both chemical and physical properties is, to say the least, difficult. It is possible, nevertheless, to formulate a definition which is adequate in the majority of cases. In the present discussion we shall think of metals as those crystalline solids which exhibit such physical properties as high thermal and electrical conductivity, a metallic luster, and a large coefficient of thermal expansion. The melting point and degree of hardness vary over rather wide limits, but most pure metals are soft and malleable. From a chemical point of view, the metallic elements are characterized by a low ionization energy, so that in crystalline salts and polar solvents they usually exist as positive ions.

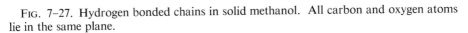

* *The Hydrogen Bond.* G. C. Pimentel and A. L. McClellan. San Francisco: W. H. Freeman, 1959.

TABLE 7-8.   STRUCTURE AND PROPERTIES OF METALS

Metal	Structure	Lattice spacing, angstroms	s_e, angstroms	ΔH°_{298},† kcal/mole	mp, °K
Li	BCC	3.50	3.03	38.44	459
Na	BCC	4.28	3.72	25.9	380.7
K	BCC	5.24	4.51	21.5	335.5
Rb	BCC	5.69	4.94	19.5	311.7
Cs	BCC	6.08	5.25	18.7	301.7
Be	HCP	2.28, 3.58	2.22, 2.28	77.9	1623
Mg	HCP	3.20, 5.20	3.19, 3.20	35.6	924
Ca	CCP	5.58	3.94	42.2	1083
Sr	CCP	6.07	4.29	39.2	1030
Ba	BCC	5.01	4.34	42.5	1123
Al	CCP	4.04	2.86	77.5	933
Sc	CCP	4.53	3.21	93	1470
Ti	HCP	2.95, 4.68	2.89, 2.95	113	2070
V	BCC	3.03	2.62	123	1980
Cr	BCC	2.88	2.49	95.0	1888
Mn	*		~2.7	67.2	1533
Fe	BCC	2.86	2.48	99.5	1808
Co	CCP	3.54	2.50	102	1768
Ni	CCP	3.52	2.49	103	1728
Cu	CCP	3.61	2.55	81.1	1356
Zn	HCP	2.66, 4.94	2.66, 2.91	31.2	1180
Y	HCP	3.65, 5.73	3.54, 3.64	103	1763
Zr	HCP	3.23, 5.15	3.17, 3.22	146	2170
Nb	BCC	3.29	2.85	185	2223
Mo	BCC	3.14	3.71	158	2893
Tc	HCP	2.74, 4.39	2.70, 2.73	46?	
Ru	HCP	2.70, 4.27	2.65, 2.70	160	
Rh	CCP	3.80	2.69	138	2258
Pd	CCP	3.88	2.75	93	1822
Ag	CCP	4.08	2.88	68.4	1234
Cd	HCP	2.97, 5.61	2.97, 3.29	26.8	594
In	*		3.25, 3.36	58.2	429
Sn	*		3.02, 3.18	72.0	505
La	CCP	5.29	3.74	88	1099
Hf	HCP	3.20, 5.05	3.12, 3.19	168	
Ta	BCC	3.29	2.85	187	3300
W	BCC	3.16	2.74	200	3643
Re	HCP	2.76, 4.46	2.74, 2.75	189	3440
Os	HCP	2.73, 4.31	2.67, 2.73	174	2970
Ir	CCP	3.83	2.71	165	2727
Pt	CCP	3.92	2.77	135	2047
Au	CCP	4.07	2.88	87.3	1336
Hg	*		3.00	14.7	234.3
Tl	HCP	3.45, 5.51	3.40, 3.45	43.0	575
Pb	CCP	4.94	3.49	46.8	600

* Other than simple close-packed structure.
† ΔH°_{298} = heat of formation of gaseous atoms.

It should be realized that, in the case of metals, physical properties are remarkably sensitive to the presence of even trace impurities, and in some cases they vary according to the history of the sample as well. In part, this variance results from the formation of alloys, and variations in the degree of order they exhibit. There is little doubt that structural characteristics on a superatomic scale are also very important in determining physical properties. A crystal of any type which possessed a perfectly regular structure from one boundary to another would be classified as an *ideal crystal*, and although such perfection has been approached, it has never been found in the laboratory. Commonly, the symmetry expressed by the space lattice extends only over regions of about 10^{-5} cm, corresponding to some hundreds of unit cells. A normal single crystal is therefore described as a *mosaic*, in which these units are very slightly displaced relative to one another.

To return to the subject of metals specifically: It is, then, the size and disposition of these mosaic units which so profoundly affects the physical properties. The fact that they may change with time reflects the lack of true equilibrium in the original structures.

(a) Structure of pure metals

With few exceptions, the crystal structures displayed by the metallic elements (Table 7–8) are close-packed ones of the body-centered, face-centered, or hexagonal type. As Table 7–9 illustrates, polymorphism is common, with some elements exhibiting three or even four modifications, usually at different temperatures. Beyond noting that there is some system in Table 7–8 (all of the alkali metals have body-centered structures, for example), there is little that can be done in establishing simple rules governing the structure type.

TABLE 7–9

STRUCTURES OF SOME POLYMORPHIC METALS

	Structure	s_e, angstroms	Temperature, °K
αCa	CCP	3.94	291
γCa	BCC	3.87	770
αFe	BCC	2.48	293
γFe	CCP	2.57	1189
δFe	BCC	2.53	1667
αSr	CCP	4.29	298
βSr	HCP	4.31	521
γSr	BCC	4.19	887
Li	BCC	3.03	293
Li	HCP	3.11	351

TABLE 7–10

METALLIC RADII FOR TWELVE-COORDINATION
(in angstroms)

Li 1.58	Be 1.12												
Na 1.92	Mg 1.60	Al 1.43											
K 2.38	Ca 1.97	Sc 1.66	Ti 1.47	V 1.35	Cr 1.29	Mn 1.37	Fe 1.26	Co 1.25	Ni 1.25	Cu 1.28	Zn 1.37	Ga 1.53	Ge 1.39
Rb 2.53	Sr 2.15	Y 1.82	Zr 1.60	Nb 1.47	Mo 1.40	Tc 1.35	Ru 1.34	Rh 1.34	Pd 1.37	Ag 1.44	Cd 1.52	In 1.67	Sn 1.58
Cs 2.72	Ba 2.24	Rare earths 1.82	Hf 1.59	Ta 1.47	W 1.41	Re 1.37	Os 1.35	Ir 1.36	Pt 1.39	Au 1.44	Hg 1.55	Tl 1.71	Pb 1.75

In the further discussion of metals and alloys, it is of value to derive an empirical set of metallic radii. This project presents two problems: (1) the radii are found to be functions of the coordination number, and (2) in some cases not all of the nearest neighbors are equidistant. The latter difficulty is not encountered in the cubic structures, but is present in HCP structures when the axial ratio departs from the ideal close-packed one of 1.633.

In this case, for a given atom there will be six equidistant nearest neighbors in the same plane, and six more (three above and three below) which are closer or more distant, depending on the axial ratio. In deriving the metallic radii, when the deviation from true HCP is small, it suffices to take half of the mean of the two distances. In the few cases where the deviation is large, it is probably better to consider the coordination number as less than 12.

The dependence of the metallic radius on coordination number presents a more difficult problem but, for the restricted group of elements we are considering, the empirical ratios of Goldschmidt are probably adequate. By studying a large number of metallic crystals, he deduced that the relative radii for different coordination numbers are:

Coordination number 12   ...   1.00

8   ...   0.97

6   ...   0.96

The radii derived in the above manner for the coordination number 12 are listed in Table 7–10. Qualitatively, these show roughly the expected trends; but, as in the case of the structures themselves, it appears that detailed quantitative treatment is required to relate the radii to atomic structure.

(b) Simple alloys

Alloys are essentially solid solutions of one metal in another and, from a structural point of view, it is convenient to distinguish between two basic types: (1) substitutional solid solutions, and (2) intermediate phases.

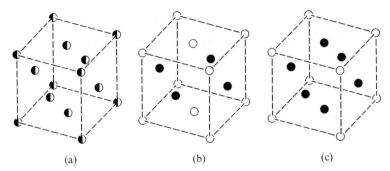

(a)   (b)   (c)

FIG. 7–28. Structure of copper–gold alloys: (a) statistical CCP structure in which the half-shaded atoms may be either Cu or Au; (b) and (c) ordered structures of CuAu and Cu₃Au (Cu atoms shaded).

The first type refers to alloys in which atoms of one kind in a crystal are replaced by atoms of another kind of similar size and valence, so that a continuous series of solid solutions may be formed. A good example of a *substitutional solid solution* is provided by the system copper—gold. Both pure metals have CCP structures, and the solid solution is a disordered one in which Cu and Au atoms are located randomly at the different sites (Fig. 7–28). One might refer to a statistical Au-Cu atom, since the probability of finding a given atom on any site is dependent only on the mole ratio of the constituents. While the disordered structure is the more stable at high temperatures, it is found that, below about 450°C, more ordered arrangements exist. The structures of the ordered arrangements observed for the Cu-Au systems are also illustrated in Fig. 7–28. The disorder-order transformation is assisted by the process of annealing.

Relatively few pairs of metals are completely miscible in ane another and able to form continuous solid solutions of the type described. Hume-Rothery has shown, in fact, that the possible combinations are determined by a relatively simple set of empirical rules. These are:

(1) The atoms should have metallic radii that differ by less than 15%. (Sodium and potassium, for example, will not form extensive solid solutions, despite their chemical and structural similarity in the pure state.)

(2) The crystal structures of the two metals must be identical.

(3) The metals must be chemically similar.

If only one or two of these rules are obeyed, then random solid solutions will be formed only over a very limited compositional range at the two extremes. Between these, we find phases whose structures may bear little relation to those of the pure metals. Some of these may, in fact, have properties which justify their being regarded as compounds of the constituent metals, although they are usually stable over a limited compositional range and do not have a fixed stoichiometry.

A good example is the copper—zinc system, in which five different structures are distinguished as follows:

$$\alpha \quad 0–\ 35\%\ Zn$$

$$\beta \quad 45–\ 50\%\ Zn \quad CuZn$$

$$\gamma \quad 60–\ 65\%\ Zn \quad Cu_5Zn_8$$

$$\epsilon \quad 82–\ 88\%\ Zn \quad CuZn_3$$

$$\eta \quad 97–100\%\ Zn$$

The α- and η-phases are random solid solutions of Zn in Cu and Cu in Zn, respectively, and have structures based on the CCP and HCP structures of the pure metals. The β-phase (β-brass) has a cubic structure like that of cesium chloride, with the Cu and Zn atoms taking the part of the cations and anions. The γ-phase, however, has a complicated cubic structure with a large unit cell containing 52 atoms, and might be considered a compound. Finally, the structure of the ϵ-phase is a modified form of hexagonal close-packing.

(c) Interstitial compounds

While closely related to alloys, interstitial compounds exhibit unique properties which merit giving them separate treatment. Composed mainly of the carbides, nitrides, borides, and hydrides of the transition metals, they derive the name interstitial from the fact that they are regarded as close-packed structures of these metals, with the smaller nonmetallic atoms located in interstices.

Referring to Section 7–2(a), where these interstitial sites or holes were discussed, we recall that they are of two types: octahedral holes and tetrahedral holes. The filling of all of the octahedral holes gives a structure geometrically identical with the NaCl structure, and it is this type which is most common among the carbides, etc., which we are considering here. Table 7–11 lists some of the important properties of these compounds. We see that all of the interstitial compounds listed have the NaCl structure, regardless of the structure of the pure metal.

If, as we have assumed, the metal atoms are close-packed, then they will be in contact along the diagonal of the cube face, and their radius in the interstitial compound may be derived from the lattice constant. This has been done in Table 7–11, and we observe that there is only a slight increase in the radii of the metals. From this we might infer little change in the metal-to-metal bonding, in keeping with the property of true metallic conduction exhibited by these compounds. On the other hand, the octahedral hole is rather small, and has a radius $[0.41\ r(M) \approx 0.7\ A]$ approximately equal to the covalent radii of the interstitially located atoms. This gives us an insight into the metal–nonmetal bonding which is apparently responsible for the remarkable properties of the interstitial compounds.

TABLE 7-11

PROPERTIES OF SOME INTERSTITIAL COMPOUNDS

	Structure	Lattice spacing, angstroms	Metallic radius, angstroms	mp, °K
HfB	FCC	4.62	1.63	
TiB	FCC	4.20	1.48	2900
ZrB	FCC	4.65	1.64	
HfC	FCC	4.65	1.64	4160
NbC	FCC	4.44	1.57	4100
TaC	FCC	4.46	1.57	4150
TiC	FCC	4.32	1.53	3400
VC	FCC	4.18	1.47	3080
ZrC	FCC	4.69	1.66	3810
ScN	FCC	4.44	1.57	
TiN	FCC	4.24	1.50	3220
VN	FCC	4.17	1.48	2320
ZrN	FCC	4.56	1.61	3250

Apart from their very high melting point and extreme hardness (only slightly less than that of diamond), all of these interstitial carbides, nitrides, and borides are extremely inert chemically. They are attacked by strong oxidizing agents (e.g., aqua regia), or by oxygen at very high temperatures.

The interstitial hydrides of the transition metals are much less well defined than the carbides, etc., discussed above. Their composition is variable, and the process of their formation is usually described as adsorption of the hydrogen by the metal, since the amount of gas taken up is strongly dependent on such conditions as the temperature, pressure, and the state of subdivision of the metal. Furthermore, the process is a reversible one, and the hydrogen may be removed by pumping on the system at higher temperatures. These results are apt to be misleading, because more often than not the metallic structure changes substantially in the adsorption process.

In addition, the heats of formation of the interstitial hydrides from hydrogen and the metal are fairly large, and are, in fact, of the same order as those of the ionic hydrides (LiH, NaH, CaH_2, BaH_2, etc.). These compounds are, however, definitely metallic in character, so that, like the carbides, they are regarded as interstitial compounds. The CCP structure is common among these hydrides, and it has been suggested that the hydrogen atoms, because of their small radii, occupy the tetrahedral holes in the face-centered array. More recent neutron-diffraction work does not bear this out, but indicates structures that are rather more complicated.

(d) Bonding in metals

A qualitative analysis of the data of Table 7–8 reveals several interesting facts concerning metallic bonding. The binding energy for metals is defined experimentally as the heat of formation of the crystalline solid from the gaseous monatomic atoms. In other words, it is the enthalpy of the reaction

$$M \text{ (gas)} \xrightarrow{\Delta H} M \text{ (crystal).}$$

In Table 7–8, this enthalpy change is quoted for 1 atm pressure and 298°K (ΔH_{298}°). Like molecular solids, the atomic crystals are all close-packed ones; hence the forces responsible for cohesion in metals must be nondirectional in nature. The cohesion energy in metals is much larger than in molecular crystals and, although varying over a rather wide range (−18 to −200 kcal/mole), approaches the crystal energies of ionic crystals. Metallic cohesion energies, like crystal energies, appear to exhibit an inverse dependence on the internuclear separations (Fig. 7–29).

Another important and characteristic property of metals is their high thermal and electrical conductivity. It is logical to infer from these properties the presence of free electrons in the metal, and such thinking has had a profound influence on the development of the theory of metallic bonding. In its simplest form, the free-electron theory regards a metal as consisting of positive ions embedded in a gas of free valence electrons. Such a model can be treated in a classical manner analogous to that used by Born for ionic crystals, except that, in the case of metals, the cohesion results from the electrostatic interaction between the ions and the electron cloud. This simple treatment is far less successful in the case of metals, however.

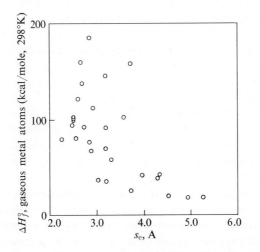

FIG. 7–29. Cohesion energies of metallic crystals as a function of internuclear separation.

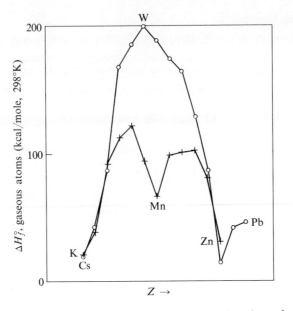

FIG. 7–30. Cohesion energies of metallic crystals as a function of atomic number. The second 18-membered period, which has been omitted to avoid confusion, lies between the first and third, with a minimum at technetium.

The free-electron approach can be improved on by the application of quantum mechanics, but such a treatment is far beyond the scope of this book. In any event, the complexities encountered have resulted in very few detailed calculations being carried out. Fortunately, there are alternative approaches which, although they are qualitative, assist in an appreciation of the important factors involved.

Note, for example, in Table 7–8, that the cohesion energies of the alkaline earths are all higher than those of the corresponding alkali metals. This suggests a relation between the cohesion energy and the number of valence electrons of the elements concerned. To test the hypothesis further, we may, as in Fig. 7–30, plot the cohesion energies for the 18-membered periods as a function of atomic number. It is then seen that the binding energy increases to a maximum in the region of the vanadium or chromium groups, falls off to a minimum with the zinc group, and then begins to increase again. In other words, the cohesion energy decreases as electrons are available to doubly fill the d-orbitals, and does not increase again until the p-orbitals are occupied by unpaired electrons.

Obviously the hypothesis is an oversimplification, because it predicts a maximum cohesion energy for the chromium group; and, except for tungsten, this is not so. There is furthermore an unexplained dip in energy at manganese (which also has a complex and unusual crystal structure), and at technetium, but it is still difficult to avoid the conclusion that the presence of these unpaired electrons plays an essential role in the bonding process. Alternatively, we might regard the decrease in cohesion energy to zinc as paralleling the gradual conversion of the *d*-orbitals from outer to inner orbitals, so that for thallium and lead, for example, only the *p*-electrons are available for bonding. [See also Section 7–5(b).]

In valence-bond terms, this phenomenon is explained through the resonance of electron-pair bonds between an atom and its nearest neighbors. Thus, in the case of lithium with a single valence electron, the bond resonates among the positions between each atom and its nearest neighbors. Two types of resonance are distinguished: synchronized resonance, in which each atom forms only one bond according to the scheme

$$
\begin{array}{cccc}
\text{Li---Li} & & \text{Li} & \text{Li} \\
 & & | & | \\
\text{Li---Li} & & \text{Li} & \text{Li}
\end{array}
$$

and unsynchronized resonance,

$$
\begin{array}{cccc}
\text{Li---Li} & & \text{Li---Li}^- \\
 & & | \\
\text{Li---Li} & & \text{Li}^+ \quad \text{Li}
\end{array}
$$

where, through ionization, a single atom may form two bonds. The latter requires the use of a second orbital but, as we shall see shortly, low-energy unoccupied orbitals are available in metals.

Consideration reveals that there is an extremely large number of resonance structures in any finite crystal, hence the resonance energy and therefore the cohesion energy are large. This argument explains the fact that the cohesion energy of crystalline lithium is almost three times the dissociation energy of Li_2. It should also be pointed out that, while energy is required to bring about ionization in the unsynchronized structures, the latter are also essential for the explanation of metallic conduction.

The application of the VB treatment to the 18-membered periods is now quite straightforward. The alkaline earths, with two valence electrons per atom, have a larger cohesion energy than the alkali metals, because they are capable of forming two bonds per atom in any resonance structure. The trend may be expected to continue as the number of valence electrons increases, until pairing of the electrons in the *d*-orbitals prevents their use in bond formation.

The existence of unoccupied, low-lying energy levels or orbitals (Pauling's metallic orbital) follows from the wave-mechanical treatment of the free-electron model. The same result may be demonstrated, however, by an approach closely related to the MO method. Thus, regarding the metallic crystal as a large molecule, one can conceive that interaction between AO's of the constituent atoms leads to the formation of MO's. In contrast to small molecules, however, in a metallic crystal there are a large number of MO's of similar energy. In other words, the AO's which are of the same energy in the free atoms split into a band of allowed energy levels in the crystal. The degree of splitting or width of the band depends,

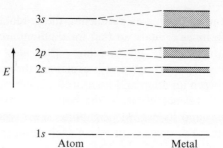

FIG. 7–31. Schematic illustration of the relationship between the energy levels of atomic sodium and the energy bands in metallic sodium.

of course, on the degree of interaction, and is largest for the outermost orbitals and very small for the inner orbitals which participate little in the bonding.

The situation in metallic sodium is illustrated schematically in Fig. 7–31. The outermost orbitals are delocalized throughout the whole crystal in three dimensions, and provide the basis for an explanation of metallic conduction. They may be compared with the π MO's binding the layers of graphite, where metallic conduction is observed parallel to the layers.

From the standpoint of bonding, the interstitial carbides, nitrides, etc., of the transition metals are most interesting. The presence of the interstitial atoms obviously has a profound effect on such properties as hardness and melting point, but the compounds still retain the property of metallic conduction, although to a lesser extent than the pure metals. Most of them assume the rock-salt structure, with octahedral coordination about the metal and nonmetal atoms. As we saw in Chapter 6, octahedral coordination is not unusual among the transition metals, but it is rare indeed for the nonmetallic elements involved here. One explanation proposes the use of three $2p$ orbitals, octahedrally directed, with a resonance similar to that suggested by Pauling for metals. To account for the conductivity, the metal–metal bonds must remain relatively delocalized.

7–4. COVALENT CRYSTALS

Crystals in which covalent bonding alone gives rise to infinite three-dimensional complexes are relatively rare. All of the examples, silicon, germanium, grey tin, and diamond itself are characterized by tetrahedral coordination, and have the diamond structure of Fig. 7–9.

That the bonding in these structures is in fact predominantly covalent follows from a number of observations. The physical and chemical properties (high mp, large heat of sublimation, electrical nonconductivity, chemical inertness) suggest strong bonds, but are not consistent with the presence of ions or metallic bonding. On the other hand, the atoms are inefficiently packed and the bonding forces directional in character. Furthermore, the observed internuclear distances are

TABLE 7–12

PROPERTIES OF COVALENT CRYSTALS

Element	Structure	a, angstroms	s_e, angstroms	ΔH°_{298}, kcal/mole	mp, °K
Diamond	Diamond	3.57	1.55	170	3770
Silicon	Diamond	5.43	2.36	105	1693
Germanium	Diamond	5.63	2.44	90	1232
Grey tin	Diamond	6.47	2.81	72	505

ΔH°_{298} = heat of formation of gaseous atoms.

almost exactly twice the covalent single bond radii for these atoms. (See Table 7–12.)

The bonding in these crystals may then be assumed to be essentially covalent, and may be described more or less accurately through sp^3 hybridization, as in Chapter 5. At the same time, an interesting transition is observed in the group for, while diamond is an insulator, silicon, germanium, and grey tin are semiconductors. In addition, the more commonly encountered white tin (the stable form above 18°C), which exhibits a distorted diamond structure, is definitely metallic.

Carbon also assumes another structure, the well-known graphite, and it is interesting to compare the two polymorphs in detail. In some respects they differ radically. Thus diamond is chemically inert, very hard, and a nonconductor. Graphite, in contrast, is chemically much more reactive, relatively soft, and is a moderate conductor in a direction parallel to the layers. On the other hand, both have a high mp, and almost identical heats of sublimation. All of these properties are readily correlated with the difference in structure of the two crystalline forms.

The bonding in a layer of graphite is similar to that in benzene or in one of the larger aromatic molecules such as coronene, with sp^2 hybrid orbitals being used to form σ-bonds linking the carbons. There are also π-bonds described in VB terms, as in Fig. 7–32. The MO approach considers the crystal as simply a large aromatic molecule with π MO's delocalized parallel to the layers. As shown in Fig. 5–41, such an interpretation yields a bond order consistent with those for other C—C bonds. The layers themselves are held together by much weaker forces, presumably those of the van der Waals type. Thus, because of the delocalization or resonance energy, we might expect the total cohesion energy in graphite to be much the same as in diamond. On the other hand, the delocalized π MO provides a medium for electron conduction parallel to the layers.

Until recently, the lubricating properties of graphite were attributed to the sliding of the layers relative to one another permitted by the weak interlayer forces. However, the failure of graphite as a lubricant in instruments used in the upper atmosphere has stimulated further research in the matter. It is now

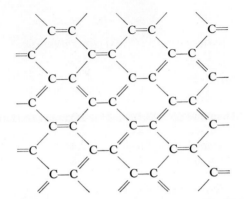

FIG. 7–32. One of the VB resonance structures for the bonding in graphite layers. Since the only restriction is that each carbon form one and only one double bond, it can be seen that there will be a great many resonance structures for a finite crystal.

known that graphite loses its lubricating properties under vacuum, so we may infer that adsorbed gases play an essential role. While the phenomenon is not completely understood, it is possible that oxygen and/or nitrogen molecules trapped between the bonded layers are responsible for the lubricating properties of graphite.

The chemical reactivity of graphite is also largely a result of the weak forces binding the layers. Two types of crystal compounds of graphite may be distinguished: (1) *intercalation compounds*, in which the lamellar skeleton of carbon rings is preserved, and (2) those compounds such as graphite oxide or fluoride, in which the carbon skeleton is buckled. The intercalation compounds may be likened to interstitial compounds, since the original graphite structure is largely preserved, although the interlayer distance is increased. Crystal compounds of this type are formed with a wide variety of chemical species, including the halogens, the alkali metals, and others. Typical are the compounds C_8Br, C_5ICl, C_8Cl, and C_8K, $C_{24}K$, $C_{36}K$.

The structure of C_8K, illustrated in Fig. 7–33, is characteristic of many of the intercalation compounds. Although the graphite layers are not distorted, the physical properties may change considerably in the formation of the crystal compounds. The electrical conductivity diminishes, for example, and the compounds are often highly colored, such as C_8K, which is orange, and $C_{24}K$, which is deep blue.

The reactions in which the intercalation compounds are formed are usually reversible, and the graphite may be recovered in its original form. In contrast, the fluorine in CF or C_4F is very difficult to remove. If these compounds are heated strongly, explosive decomposition occurs to give CF_4, C_2F_6, and other products. Graphite oxide or graphitic acid is much less well defined but behaves in a similar manner. In both cases X-ray diffraction investigations of the structure indicate a buckled nonaromatic ring, such as exists in diamond. It can be assumed, therefore, that the fluorine and oxygen are covalently bonded to the carbon atoms.

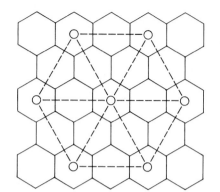

FIG. 7–33. Location of the interlayer potassium atoms relative to the carbon atoms in graphite layers of C_8K. The interlayer spacing (5.40 A) is increased over that in graphite (3.34 A) to accommodate the potassium atoms, and the layers are not displaced relative to one another, as they are in graphite.

In view of the recent successful attempts to synthesize diamond from graphite, it is interesting to examine the reaction involved, and to look at some of the problems encountered. At room temperature and atmospheric pressure, graphite is the thermodynamically stable allotrope to the extent of 0.45 kcal/mole. On the other hand, the diamond structure is slightly more dense than that of graphite. The volume occupied by an atom in the diamond structure is only 2.98 times the volume of a carbon atom, with a radius of 0.77 A, while in graphite the ratio is 3.07. Thus, in accord with geological observations and laboratory experiments, high pressures favor the formation of diamond.

The conversion of graphite to diamond is an interesting example of the need to balance thermodynamic and kinetic requirements in considering a chemical reaction, for the conditions which favor the conversion thermodynamically (high pressures and low temperatures) lead to an extremely small rate of reaction. A reasonable rate of reaction requires high temperatures, which necessitate still further increases in pressure. Thus the laboratory synthesis of diamond from graphite was accomplished under pressures of about 95,000 atmospheres at a temperature of approximately 1920°K. [See H. T. Hall, "The Synthesis of Diamond," *J. Chem. Ed.*, **38**, 484 (1961).]

7–5. IONIC AND INTERMEDIATE TYPES OF CRYSTALS

Having discussed the nature of van der Waals forces and covalent bonding in crystals, we can now make an assessment of the part these play in determining the structures of ionic and intermediate crystal types. We shall, in addition, survey briefly the structure of some complex ionic crystals.

(a) Van der Waals and covalent bonding in ionic crystals

To begin, we shall review briefly the characteristics associated with each bond type.

(1) *Ionic bonding.* The forces involved are nondirectional and the crystal energy, as we saw in Chapter 2, can be represented by an expression which shows an inverse dependence on s. This latter fact leads to close-packed structures which, on the basis of ionic interactions alone, are expected to be: CsCl if the radius ratio exceeds 0.73, NaCl if the radius ratio is between 0.73 and 0.41, and ZnS if the radius ratio is less than 0.41.

(2) *Van der Waals bonding.* Here again the forces are nondirectional, but the energy is proportional to $1/s^6$ and, for dispersion forces, a function also of the polarizabilities of the species involved. In general, these interactions lead to a small binding energy in comparison with ionic or covalent bonding.

(3) *Covalent bonding.* The most characteristic property in this case is the directional nature of the forces. In practice, this leads to lower coordination, commonly fourfold, with tetrahedral symmetry.

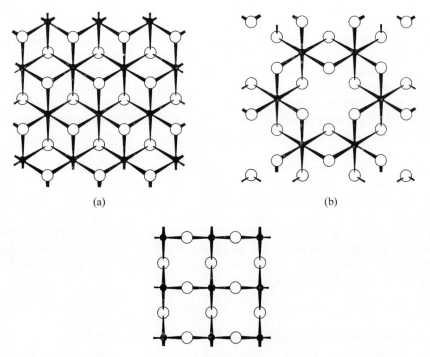

(a)   (b)

(c)

FIG. 7–34. Structure of the layers in crystals of (a) CdI_2 or $CdCl_2$ (differ in the packing of the layers); (b) $CrCl_3$ and (c) HgI_2. In (a) and (b) the halogen ions (unshaded) are close-packed, with the smaller metal ions (shaded) occupying one-half and one-third, respectively, of the octahedral holes.

The influence of the van der Waals forces in determining the structure of the alkali halides was mentioned in Chapter 2. In this group of compounds, contrary to the predictions of the radius-ratio rule, only three, CsCl, CsBr, and CsI, assume the simple cubic structure under normal conditions. The difference in ionic crystal energy for the NaCl and CsCl lattices is small, however, and noting that the three compounds assuming the latter structure are composed of the largest and most polarizable ions (Table 7–3), we can conclude that it is the van der Waals forces which determine the structure. The reason why these will be higher for the eightfold as opposed to the sixfold coordination lies in the different dependence on internuclear distance. In the case of the van der Waals forces, where the energy is inversely proportional to s^6, the number of nearest neighbors is by far the most important factor and the CsCl structure is favored, despite the slightly (3%) larger internuclear distance for eightfold coordination.

Although it is important in determining the structure, the van der Waals contribution to the total bonding energy in the alkali halides is small (5 kcal/mole in LiF, 13 kcal/mole in CsI) because of the high symmetry of coordination. In less symmetrical structures, the van der Waals energy may be much larger. Important examples of this type are the layer structures assumed by CdI_2, $CdCl_2$, $CrCl_3$, and HgI_2 (Fig. 7–34). The layers themselves exhibit a form of close-packing of the large anions, with the cations located centrally in the layer. Thus, when we view them end on, we find a sequence of layers $- - + - - + - -$, so that the highly polarizable anions are surrounded asymmetrically by anions on one side and cations on the other. From the point of view of Coulomb repulsion between the anions, such a configuration is undesirable, but it leads to large van der Waals contributions which stabilize the structure. The chain analog of this type of structure is much less common, but it is observed in the case of $PdCl_2$ (Fig. 7–35).

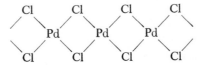

FIG. 7–35. Planar chains in crystalline $PdCl_2$.

The influence of covalent bonding in ionic crystals is difficult to ascertain. Structure type alone is not a very useful criterion, since tetrahedral coordination is expected not only in the case of directional bonding but also in purely ionic bonding when the radius ratio is less than 0.41. Thus, zinc sulfide with a radius ratio of 0.3 exhibits tetrahedral coordination in both the zincblende (sphalerite) and wurtzite structures (Fig. 7–36). On the other hand, there are far more examples of crystals which do not obey the radius ratio rule. Magnesium sulfide and selenide, for example, both have radius ratios of less than 0.41, yet assume the rock-salt structure, while Table 7–13 lists many tetrahedral structures in which the radius ratio is greater than 0.41.

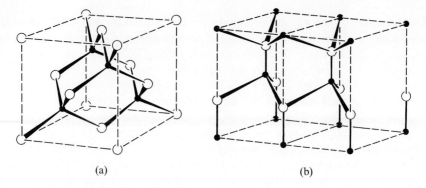

Fig. 7–36. Tetrahedral coordination in the zincblende (a) and wurtzite (b) forms of zinc sulfide. Note the similarity of these structures to those of diamond and ice I.

TABLE 7–13

STRUCTURES OF SOME AB COMPOUNDS

	Structure	Radius ratio	Experimental crystal energy, kcal/mole
CuCl	Zincblende	0.53	−234
CuBr	Zincblende	0.48	−232
CuI	Zincblende	0.43	−229
AgF	NaCl	0.85	−231
AgCl	NaCl	0.62	−219
AgBr	NaCl	0.58	−217
AgI	Zincblende	0.52	−214
ZnS	Zincblende	0.37	−865
ZnSe	Zincblende	0.35	−863
CdS	Wurtzite	0.48	−813
CdSe	Zincblende	0.46	−808
HgS	Zincblende	0.55	−854
HgSe	Zincblende	0.52	−867

Comparison of theoretical and experimental crystal energies might be expected to be of assistance, but this is not generally so. Crystals with the zinc sulfide structure are usually composed of a large anion with high polarizability and a small highly charged cation, so that the van der Waals contribution will be relatively large. Since this part of the total energy cannot be calculated with much accuracy, it is difficult to ascertain the source of the difference between the experimental and theoretical crystal energies.

Pearson has adopted an approach to this problem which, while largely empirical, is interesting and useful. He points out that the influence of directional bonding should be a function of two parameters: the average principle quantum number and the difference in electronegativity of the ions involved. Restricting ourselves to simple AB type compounds, these parameters may be defined as

$$\bar{n} = \frac{n_A + n_B}{2} \quad \text{and} \quad \Delta x = x(B) - x(A).$$

The relation between $\bar{n}$ and directional bonding may be observed in the series C, Si, Ge, Sn, and Pb, where a transition occurs from a purely covalent diamond crystal to the metallic tin. It has been noted previously that a large Δx gives rise to ionic bonding. To illustrate the relationship, graphs such as that in Fig. 7–37 for AB type compounds are most convenient. The sharp separation between the octahedrally and tetrahedrally coordinated structures is remarkable indeed. Furthermore, similar relationships are observed for other structure types, such as AB_2, AB_3, A_2B_3, etc.

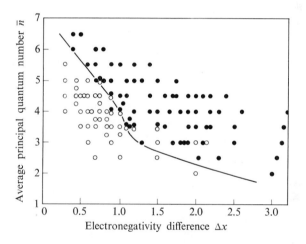

FIG. 7–37. Relationship between coordination number and $\bar{n}$ and Δx for AB type structures. The shaded circles are for crystals with octahedral coordination, and the open circles are for those exhibiting tetrahedral coordination. (E. Mooser and W. B. Pearson, reproduced from *Acta Crystallographica*, **12**, 12, 1959.)

(b) Crystal chemistry of the transition metals

As in other aspects of their chemistry, the crystal structures of transition metal compounds require special consideration because of the use, in bonding, of d-orbitals which have a principal quantum number one less than that of the valence shell. This feature has a number of interesting manifestations in crystals involving these ions, and it is the purpose of the present section to illustrate some of these.

Particularly useful for this purpose are the divalent halides of the first transition series, the majority of which assume the rutile, cadmium iodide, or cadmium

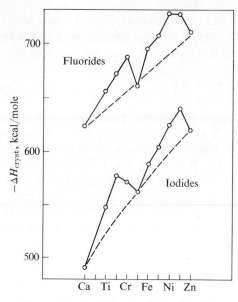

Fig. 7–38. Ionic crystal energies ($-\Delta H_{\text{cryst}}$) of the fluorides and iodides of the first transition series. The curves for the chlorides and bromides lie between those shown, and are similar in shape.

chloride structures. While there is, in these structures, octahedral coordination of the halide ions about the metal ion, this does not necessarily imply ionic bonding. On the contrary, as has been pointed out in Section 5–3(e) and Chapter 6, it is a simple matter to formulate hybrid orbitals with octahedral symmetry when d-orbitals are available for bonding. As in the discussion of the previous section concerning tetrahedral coordination, we are forced to the conclusion that structure type alone does not allow us to distinguish the type of bonding. Regardless of the bond type, it is possible, employing the usual cycles, to evaluate the experimental crystal energy as defined in Section 2–4(b). These are plotted in Fig. 7–38 as a function of atomic number. In every case the curves are double-humped ones, with minima at $Ca^{2+}(d^0)$, $Mn^{2+}(d^5)$ and $Zn^{2+}(d^{10})$.

These discontinuities can be related qualitatively to the effects of the octahedral crystal field of the anions, and to a first approximation, the treatment is a simple one. From Chapter 6, it will be recalled that in a field of octahedral symmetry the d-orbitals split into two groups according to their symmetry (see Fig. 6–14). The two e_g orbitals, being most affected by the presence of the ligands, are raised in energy by an amount Δ over that of the three orbitals of the t_{2g} group. Alternatively, if zero is defined arbitrarily as the weighted mean of the energies of the split d-orbitals, then the energy of the e_g orbitals is $+\frac{3}{5}\Delta$ and that of the t_{2g} orbitals $-\frac{2}{5}\Delta$. This zero level will not, of course, coincide with the d-orbital energy in the free ion, but is useful nevertheless because of the direct relation of Δ to both theory and experiment. On the other hand, when calculating the total crystal energies, it is the absolute energy which is of importance, and the arbitrarily defined zero must be taken into account. The difference would, however, be expected to vary continuously across the series and, since we are interested in the discontinuities, we can ignore it.

We may, therefore, estimate the *crystal-field stabilization energy* for these crystals by simply summing the energies of the electrons relative to the arbitrary zero. Since Δ is relatively small for the dihalides we are considering, they may be regarded as high-spin compounds, and the energy will vary, as in Table 7–14. The remarkable correlation between these stabilization energies and the double-humped curves makes it clear that the discontinuities find their origin in crystal-field effects. Note that, when we are considering the experimental data, it is the difference between the solid curves and the smooth dotted curves which is of significance. Even then, because of variations in Δ along the series and because of errors due to other approximations, we need not expect perfect agreement.

In crystals of the metallic elements themselves, it might be expected that the above arguments will no longer be valid because of the much greater interaction between the metal atoms. There is, nevertheless, sufficient similarity between the curves of Figs. 7–30 and 7–38 to indicate that the explanation must be much the same in the two cases.*

TABLE 7–14

CRYSTAL-FIELD STABILIZATION ENERGIES
FOR HIGH-SPIN COMPOUNDS

Number of d-electrons	Octahedral field	Tetrahedral field
1, 6	$-\frac{2}{5}\Delta$	$-\frac{3}{5}\Delta$
2, 7	$-\frac{4}{5}\Delta$	$-\frac{6}{5}\Delta$
3, 8	$-\frac{6}{5}\Delta$	$-\frac{4}{5}\Delta$
4, 9	$-\frac{3}{5}\Delta$	$-\frac{2}{5}\Delta$
5, 10	0	0

---

* For proper comparison, the curves of Fig. 7–30 should be adjusted to give the crystal energies of a lattice of divalent ions; that is,

$$-\Delta H_{\text{cryst}} = \Delta H^{\circ}_{298} + I_1 + I_2,$$

where I_1 and I_2 are the first and second ionization energies. The curves thus obtained are even more similar to those of Fig. 7–38 than the uncorrected ones. The lack of a minimum in the third transition series, corresponding to the d^5 configuration, could reasonably be explained as the result of a large Δ in those cases leading to low-spin configurations. The ligand-field stabilization energies would then increase to a maximum for the d^6 configuration, and drop to zero for d^{10} without a central minimum.

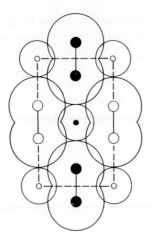

FIG. 7–39. Close-packing of the C_2^{2-} and Ca^{2+} ions
in the calcium carbide structure. Crystalline KO_2 has a
very similar structure.

The ligand-field stabilization may also be a factor in determining the crystal structure. Thus, in the first transition series, the Co^{2+} ion is the only one apart from Zn^{2+} which shows much tendency to form tetrahedral complexes. An examination of Table 7–14 reveals that the stabilization energy for tetrahedral crystal fields is a maximum for the d^7 configuration of Co^{2+}. Although the Δ for tetrahedral coordination is generally smaller than in the octahedral case, apparently it is sufficient to lead to fourfold coordination for Co^{2+}.

(c) Complex ions in crystals

Bearing in mind the nondirectional nature of coulombic forces, it is not surprising that complex ions incorporate themselves into essentially close-packed structures. In many respects, the packing is similar to that encountered in molecular crystals. With the smaller complex ions, the structures may be quite simple, like those of the alkali halides. Ammonium chloride, for example, assumes several different structures according to the temperature, among them the NaCl and CsCl configurations. The transitions are related to the degree of rotation allowed the ammonium ions.

With less symmetrical ions, the structures encountered are often arrangements of a simple type, distorted to accommodate the shape of the ion. The tetragonal structure of CaC_2 (Fig. 7–39) and the orthorhombic structure of $NaNO_2$ (Fig. 7–8) are like this. Figure 7–40 shows the packing of SO_4^{2-} ions in $CaSO_4$.

The water of crystallization, frequently incorporated into ionic crystals, may be considered in much the same light as complex ions. That hydrates are common is a result of the lone pairs on the oxygen atoms and the polarity of the O—H bond. In many structures the water molecules are grouped octahedrally or tetrahedrally about the metallic cation, presumably with lone pairs oriented toward the positively charged ion. Alternatively, the water molecules may be hydrogen bonded to an oxyanion such as SO_4^{2-} or even to other water molecules. In all cases, the preferred orientation of the water molecules implies directional forces which will, in part, determine the structure adopted. These are often quite complicated, and none will be described in detail. In hydrated acids, such as $HNO_3 \cdot H_2O$ or $H_2SO_4 \cdot H_2O$, the water of crystallization is frequently present as H_3O^+.

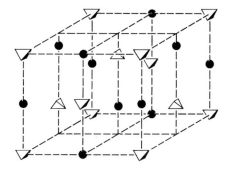

FIG. 7–40. Crystal structure of $CaSO_4$. The tetrahedra show the position and orientation of the SO_4^{2-} ions. Both the Ca^{2+} ions and the SO_4^{2-} tetrahedra are much larger, relative to the cell dimensions, than is shown.

(d) Silicates

Silicon combines with oxygen to form a group of compounds which are remarkable for the variety of physical and structural properties which they display. There is, in fact, such a bewildering array of silicates that it is only since the advent of X-ray structural analysis that a useful systematic classification has been possible. As Table 7–15 indicates, they fall into four main groups, according to whether the Si_nO_m complex is finite, or whether it extends infinitely in one dimension (chains), in two dimensions (layers), or in three dimensions (lattices). The negatively charged complex ions are then bonded together in the crystal in a complicated way through the medium of the metallic cations. Fortunately, silicates rarely contain more than one type of complex ion, but complications arise through the isomorphous replacement of silicon by Al^{3+}. In addition, it is not uncommon to find OH groups bonded to the metal ions, but not to the silicon itself.

The mineral olivine is one of the simplest silicates, and contains SiO_4^{4-} complexes and Mg^{2+} ions in a close-packed array. Several more finite complexes have been observed, including rings of varying size. The $Si_6O_{18}^{12-}$ ring in beryl is one of the larger ones, and leads to an open structure, in which helium atoms are often found trapped. (See Fig. 7–41.)

Two types of chain structures are distinguished, the simplest consisting of corner-linked tetrahedra, as in diopside (pyroxenes). If cross-linking occurs, then $Si_4O_{11}^{6-}$ chains such as those in tremolite are formed (amphiboles). Because of the relatively open framework of the chains, OH groups are often incorporated into the

280

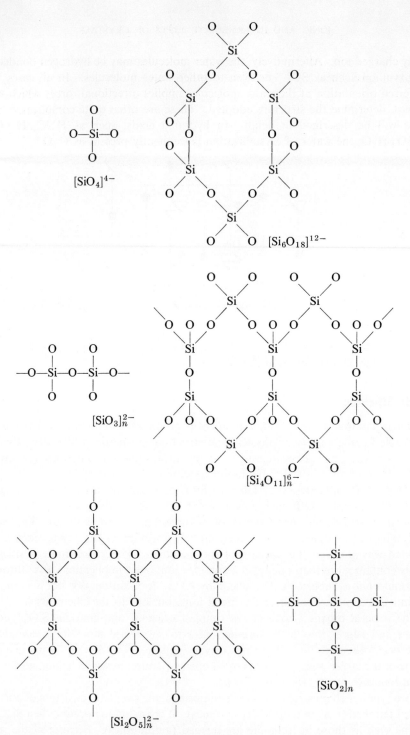

FIG. 7–41. Schematic illustration of the silicate complexes. In all cases, the coordination about the silicon atoms is approximately tetrahedral.

TABLE 7–15

CLASSIFICATION OF SILICATES

Mineral	Class	Formula	Type
Olivine	Finite complex	Mg_2SiO_4	$[SiO_4]^{4-}$
Beryl	Finite complex	$Be_3Al_2(Si_6O_{18})$	$[Si_6O_{18}]^{12-}$
Diopside	Chains	$CaMg(SiO_3)_2$	$[SiO_3]_n^{2-}$
Tremolite	Chains	$Ca_2Mg_5(Si_4O_{11})_2(OH)_2$	$[Si_4O_{11}]_n^{6-}$
Talc	Layers	$Mg_3(Si_2O_5)_2(OH)_2$	$[Si_2O_5]_n^{2-}$
Muscovite	Layers	$KAl_2(Si_3AlO_{10})(OH)_2$	$[Si_2O_5]_n^{2-}$
Quartz	Lattice	SiO_2	$[SiO_2]_n$
Orthoclase	Lattice	$KAlSi_3O_8$	$[SiO_2]_n$

structure. Asbestos, like the pyroxenes and amphiboles, displays a fibrous cleavage, but its structure is unknown.

If the cross-linking of the amphibole chains is extended indefinitely, then layers are formed with the composition $Si_2O_5^{2-}$. Each silicon in the hexagonal rings of the layers is then linked through oxygens to three other silicon atoms. Talc and muscovite mica are typical of the layer-type silicates, although in the latter case one silicon in four is replaced by an Al^{3+} ion, so that the repeating unit is actually $Si_3AlO_{10}^{5-}$. The reasons for the pseudo-hexagonal symmetry of muscovite and its pronounced lamellar cleavage are now apparent. Apart from the numerous packing arrangements possible for the layers, variations are observed in the layers themselves. The mineral apophyllite, for example, has layers with alternate four- and eight-membered rings.

Extension of the cross-linking in three dimensions gives silica, with the formula SiO_2^0, but even here many variations are possible. Three major types are distinguished: quartz, tridymite, and cristobalite, with minor modifications of each of these in their low (α) and high (β) temperature forms. The tridymite and cristobalite structures are similar to the wurtzite and zincblende forms of zinc sulfide. The SiO_2 complex is, of course, uncharged, but the replacement of the silicon by Al^{3+} leaves excess charge on the silica framework. This occurs in the feldspars, of which orthoclase ($KAlSi_3O_8$) and anorthite ($CaAl_2Si_2O_8$) are typical.

BIBLIOGRAPHY

A

BIJVOET, J. M., N. H. KOLKMEYER, and C. H. MACGILLAVRY, *X-ray Analysis of Crystals*. London: Butterworth, 1951.

COULSON, C. A., *Valence*. New York: Oxford, 1961.

DAY, M., and J. Selbin, *Theoretical Inorganic Chemistry*. New York: Reinhold, 1962.

EMELEUS, H. J., and J. S. ANDERSON, *Modern Aspects of Inorganic Chemistry*. London: Routledge and Kegan Paul, 1952.

HESLOP, R. B., and P. L. ROBINSON, *Inorganic Chemistry*. Amsterdam: Elsevier, 1960.

KETELAAR, J. A. A., *Chemical Constitution*. Amsterdam: Elsevier, 1960.

MOELWYN-HUGHES, E. A., *States of Matter*. London: Oliver and Boyd, 1961.

ORGEL, L. E., *Transition-Metal Chemistry*. London: Methuen, 1958.

PAULING, L., *The Nature of the Chemical Bond*. Ithaca, New York: Cornell, 1960.

VAN ARKEL, A. E., *Molecules and Crystals*. London: Butterworth, 1956.

WELLS, A. F., *The Third Dimension in Chemistry*. New York: Oxford, 1956.

WHEATLEY, P. J., *Molecular Structure*. New York: Oxford, 1959.

B

EVANS, R. C., *An Introduction to Crystal Chemistry*. New York: Cambridge, 1962.

KITTEL, C., *Introduction to Solid-State Physics*. New York: Wiley, 1956.

PEARSON, W. B., *Lattice Spacings and Structures of Metals and Alloys*. London: Pergamon, 1958.

SEITZ, F., *Modern Theory of Solids*. New York: McGraw-Hill, 1940.

SUTTON, L. E., *Tables of Interatomic Distances and Configuration in Molecules and Ions*. London: Chemical Society, 1958.

WADDINGTON, T. C., "Lattice Energies and Their Significance in Organic Chemistry," *Advances in Inorganic Chemistry and Radiochemistry*, Vol. 1. New York: Academic Press, 1959.

WANNIER, G. H., *Solid State Theory*. New York: Cambridge, 1959.

WELLS, A. F., *Structural Inorganic Chemistry*. New York: Oxford, 1961.

WYCKOFF, R. W. G., *Crystal Structures*. New York: Interscience.

PROBLEMS

7–1. Illustrate the primitive unit cells for (a) the sodium chloride structure and (b) a body-centered cubic structure such as that of sodium metal. What is the symmetry of the lattice corresponding to these primitive cells?

7–2. Show that monoclinic and tetragonal C-lattices are equivalent to simpler lattice types. Why is there not a cubic C-lattice?

7–3. Calculate the efficiency of packing in the HCP, CCP, and body-centered cubic structures; i.e., the ratio of the unit cell volume to the volume of spheres. Show that the axial ratio c/a for perfect HCP is 1.63.

7–4. While slightly less efficient than CCP, the body-centered cubic structure is still a common form of packing. Illustrate the relationship between the two types of structure by showing that a larger face-centered (pseudo-cubic) cell may be chosen for the BCC structure. What is the true symmetry of the alternative cell?

7–5. Calculate the radius of the spheres which may be accommodated in the tetrahedral and octahedral holes of a CCP structure of spheres of radius r.

7–6. Explain why, despite the stronger hydrogen bond, HF has a smaller ΔH_{vap} than H_2O.

7–7. Noting in Table 7–5 that only a small part of the total cohesion energy of H_2O is involved in the fusion process, suggest an explanation for the fact that the density of ice is less than that of water.

7–8. There is some evidence to indicate that an ordered structure Au_3Cu is also formed in the copper–gold system. What structure would you expect the alloy to have?

7–9. Prepare graphs similar to that of Fig. 7–30 for (a) the internuclear distance s_e, and (b) the mp of the metals. Compare with Fig. 7–30.

7–10. Calculate the crystal energies (Born-Mayer) for the cuprous and silver halides of Table 7–13. Compare your results with the experimental crystal energies, and suggest a qualitative explanation for the discrepancies.

CHAPTER EIGHT

Thermodynamics

The science of thermodynamics concerns the chemical and physical processes which involve the conversion of energy among its various forms. It is developed mathematically on the basis of a number of postulates which have been thoroughly supported by experiment. Although its application to chemical processes is quite general, thermodynamics is not at all concerned with either the time element (rate of a process) or the detailed path (mechanism of a process). This is not to say that thermodynamics is not important in the latter cases, because it is futile to inquire into either the rate or mechanism of a reaction that simply cannot occur to any appreciable extent on a thermodynamic (or energetic) basis.

In the present context, the mathematical development of thermodynamics will not be used, except in certain special cases. Instead, the intent of this chapter is to develop in the reader a "feeling" for thermodynamics. Many of its concepts are difficult to grasp, particularly if they are treated in a mathematical sense at first meeting. We shall assume in the following that the idea of temperature is understood, despite the fact that the precise meaning of temperature in thermodynamics bears no direct relation to definitions found in a dictionary.

8–1. EQUILIBRIUM

Of fundamental importance to thermodynamics is the concept of the equilibrium state. Thermodynamic equilibrium in the true sense refers to a condition in which the properties of a system are absolutely unchanging with time such that, if the

284

system is disturbed slightly in some way, it will return to essentially the same condition after the disturbing force is removed. This latter criterion may differentiate between a true state of equilibrium and a metastable one. If a metastable equilibrium is disturbed, as, for example, by introduction of a catalyst or by local heating, it may spontaneously undergo a drastic change to some new state.

Consider a container filled with chlorine gas. Provided that the container is sealed and thermally insulated from its surroundings, a state of true thermodynamic equilibrium will be established in which the temperature and pressure are uniform. If we disturb the system by shining a light on it, some of the chlorine molecules will absorb radiation and dissociate into atoms. When we turn off the light, the chlorine atoms recombine and the system, except for the addition of a small amount of energy from the light beam, returns to its original condition.

By way of contrast, a mixture of hydrogen and chlorine is metastable. Although chlorine and hydrogen react with one another at room temperature, the rate is so slow as to be virtually undetectable. Hence the system seems to behave in just the same way as the pure chlorine system, in that uniform temperature and pressure are established. However, if we direct a beam of light through this mixture, it explodes, forming hydrogen chloride and evolving a large amount of heat. After being disturbed in this way, the system cannot revert spontaneously to its original condition. In fact, the change which does occur (the explosion) is toward a state of true thermodynamic equilibrium.

Although thermodynamics cannot deal with the rate at which reactions occur, it does establish the direction in which a reaction can proceed. Metastable or unstable compounds can be treated by the methods of thermodynamics, provided that they have a lifetime sufficiently long for thermodynamic measurements to be made. This requirement may vary, depending on the type of experiment, from a minute fraction of a second to hours, or even days. In this regard, we can make the distinction between a substance which exists by virtue of its thermodynamic stability (discussed in a later section), or by reason only of its slow rate of reaction or decomposition. We shall reserve the word stable for the first case, while the second will be described as an *inert* substance.

There is a wide range in degree of inertness of unstable systems. Diamond, on the one hand, is inert to the extent that there is no observable conversion (under ordinary conditions) to the stable state of graphite. At the other extreme are such unstable substances as a supercooled liquid, or a sensitive explosive. In either of these cases only a slight perturbation is necessary to change these systems drastically; it would obviously be improper to call them inert. Lewis and Randall, in their classic treatment of thermodynamics, found that water and air, although inert, are thermodynamically unstable with respect to the formation of nitric acid. They conclude: "It is to be hoped that nature will not discover a catalyst for this reaction, which would permit all of the oxygen and part of the nitrogen of the air to turn the oceans into dilute nitric acid."

Those substances which are quite inert chemically can generally be treated by the methods of thermodynamics. As an example, both NO and NO_2 are unstable with respect to decomposition into their elements, yet we can not only consider the reaction

$$2NO_2 \rightleftharpoons 2NO + O_2 \qquad (8-1)$$

but also study the equilibrium by a direct experiment. The practical criterion is that those processes which lead to negligible change during the time required for thermodynamic measurements can be ignored. In the case of the reaction of Eq. (8-1), the processes of decomposition of NO_2 and of NO into oxygen and nitrogen can be completely neglected.

(a) Quantitative aspects of equilibrium

Thermodynamics is most useful when it provides quantitative information. However, even crude information can be put to good use in some cases, so that later on we shall study in some detail useful methods of estimating thermodynamic parameters. Some data can even be calculated theoretically from molecular constants far more accurately than they can be measured by direct experiment. Our approach here will be largely empirical and based on experimental studies, because it is not intended, nor would it be desirable at this stage, to present a rigorous mathematical development of thermodynamics.

One of the simplest, yet nontrivial, equilibrium systems to deal with is that of a pure compound existing in two phases, such as the vapor of water in equilibrium with the liquid. It is observed experimentally that at a fixed uniform temperature there is a characteristic pressure of water vapor, the vapor pressure. Thus, at 10°C, water vapor in equilibrium with liquid water exerts a pressure of 9.209 mm Hg (0.0121 atmospheres). If the containing vessel is suddenly expanded, there will be a momentary decrease in pressure, but some of the liquid will rapidly evaporate and, provided there is still some liquid left and the temperature is constant, the same vapor pressure will be established. Conversely, if the volume of the vessel is rapidly decreased, the pressure will increase, but will be immediately compensated for by some condensation of vapor, so that again the same vapor pressure will be found. This system fits the basic criterion of equilibrium: that the equilibrium pressure obtained is the same whether we start from nonequilibrium states which have higher or lower pressure.

It is true, however, that the vapor pressure changes with temperature. This behavior, to be explored in a later section, will provide an important basis for the thermodynamic treatment of equilibria.

We now move on to examine a chemical equilibrium, that between nitrogen dioxide and its dimer, nitrogen tetroxide, both in the gas phase. The chemical equation for the reaction is

$$N_2O_4(g) \rightleftharpoons 2NO_2(g). \qquad (8-2)$$

This is a particularly mobile equilibrium which is often investigated qualitatively in undergraduate chemistry laboratories. In Table 8-1, a random selection of the

TABLE 8–1

EXPERIMENTAL VALUES OF K_p FOR THE EQUILIBRIUM
BETWEEN NITROGEN DIOXIDE AND NITROGEN TETROXIDE AT 298°K
(by Verhoek and Daniels, 1931)

Total pressure, atmospheres	K_p
0.1566	0.1380
0.2118	0.1419
0.3357	0.1349
0.3941	0.1340
0.4369	0.1265
0.4843	0.1290
0.5443	0.1274
0.6007	0.1272
0.6543	0.1325
0.8081	0.1236

extensive data of Verhoek and Daniels (1931) is given for this reaction at 298°K. The experiments were performed by expanding a weighed amount of a mixture into a carefully thermostated glass bulb of accurately known volume. The total pressure in the system was measured after no further change could be detected. The data fit reasonably well an equation of the form

$$K_p = \frac{4P\alpha^2}{1 - \alpha^2},$$ (8–3)

in which P is the total measured pressure and α is given by

$$\alpha = \frac{P - p^{\circ}_{N_2O_4}}{p^{\circ}_{N_2O_4}}.$$ (8–4)

The pressure that would be obtained if no dissociation occurred, $p^{\circ}_{N_2O_4}$, is calculated from the weight taken and the volume and temperature of the system, using the ideal gas law. Analysis of the data in this form yields K_p, the *equilibrium constant*. Equation (8–3) can be converted to the more familiar form

$$K_p = \frac{p^2_{NO_2}}{p_{N_2O_4}},$$ (8–5)

in terms of the partial pressures of the two components. Some of the data are shown in Fig. 8–1, with the mole fraction of nitrogen dioxide, x_{NO_2}, plotted

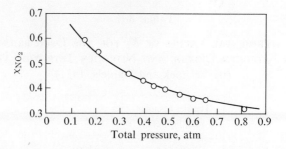

FIG. 8–1. Mole fraction of NO_2 (x_{NO_2}) as a function of pressure in equilibrium mixtures of NO_2 and N_2O_4 at 298°K.

against the total pressure. The line is given by the equation

$$K_p = \frac{x_{NO_2}^2 P}{1 - x_{NO_2}}, \tag{8–6}$$

which can be obtained directly from Eq. (8–5).

It is frequently convenient to deal with concentrations of gases rather than with partial pressures. We can convert Eq. (8–5) to concentration units (moles/liter) with the ideal gas law

$$[NO_2] = \frac{p_{NO_2}}{RT}, \tag{8–7}$$

$$[N_2O_4] = \frac{p_{N_2O_4}}{RT}, \tag{8–8}$$

in which R is the gas constant (see Appendix I). Substitution of these expressions into Eq. (8–5) gives, on rearrangement,

$$\frac{K_p}{RT} = K_c = \frac{[NO_2]^2}{[N_2O_4]}. \tag{8–9}$$

The new equilibrium constant K_c, which describes the equilibrium in terms of concentrations, is related in this case to K_p by the factor RT, in appropriate units.

In the general case, for the reaction

$$aA + bB + \cdots \rightleftharpoons xX + yY + \cdots. \tag{8–10}$$

The *Law of Mass Action* leads to the equilibrium constants

$$K_p = \frac{p_X^x p_Y^y \cdots}{p_A^a p_B^b \cdots} \tag{8–11}$$

and

$$K_c = \frac{[X]^x[Y]^y \cdots}{[A]^a[B]^b \cdots}.$$ (8-12)

Further, K_p and K_c are related by

$$K_p = (RT)^{\Delta n}K_c,$$ (8-13)

in which Δn is the difference between the number of moles (of gas) of product and of reactant in Eq. (8-10). In the example of the nitrogen oxide equilibrium, Eq. (8-2), Δn is 1.

Now consider a heterogeneous equilibrium, that between solid graphite, carbon dioxide and carbon monoxide:

$$C(graphite) + CO_2 \rightleftharpoons 2CO.$$ (8-14)

Application of Eq. (8-11) gives the expression

$$K_p = \frac{p_{CO}^2}{p_{CO_2}}$$ (8-15)

for the equilibrium constant. Graphite is not included in the equilibrium expression because its concentration is not a variable, even though its presence is demanded for the establishment of equilibrium. Therefore, at a particular temperature, one partial pressure uniquely determines the other partial pressure. At 900°C, K_p is 14.11, for partial pressure measured in atmospheres. The variation of the partial pressures with total pressure of carbon monoxide, and of carbon dioxide in equilibrium with graphite, at this temperature, is shown in Fig. 8-2.

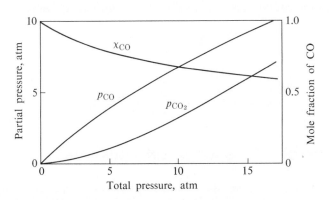

FIG. 8–2. Experimental data for the equilibrium $C(graphite) + CO_2 \rightleftharpoons 2CO$. The mole fraction of CO (X_{CO}) and the partial pressures of CO (p_{CO}) and CO_2 (p_{CO_2}) are shown as a function of total pressure.

The mole fraction of carbon monoxide, also given in Fig. 8–2, changes with pressure in the same way as that of nitrogen dioxide in Fig. 8–1, as it must, since the form of the equilibrium constant expression is the same [compare Eqs. (8–5) and (8–15)]. It is in general true that, in heterogeneous equilibria, pure components in condensed phases do not appear in the equilibrium expression.

Compare, for example, the following two equilibria:

$$2CoTe(s) + Te_2(g) \rightleftharpoons 2CoTe_2(s)$$

and

$$2Cu_2O(s) + O_2(g) \rightleftharpoons 4CuO(s).$$

The first has only one solid phase, whose composition can vary from 50 atom percent Te (CoTe) to 66.7 atom percent Te (CoTe$_2$), while in the second, two distinct, essentially pure phases are formed, Cu$_2$O and CuO. At a fixed temperature, the equilibrium pressure of tellurium vapor is a function of the extent of reaction, i.e., of the composition of the single solid phase. However, as long as both Cu$_2$O and CuO phases are present in the second equilibrium, the oxygen pressure is fixed only by the temperature, and remains constant regardless of the relative amounts of the two solid phases.

In solution reactions (discussed more fully in later chapters), it is common practice to omit the solvent concentration from the equilibrium expression, on the basis that if the solution is dilute, the concentration of the solvent does not change appreciably, even if it partakes of the equilibrium. Thus, the equilibrium involving hydrogen and hydroxyl ions in water is represented by

$$K = [H^+][OH^-], \tag{8–16}$$

even though the equilibrium could be written in several equivalent forms:

$$H_2O \rightleftharpoons H^+ + OH^-,$$

$$2H_2O \rightleftharpoons H_3O^+ + OH^-, \tag{8–17}$$

$$(m + n)\,H_2O \rightleftharpoons H_{2m+1}O_m^+ + O_nH_{2n-1}^-.$$

8–2. EFFECT OF TEMPERATURE ON EQUILIBRIA

We have specified that the equilibrium constants are indeed constant for a given chemical equation and a given set of units, but that their numerical values change with temperature. Our purpose now is to examine this temperature dependence, which is of far-reaching significance.

TABLE 8–2

VAPOR PRESSURE OF WATER

T, °K	Pressure, mm Hg
283	9.21
293	17.54
303	31.82
313	55.32
323	92.51
333	149.4
343	233.7
353	355.1
363	525.8
373	760.0

The dependence of the vapor pressure of water on temperature provides an instructive approach to the problem. Table 8–2 gives the vapor pressures at a series of temperatures. These vapor pressures are plotted in Fig. 8–3, from which it should be clear that although the vapor pressure is not directly proportional to the temperature, the two are in some way related mathematically. In fact, it has long been known that if, as shown in Fig. 8–4, the logarithm of the vapor pressure is plotted against the reciprocal of the absolute temperature T, the resulting data lie on a reasonably straight line, even for extended temperature ranges. Mathematically this means that

$$\ln P = \frac{a}{T} + b. \tag{8–18}$$

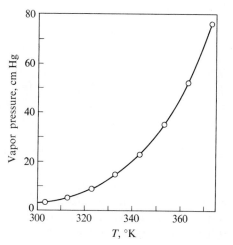

FIG. 8–3. Vapor pressure of water as a function of temperature. Data are from Table 8–2.

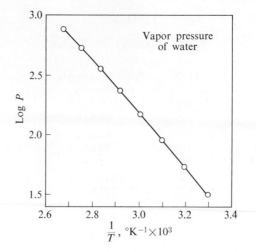

FIG. 8–4.   Logarithmic plot of the vapor pressure of water.

Furthermore, it is found that the slope of the line a and the enthalpy of the reaction ΔH_{vap} are simply related, according to the equation

$$\Delta H_{vap} = -Ra,$$

so that

$$\ln P = \frac{-\Delta H_{vap}}{RT} + b. \tag{8–19}$$

From Fig. 8–4, the slope is seen to be $-4{,}970°$, and with $R = 1.9872$ cal/mole-deg we obtain

$$\Delta H_{vap} = 9880 \text{ cal/mole}.$$

This is to be compared with the experimental value of 9705 cal/mole measured at the normal boiling point by calorimetry.

While we may quite legitimately regard the relationship of Eq. (8–19) as empirical, it may also be derived from the fundamental principles of thermodynamics. We do not propose to derive it from first principles, but it can be seen to be an immediate consequence of the equation

$$\frac{dP}{dT} = \frac{\Delta H_{vap}}{T \, \Delta V}, \tag{8–20}$$

due to Clapeyron. In the present example, the volume change attendant on the transition is, to a first approximation, equal to the volume of the vapor formed (30,165 ml/mole); i.e., we may neglect the volume of liquid (18.80 ml/mole).

Then, assuming the vapor to be an ideal gas, we obtain

$$\frac{1}{P}\frac{dP}{dT} = \frac{\Delta H_{vap}}{RT^2}$$

or

$$\frac{d\ln P}{dT} = \frac{\Delta H_{vap}}{RT^2}. \tag{8–21}$$

This equation, the Clausius-Clapeyron equation, may now be integrated to give

$$\ln P = \frac{-\Delta H_{vap}}{RT} + \text{const}, \tag{8–22}$$

which is of the same form as Eq. (8–19). The error of about two percent in the value of ΔH_{vap} given by the Clausius-Clapeyron equation can be traced to approximately equal contributions from the nonideality of the vapor and the neglect of the liquid volume. If Eq. (8–20) is used directly, then a value of 9736 cal/mole is obtained for the enthalpy of vaporization. This is within the experimental error of the calorimetric value.

While we are discussing the dependence on temperature of the vapor pressure of water, we recall that in this case $P_{vap} = K_p$. We then inquire whether the relationship described might be true for equilibrium constants generally. This is, in fact, found to be the case [see Eq. (8–21)] and in the form

$$\frac{d\ln K_p}{dT} = \frac{\Delta H}{RT^2},$$

it is known as the Van't Hoff equation. When integrated, the Van't Hoff equation gives

$$\ln K_p = -\frac{\Delta H}{RT} + \text{const}. \tag{8–23}$$

The usefulness of the Van't Hoff equation may be illustrated by the example given in the previous section, the equilibrium between NO_2 and N_2O_4. In Table 8–3 are shown some of the data obtained by Bodenstein and his coworkers (1922) for the equilibrium constant at a series of temperatures. These fit the equation (Fig. 8–5)

$$\ln K_p = \frac{-6.80 \times 10^4}{T} + 20.84. \tag{8–24}$$

In this case, the slope is again related to the standard enthalpy change of the reaction at the temperature at which the slope is measured. Such treatments do not, in fact, show exactly a straight-line dependence, because the enthalpy change itself is a function of temperature. However, over a narrow temperature range such as that considered here, ΔH is essentially constant. From the slope in Fig. 8–5,

TABLE 8–3

THE EQUILIBRIUM CONSTANT FOR THE NITROGEN DIOXIDE–NITROGEN TETROXIDE SYSTEM AS A FUNCTION OF TEMPERATURE
(by Bodenstein and Boës, 1922)

$T°K$	Log K_p	$T°K$	Log K_p
281.82	−1.449	324.15	−0.036
285.83	−1.273	334.88	0.255
288.85	−1.197	339.54	0.379
293.05	−1.022	343.41	0.474
302.07	−0.729	353.21	0.709
305.97	−0.587	361.96	0.903
315.95	−0.284	366.84	1.024

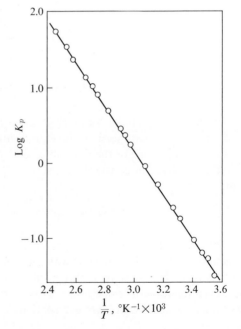

FIG. 8–5. Temperature dependence of the equilibrium constant (K_p) for the equilibrium $N_2O_4 \rightleftharpoons 2NO_2$. Data are from Table 8–3.

ΔH is found to be 13,500 cal (13.5 kcal). A slightly larger value ($\Delta H^\circ = 13.87$ kcal) is obtained when the nonideal behavior of the gases is taken into account by extrapolating the equilibrium constants found at each temperature to zero pressure. [See Section 8–4(a) and Problem 8–7.]

Thus, thermochemical data can be derived from equilibrium studies without recourse to calorimetric measurements, which in many cases would be difficult to make. The enthalpy change found in this way is that for the reaction with all reactants and products in their standard states, that is, ΔH° when the zero-pressure equilibrium constants are employed. If the equilibrium constant K_c [Eq. (8–9)] were used instead, the slope would yield the internal energy change, ΔU°.

It will be observed that the dependence of the equilibrium constant on temperature is in agreement with the qualitative predictions of Le Chatelier's principle. Furthermore, the relationship between the equilibrium constant and the heat of reaction is in accord with our previous remarks concerning the energetics of chemical reactions. Thus we find that an exothermic reaction should have a numerically large equilibrium constant, favoring the chemical reaction as written. Similarly, an endothermic reaction, in which the products lie at a higher energy than the reactants, should be associated with a small equilibrium constant. Hence, other things being equal, an exothermic reaction will proceed more readily on a thermodynamic basis than will an endothermic reaction. However, the "other things" are not always "equal," as will be seen in the following section.

8–3. ENTROPY

That the enthalpy change in a reaction does not uniquely determine the equilibrium constant is readily illustrated. Consider the three equilibria

$$2NH_3(g) \rightleftharpoons N_2(g) + 3H_2(g), \tag{8–25}$$

$$SO_3(g) \rightleftharpoons SO_2(g) + \tfrac{1}{2}O_2(g), \tag{8–26}$$

$$HCl(g) \rightleftharpoons \tfrac{1}{2}H_2(g) + \tfrac{1}{2}Cl_2(g). \tag{8–27}$$

Although they are all endothermic to approximately the same extent (22.08, 23.49, and 22.06 kcal, respectively), the equilibrium constants are entirely different, as is shown in Table 8–4 and illustrated in Fig. 8–6. These equilibrium constants cover a range of eleven powers of ten, clearly demonstrating the fact that the enthalpy alone does not determine the value of the equilibrium constant. In addition, if we compare the reaction of Eq. (8–25) with the following two reactions,

$$NO_2(g) \rightleftharpoons NO(g) + \tfrac{1}{2}O_2(g), \tag{8–28}$$

$$H_2S(g) \rightleftharpoons H_2(g) + S(s), \tag{8–29}$$

we find (Table 8–4) that these have the same equilibrium constant within a factor

TABLE 8–4

CHEMICAL EQUILIBRIA AT 298°K

Reaction	K_p	$\Delta H°$, kcal	$\Delta S°$, cal/deg
$2NH_3(g) \rightleftharpoons N_2(g) + 3H_2(g)$	1.5×10^{-6}	22.08	47.4
$SO_3(g) \rightleftharpoons SO_2(g) + \frac{1}{2}O_2(g)$	5.5×10^{-13}	23.49	22.6
$HCl(g) \rightleftharpoons \frac{1}{2}H_2(g) + \frac{1}{2}Cl_2(g)$	2.0×10^{-17}	22.06	-2.37
$NO_2(g) \rightleftharpoons NO(g) + \frac{1}{2}O_2(g)$	0.8×10^{-6}	13.51	17.4
$H_2S(g) \rightleftharpoons H_2(g) + S(s)$	1.7×10^{-6}	4.82	-10.3
$\frac{1}{2}N_2(g) + \frac{1}{2}O_2(g) + \frac{1}{2}Cl_2(g) \rightleftharpoons NOCl(g)$	2.4×10^{-12}	12.57	-11.1
$N_2(g) + 2O_2(g) \rightleftharpoons N_2O_4(g)$	6.0×10^{-18}	2.31	-71.0

of two, despite the fact that they are endothermic by quite different extents. This point is illustrated in Fig. 8–6. By the time we include the additional equilibria,

$$\tfrac{1}{2}N_2(g) + \tfrac{1}{2}O_2(g) + \tfrac{1}{2}Cl_2(g) \rightleftharpoons NOCl(g), \qquad (8\text{–}30)$$

$$N_2(g) + 2O_2(g) \rightleftharpoons N_2O_4(g), \qquad (8\text{–}31)$$

in Fig. 8–6, there can be no question that there is no direct correlation between $\Delta H°$ and K_p or $\log K_p$. The relationship between $\log K_p$ and $1/T$ for the individual equilibria is shown in Fig. 8–7.

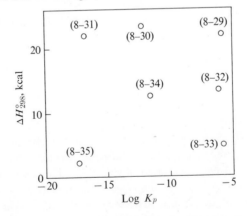

FIG. 8–6. Enthalpy changes and $\log K_p$ for reactions (8–25) to (8–31). Data are from Table 8–4.

From these examples, it is quite apparent that the integration constant of Eq. (8–23) can be very important in determining the value of the equilibrium constant. Examination of Eq. (8–23) shows that it is equal to $\ln K_p$ when $1/T = 0$,

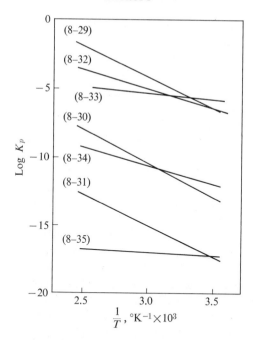

Fig. 8–7. Temperature dependence of the equilibrium constants of reactions (8–25) to (8–31). Data are from Table 8–4.

and may readily be evaluated by graphical or analytical extrapolation of the $\ln K_p$ versus $1/T$ straight line to $1/T = 0$. More important, however, is the fact that the intercept so obtained is related to a fundamental quantity, the *entropy* change $\Delta S°$, by the equation

$$\text{const} = \frac{\Delta S°}{R}.$$

Combining this with Eq. (8–23) gives

$$\ln K_p = -\frac{\Delta H°}{RT} + \frac{\Delta S°}{R},$$

or

$$RT \ln K_p = -\Delta H° + T\,\Delta S°. \qquad (8\text{–}32)$$

According to this equation, the equilibrium constant is determined by three parameters: temperature, enthalpy change and entropy change. In Table 8–4 we list, for each of the reactions discussed above, the values of $\Delta S°$ as well as the equilibrium constant and enthalpy change at $298.15°K$.

The equilibrium constant is completely determined by the enthalpy and entropy changes at a particular temperature, as is shown in Eq. (8–32). It is important in dealing with these thermodynamic quantities to have a feeling for the effect of the magnitude of each on the value of the equilibrium constant. At 298°K, Eq. (8–32) can be put in the following form:

$$\log_{10} K_p = \frac{-\Delta H^\circ}{1.364} + \frac{\Delta S^\circ}{4.57}, \tag{8–33}$$

with ΔH° measured in kcal and ΔS° in cal/deg.

Consider now a hypothetical reaction in which both ΔH° and ΔS° are zero. This would mean, in turn, that K_p is unity. Now if we imagine the reaction to become endothermic, then K_p will decrease by a factor of ten for each 1.364 kcal the reaction is endothermic; for example, K_p would be 10^{-10} if ΔH° were 13.64 kcal. Similarly, if we fix ΔH° at zero, and consider a negative entropy change, then K_p is reduced by a factor of ten for each 4.57 cal/deg. Also K_p becomes greater than unity by the same factors if ΔH° is made negative and ΔS° is made positive. Therefore, an exothermicity of 13.64 kcal, for example, is just balanced by an entropy change of -45.7 cal/deg, and K_p would still be unity. These conclusions are valid at the temperature chosen, 298°K. Qualitatively, it can be seen from a consideration of Eq. (8–32) that at very high temperatures, the entropy change becomes very important, since the first term involving ΔH° is divided by T.

The entropy changes given in Table 8–4 are state functions, just as are enthalpy changes; both are independent of the path by which the reaction is carried out. Hence for a given reaction there is a unique value of ΔS°, provided only that the initial and final conditions are specified. One of the major conceptual difficulties concerning entropy is that if the entropy change of the surroundings of the system is included (as, for example, a water bath in which the reaction is carried out), the total entropy change is either zero or greater than zero. Unlike enthalpy (energy), entropy is not necessarily conserved in an overall process.* Only if a process is carried out reversibly (continuously at equilibrium) is the total entropy change zero. A reversible process cannot occur in nature, but it can be conceived in principle, just as an ideal gas can be conceived. For our present purpose, we can ignore this feature of entropy, since we shall only be concerned with the entropy change in a chemical reaction without regard for the associated entropy changes in the surroundings.

(a) Temperature dependence of entropy and enthalpy

It is convenient to choose for the entropy scale a rather different type of zero than that used for enthalpy. This convention is to assign zero entropy to all perfect crystalline substances, both elements and compounds, at the absolute zero of temperature. The reason for doing this will become apparent as we develop further the concept of entropy.

---

* *Die Energie der Welt ist konstant; die Entropie der Welt strebt einem Maximum zu.* ... "The energy of the world is constant; the entropy of the world tends toward a maximum." (Clausius, 1867).

Entropies at temperatures other than absolute zero can be obtained experimentally from the heat capacity measured as a function of temperature, and from the enthalpy changes associated with phase changes.

The heat capacity at constant pressure, C_p, is defined by the expression:

$$C_p = (\partial H/\partial T)_p \qquad (8\text{–}34)$$

which can be integrated to give

$$H_{T_2} - H_{T_1} = \int_{T_1}^{T_2} C_p \, dT. \qquad (8\text{–}35)$$

Hence the change in enthalpy between two temperatures is just equivalent to the area under a plot of C_p versus temperature between the limits T_1 and T_2. The experimental heat capacity of hydrogen chloride is shown in Fig. 8–8, except the region below 17°K, which is found by extrapolation with a theoretical equation. The discontinuities are characteristic of phase changes. At 98°K, the sudden increase in the heat capacity is associated with the difference between solid I and solid II (see Chapter 7). The transition at 158°K is associated with melting and that at 188°K is vaporization at the normal boiling point. At each of these discontinuities, the heat capacity is infinite, because there is an enthalpy change at constant temperature. This feature is shown in Fig. 8–9, which is the integral of the curve in Fig. 8–8, with the various enthalpies of transition added. This enthalpy is, of course, relative to the enthalpy at absolute zero.

The entropy is also related to the heat capacity of a pure substance by the equation

$$(\partial S/\partial T)_p = C_p/T, \qquad (8\text{–}36)$$

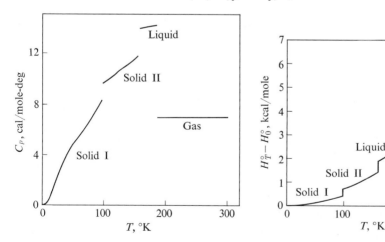

FIG. 8–8. Constant pressure heat capacity of HCl (C_p) as a function of temperature.

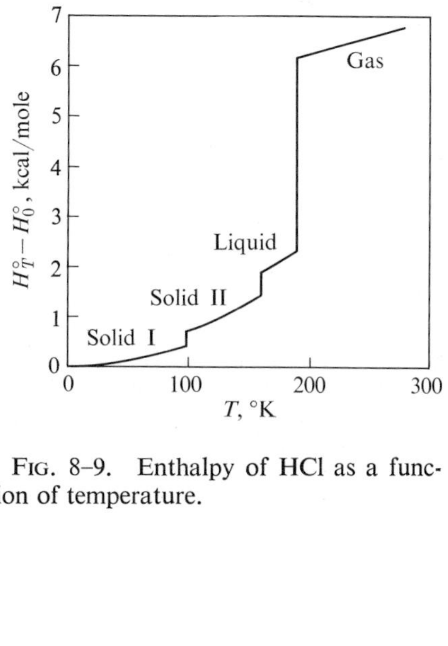

FIG. 8–9. Enthalpy of HCl as a function of temperature.

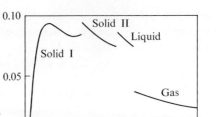

FIG. 8–10.   The function C_p/T for HCl plotted as a function of temperature.

or, in integrated form:

$$S_T - S_0 = S_T = \int_0^T (C_p/T)\, dT. \tag{8–37}$$

The function C_p/T for hydrogen chloride, Fig. 8–10, can be integrated graphically to obtain Fig. 8–11, showing the entropy of hydrogen chloride at one atmosphere pressure as a function of temperature.   There is nothing unique about the shape of the curves in Figs. 8–7 to 8–11 except for the fact that the enthalpy and entropy always increase with increasing temperature.   For the general case, the enthalpy is given by

$$H_T - H_0 = \int_0^{T_1} C_p\, dT + \Delta H_1 + \int_{T_1}^{T_2} C_p\, dT + \Delta H_2 + \cdots, \tag{8–38}$$

and the entropy by

$$S_T = \int_0^{T_1} \frac{C_p}{T}\, dT + \Delta S_1 + \int_{T_1}^{T_2} \frac{C_p}{T}\, dT + \Delta S_2 + \cdots, \tag{8–39}$$

in which, for each transition, $\Delta S_i = \Delta H_i / T_i$.

The entropies determined in this way relative to the value zero at $0°K$ are frequently called *absolute entropies*.   Although there is some justification for this name, it is preferable simply to refer to them as entropies without any connotation of their being absolute values.   Appendix II contains a list of entropies of elements and compounds evaluated in this way or by other methods.   Entropies of formation are not given directly for compounds, but can be calculated directly from the data given.   Thus the entropy of formation of hydrogen chloride at $298.15°K$ is

$$\Delta S_f^\circ(\text{HCl, g}) = S^\circ(\text{HCl, g}) - \tfrac{1}{2}S^\circ(\text{H}_2, \text{g}) - \tfrac{1}{2}S^\circ(\text{Cl}_2, \text{g}). \tag{8–40}$$

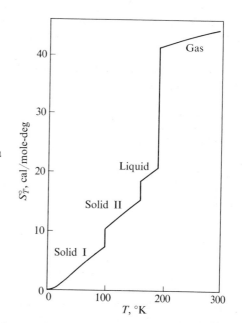

FIG. 8-11. Entropy of HCl as a function of temperature.

For a general reaction $\big($Eq. (8-10)$\big)$, the standard entropy change can be calculated from

$$\Delta S^\circ = xS^\circ(X) + yS^\circ(Y) + \cdots - aS^\circ(A) - bS^\circ(B) \cdots. \qquad (8\text{-}41)$$

Because of the difference in the conventions of zero for entropy and enthalpy, care must be taken in calculations based on tabulated thermodynamic data such as those in Appendix II. While the enthalpies of elements in their standard states are zero, and enthalpies of formation of compounds may be positive or negative, entropies of elements and of compounds are always greater than zero (except at 0°K).

Although the enthalpy (and internal energy) of a gas does not change appreciably with pressure or volume, the entropy does. If the standard molar entropy is denoted by S° for a gas at one atmosphere pressure and 298°K, then the entropy S at any other pressure P is given by

$$S = S^\circ - R \ln P, \qquad (8\text{-}42)$$

if the gas behaves according to the ideal-gas law. Thus as the pressure is increased the entropy decreases, but not without limit, as is implied by Eq. (8-42) because of gas imperfections. By means of the ideal-gas law, we may also express this relation in its equivalent form:

$$S = S^\circ + R \ln (V/V^\circ), \qquad (8\text{-}43)$$

in which $V°$ is the molar volume at standard conditions. This equation demonstrates that the entropy is determined by the volume to which the gas is restricted; the smaller the volume, the smaller the entropy. This is further illustration of the trend observed in the decrease of the entropy of a substance from gas to liquid to solid states.

(b) Trends in entropies

A survey of the data in Appendix II on entropies reveals a number of important features. Qualitatively we can see that the standard entropies are always positive (although entropy changes in reactions may be either positive or negative). In addition, the entropy of a substance always increases in the order: solid, liquid, gas.

TABLE 8–5

ENTROPIES OF GASES IN ORDER OF INCREASING
MOLECULAR WEIGHT ($S_{298}^°$, cal/mole-deg)

Diatomic		Triatomic		Tetratomic	
H_2	31.2	H_2O	45.2	NH_3	45.9
Li_2	47.0	HCN	48.2	C_2H_2	48.0
HF	41.5	H_2S	49.2	HCHO	52.4
CO	47.2	CO_2	51.1	H_2O_2	55.7
N_2	45.8	N_2O	52.6	PH_3	50.2
NO	50.2	NO_2	57.5	C_2N_2	57.6
O_2	49.0	OF_2	59.0	BF_3	60.7
HCl	44.6	COS	55.4	NF_3	62.3
F_2	48.5	MgF_2	55.9	SO_3	61.2
Na_2	54.9	SO_2	59.3	PF_3	64.6
ClF	52.1	SCl_2	67.9	ClF_3	66.3
S_2	54.5	ClO_2	60.0	$COCl_2$	67.8
Cl_2	53.3	CS_2	56.9	BCl_3	69.3
K_2	59.5	H_2Se	52.3	$SOCl_2$	73.6
HBr	47.5	Cl_2O	63.6	AsF_3	69.1
BrF	54.8	H_2Te	54.7	S_2Cl_2	75.8
BrCl	57.3	$HgCl_2$	70.3	BrF_3	69.9
HI	49.4	$HgBr_2$	76.5	PCl_3	74.6
IF	56.4	HgI_2	80.3	$AsCl_3$	78.3
Se_2	60.2			$SbCl_3$	80.8
Br_2	58.7			PBr_3	83.2
ICl	59.1			$BiCl_3$	85.2
IBr	61.8			AsI_3	92.7
I_2	62.3				
Te_2	64.1				
Bi_2	65.4				

TABLE 8–6

ENTROPIES OF GASES IN ORDER OF INCREASING MOLECULAR COMPLEXITY (S_{298}^{o}, cal/mole-deg)

$M^* \approx 20$		$M^* \approx 40$		$M^* \approx 80$		$M^* \approx 120$	
Ne	34.95	Ar	36.98	Kr	39.2	Xe	40.5
HF	41.52	F_2	48.45	Cl_2	53.3	BrCl	57.3
H_2O	45.11	CO_2	51.06	CS_2	56.9	NoBr	65.2
NH_3	46.01	H_2O_2	55.7	SO_3	61.2	$COCl_2$	67.2
CH_4	44.50			CH_2Cl_2	64.7	$CHCl_3$	70.8
				N_2O_4	72.7		

* M = molecular weight.

For the convenience of the following discussion, some entropy values from Appendix II are collected in Tables 8–5 and 8–6. Those in Table 8–5 comprise several series of gas molecules having the same number of atoms tabulated in order of increasing molecular weight. It is obvious from these data that the higher the molecular weight of a compound, the higher its entropy. In order to point out this relationship more clearly, the data have been plotted in Figs. 8–12 to 8–14. The entropies of diatomic gases (Fig. 8–12) fall readily into three classes, each of which has certain common features. The lowest entropies for a given molecular weight M (black dots) are those of the hydrogen halides and of hydrogen, which fit the empirical equation

$$S^\circ = 9.60 \log M + 29.20 \qquad (8–44)$$

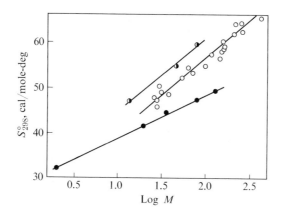

FIG. 8–12. Entropies of diatomic gases as a function of molecular weight: ● hydrides, ◑ alkali metals, ○ other diatomic gases.

reasonably well. The highest entropies for a given molecular weight are those of the diatomic alkali metals for which

$$S° = 16.7 \log M + 27.6. \tag{8-45}$$

Finally, the rest of the diatomic molecules have entropies clustered around the line

$$S° = 16.6 \log M + 23.3. \tag{8-46}$$

For the triatomic molecules (Fig. 8–13), we have to distinguish among the hydrides, the linear, and the bent molecules. For these three series we have

$$S° = 10.8 \log M + 32.0 \text{ (hydrides)}, \tag{8-47}$$

$$S° = 25.9 \log M + 9.0 \text{ (linear)}, \tag{8-48}$$

$$S° = 21.1 \log M + 22.0 \text{ (bent)}. \tag{8-49}$$

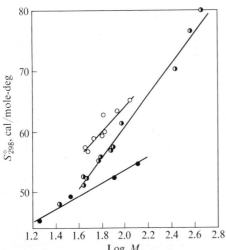
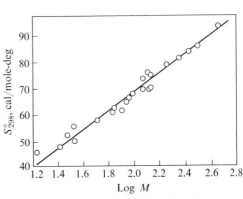

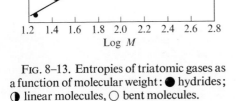

Fig. 8–13. Entropies of triatomic gases as a function of molecular weight: ● hydrides; ◐ linear molecules, ○ bent molecules.

Fig. 8–14. Entropies of tetratomic gases as a function of molecular weight.

When we consider the tetratomic gases in Fig. 8–14, such effects seem to be swamped out, and all of the data show reasonable agreement with the equation

$$S° = 35.3 \log M - 2.3. \tag{8-50}$$

These are, of course, empirical equations, and as such can provide a useful method for estimating unknown entropies. It is possible, in fact, to calculate the

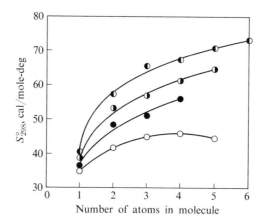

Fig. 8–15. Entropy as a function of molecular complexity for molecular weights: ○ 16–20, ● 34–40, ◐ 71–85, ◑ 92–131.

entropy of a gas molecule accurately from molecular parameters, but it is not feasible here to go into detail of these methods.

Figure 8–15 shows in graphical form the data of Table 8–6, illustrating the general increase in the standard entropy of gases as the molecular complexity (number of atoms in the molecule) increases, at approximately constant molecular weight. This is again an empirical correlation, and therefore the fact that smooth trends are not found is of no important consequence. The lowest molecular weight series does show an anomaly, in that the entropy of methane is actually less than that of ammonia.

The entropies of solids and of liquids pose more of a problem than those of gases, since the only way to determine them is by experimental measurement. Hence correlations of the type we have been considering are all the more important. We shall, however, only treat some inorganic solid salts here. In Fig. 8–16 are shown the entropies of solid compounds of formula MX, plotted against the logarithm of molecular weight. Again we note that compounds of a similar nature correlate reasonably well. The monohalide entropies fit (within one cal/mole, except for two compounds) the equation

$$S° = 22.0 \log M - 23.6 \text{ (halides)}, \tag{8–51}$$

while the oxides, and the nitrides and carbides, with much smaller entropies, fit the equations

$$S° = 14.1 \log M - 16.4 \text{ (oxides)}, \tag{8–52}$$

and

$$S° = 11.3 \log M - 13.6 \text{ (nitrides and carbides)}. \tag{8–53}$$

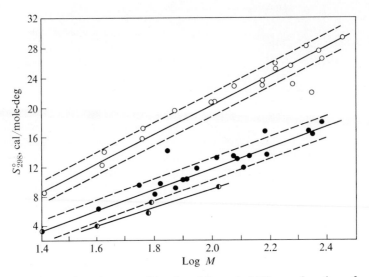

FIG. 8–16. Entropies of some solid salts of formula MX as a function of molecular weight: ○ monohalides, ● monoxides, ◐ nitrides and carbides.

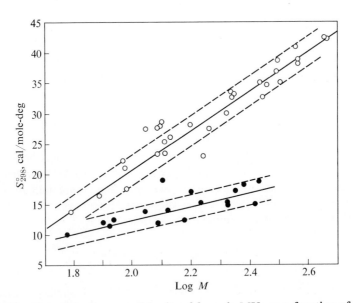

FIG. 8–17. Entropies of some solid salts of formula MX_2 as a function of molecular weight: ○ dihalides, ● dioxides.

Similar empirical relations are found when the entropies of dihalides and dioxides are plotted against the logarithm of their molecular weight (Fig. 8–17). As in the previous case, the oxides have smaller entropies than halides of similar molecular weight.

(c) Molecular basis of entropy

Although the concept of energy is generally a familiar one, that of entropy is not. This fact, coupled with the lack of an entropy conservation law, is largely responsible for the difficulty in dealing with entropy when it is first encountered. However, as has been pointed out above, the entropy change in a reaction, disregarding the entropy change in the surroundings, obeys the same rule regarding additivities (Hess' Law) as does the enthalpy change. Furthermore, it is possible on a molecular scale to establish a relationship between the entropy of a system and its state of disorder.

First of all, let us make clear what is meant by disorder, and at the same time illustrate the principle that an isolated system in equilibrium will tend to assume the state of greatest disorder. To demonstrate this, consider the probability of finding the 52 cards of a shuffled playing-card deck in various ordered arrangements. The arrangement least likely to be found is that in which the cards are arranged in order according to suit and number. Only one arrangement of the cards will satisfy this requirement, but there are a total of 52! or 8.1×10^{67} possible ways of arranging the cards. The probability of obtaining this one particular arrangement with random shuffling (and no cheating) is therefore prohibitively small. If we relax the requirement and insist only that the suits themselves be found together in the deck, then we find that this may be achieved in any one of 1.5×10^{39} possible arrangements. The probability of one of these arrangements arising is then one in 5.3×10^{28}.

Lessening our requirements still further, it can be shown that there are 1.5×10^{46} ways of arranging the cards so that each of two suits will be together, and 1.3×10^{56} arrangements that still have one suit together. The probabilities of finding such arrangements are thus one in 5.4×10^{21} and one in 6.2×10^{11}, respectively. Summarizing, we may say that the greater the disorder of a given arrangement, the larger the number of ways in which the cards may be grouped to give this arrangement, and the greater the probability that the deck of cards will be found so arranged.

In a similar manner, it is found that the greater the number of possible states which an isolated physical system may assume, i.e., the greater the disorder, then the larger the entropy. Furthermore, the isolated physical system will tend to assume the state of maximum entropy or greatest disorder. This tendency may be seen by examining the arrangement of the molecules of one mole of gas in a closed vessel. Consider the probability that all of the molecules will be found to the left of an imaginary plane bisecting the vessel. The probability that a single molecule will be found inside this boundary will be one-half. The probability that all of the molecules will be so located is one-half raised to a power equal to the number of molecules concerned, that is,

$$\text{Probability} = 0.5^N = 0.5^{6.02 \times 10^{23}}$$
$$= 10^{-1.81 \times 10^{23}}, \tag{8–54}$$

a number so small as to be beyond ordinary comprehension. On the other hand, as the size of the bounded area is increased, so will the probability increase until a value of unity is reached for free movement inside the vessel. This is obviously the most disordered arrangement, and the one most likely to be assumed.

We must now examine the phenomena of Sections 8–3(a) and (b) in the light of our proposed relationship between disorder and entropy. Consider the dependence on temperature of the entropy of HCl as shown in Fig. 8–11. We note, first of all, that the assignment of zero entropy for crystalline HCl at 0°K is a logical choice in view of the high degree of order under such conditions. In fact, the assertion that this is true for all pure crystalline phases at 0°K may be regarded as a statement of the *Third Law of Thermodynamics*. When the crystal is warmed, the vibrations of the atoms about their equilibrium position will increase in amplitude, thus promoting greater disorder and increased entropy. A further increase in disorder is encountered in the transition from Solid I to Solid II, probably because of the onset of a restricted rotation of the molecules. Further increases in entropy accompany the transitions to the liquid and finally to the gaseous state. The large increase in the latter case is quite reasonable, in view of the much increased disorder of the vapor relative to the liquid. We can also understand, now, the dependence of the entropy of an ideal gas on volume (Eq. (8–43)). An increase in volume clearly allows the gas a much greater range of spatial coordinates. Thus, there is increased disorder and increased entropy.

The relationship between the entropy and the molecular weight and complexity of a substance is more difficult to explain in simple terms. In the latter case it is helpful to consider two isolated systems: one composed of a monatomic gas and the other a diatomic gas. To avoid complications we shall, in addition, impose the condition that the diatomic molecule be equal in mass to an atom of the monatomic gas. Observe now that, since the atoms are spherically symmetrical, their orientation does not contribute to the disorder of the system. In the case of the diatomic molecule, however, both rotation and vibration are possible. Both of these forms of motion are quantized; hence there is a greater number of possible energy states for the diatomic molecule, and a higher entropy. Furthermore, the size of the rotational and vibrational quanta depend inversely on the mass of the atoms involved (Eq. (3–36)). Thus for a given total energy, the greater the mass, the larger the number of energy states available, and the larger the entropy. A larger entropy should therefore correlate with a larger molecular weight.

It is less easily seen why the entropy of a monatomic gas should be a function of its molecular weight, but the principle is the same. The total energy is quantized and the size of the quantum depends inversely on the mass of the atoms; hence an increase in the molecular weight will result in an increase in entropy. Obviously, the same considerations will also apply in regard to the translational energy of a polyatomic gas.

While we have given only a qualitative discussion of entropy in terms of molecular parameters, it is possible, as stated previously, to calculate the entropy quite accurately from spectral data on vibration and rotation. Although we cannot go into details here, it is appropriate to point out that, other things being equal, a molecule with a small amount of inertia, such as a hydride, will have a small entropy. The same reasoning applies to the contribution of vibration to the entropy; i.e., hydrides have high vibrational frequencies because of their low reduced mass (see Chapter 5), and hence make only a small contribution to the entropy. As an example, compare the gases H_2Se and Cl_2O, which have about the same molecular weight and number of atoms, yet the entropy of the latter is larger than that of the former by 11 cal/mole-deg. Other pairs, such as HI and BrCl, show a similar trend, which is illustrated in Figs. 8–12 and 8–13. Molecules such as the diatomic alkali metals have very small bond energies (Table 4–2). Although for most simple molecules vibrational disorder is not important at room temperature, these weakly bound molecules do have an appreciable additional entropy because of the low frequency vibrations, and hence their entropies are higher than "normal" (see Fig. 8–12).

The symmetry of a molecule also affects its entropy, in that molecules with symmetry have a smaller entropy than would otherwise be expected. This can be an appreciable factor for molecules such as CF_4 and SF_6, in which the reduction in S due to symmetry is 4.93 and 6.32 cal/mole-deg, respectively, or about ten percent of the total entropy of the gases. This effect is illustrated quite well in the lowest molecular weight series in Fig. 8–14. The structure HF has only a single symmetry axis, H_2O and NH_3 have two- and threefold axes of rotation, but CH_4 has four threefold axes (see Chapter 5). The decrease in entropy due to symmetry is just about enough to compensate for the increase in molecular complexity, so that the latter three have entropies very nearly the same.

Cyclic (ring) molecules have a lower entropy than their corresponding noncyclic isomers, in part because of their greater symmetry, but principally because rotation of part of the molecule with respect to the rest of the molecule is eliminated when the molecule is cyclic.

Of interest also is the entropy of mixing. The entropy of a mixture of two gases is greater than the sum of the entropies of the components at the same temperature and pressure. Qualitatively, it is easy to see that the disorder, and therefore the entropy, is larger after mixing. Consider the process in which one mole of argon at one atm is combined with one mole of neon at one atm to give two moles of mixture which are also at one atm pressure. Before mixing we have the total entropy

$$n_{Ar}S°(Ar) + n_{Ne}S°(Ne) = 36.98 + 34.95 = 71.93 \text{ cal/deg.} \qquad (8\text{–}55)$$

After mixing, each gas will have a partial pressure of 0.5 atm [see Eq. (8–42)].

Therefore, since

$$S(\text{Ar}) = S°(\text{Ar}) - R \ln p_{\text{Ar}}, \tag{8-56}$$

and

$$S(\text{Ne}) = S°(\text{Ne}) - R \ln p_{\text{Ne}}, \tag{8-57}$$

we have for the mixture

$$n_{\text{Ar}}S(\text{Ar}) = n_{\text{Ne}}S(\text{Ne}) = 36.98 + 1.38 + 34.95 + 1.38 = 74.69 \text{ cal/deg.}$$

The entropy per mole of mixing of equal quantities of two gases at constant pressure is

$$S(\text{mixing}) = -2R \ln \tfrac{1}{2} = +2.76 \text{ cal/mole-deg.} \tag{8-58}$$

If the total volume rather than the total pressure is fixed, then the entropy of the mixture is the same as the sum of the entropies of the individual gases. These considerations actually apply only to gases obeying the ideal-gas law.

We shall come back to the concept of entropy again in the treatment of solutions, since the information about entropies and entropy changes provides a powerful means of investigating the interaction between solute and solvent.

8–4. FREE ENERGY

While neither the change in enthalpy nor in entropy will individually determine the value of the equilibrium constant for a reaction, it is apparent that we can define a quantity which will do so. Thus, referring to Eq. (8–32), we define the standard free energy change* in a reaction, $\Delta G°$, as

$$\Delta G° = -RT \ln K_p = \Delta H° - T \Delta S°. \tag{8-59}$$

The superscript $°$ refers, as usual, to the substance in its standard state. The conventions with regard to the free energy are identical to those of the enthalpy.

Because of its relationship to the equilibrium constant, the free energy is a particularly useful thermodynamic function. It is conveniently tabulated in the form of standard free energies of formation, $\Delta G_f°$, as in Appendix II. Like standard heats of formation, they may be added algebraically according to Hess' law, and can be used to determine the standard free energy change and the equilibrium constant for a reaction.

---

* The free energy change, also known as the Gibbs free energy, is often given the symbol ΔF, and the student must be wary of confusion over the symbolism. Since ΔF has also been used to represent other thermodynamic quantities, the authors feel it is wise to encourage the growing trend to avoid its use altogether.

Consider the following reaction:

$$Cl_2(g) + 3F_2(g) \rightleftharpoons 2ClF_3(g). \qquad (8-60)$$

Using the data of Appendix II, we find the standard free energy change for the reaction to be

$$\Delta G^\circ = 2\,\Delta G_f^\circ(ClF_3) - \Delta G_f^\circ(Cl_2) - 3\,\Delta G_f^\circ(F_2) = -58.0\,\text{kcal}. \qquad (8-61)$$

The implication of the negative standard free energy is that a mixture of gaseous chlorine and fluorine will react spontaneously to form ClF_3. This can be seen by calculating the equilibrium constant with Eq. (8–59). At 298°K, we have

$$\ln K_p = -\frac{\Delta G^\circ}{RT} = \frac{58.0 \times 10^3}{1.987 \times 298} = 98.0,$$

so that

$$K_p = 3.1 \times 10^{42}.$$

If the total pressure of a stoichiometric equilibrium mixture is one atm, then the partial pressure of Cl_2 will be only about 10^{-11} atm.

Apart from the entropy of mixing, we have, up to this point, considered only the standard enthalpy, entropy, and free energy of pure compounds. We are concerned with reactions, however, and it is of interest to see how the free energy varies during the course of a reaction. For a simple gaseous system we can estimate this fairly simply if we assume the gases to behave ideally. We have already seen that, for an ideal gas, the entropy at any particular pressure is given by Eq. (8–42). The enthalpy, however, is independent of pressure; hence for the molar free energy of a gas at a pressure p, we have:

$$\Delta G = \Delta G^\circ + RT\ln p. \qquad (8-62)$$

For n moles, the free energy (relative to the elements) at standard conditions is

$$\Delta G = n\,\Delta G^\circ + nRT\ln p. \qquad (8-63)$$

For a mixture of gases, the total free energy (again relative to the elements) is

$$\Delta G = \sum_i n_i(\Delta G_i^\circ + RT\ln p_i), \qquad (8-64)$$

in which the summation is carried out over all the components in the mixture. Applying this equation to various mixtures of the gases NO_2 and N_2O_4, we can estimate how ΔG varies with the extent of the reaction

$$N_2O_4(g) \rightleftharpoons 2NO_2(g). \qquad (8-65)$$

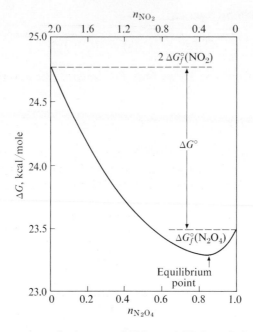

Fig. 8–18. Free energy of mixtures of NO_2 and N_2O_4 relative to the elements in their standard states. Total pressure is one atm, and total amount of gas is equivalent to one mole of N_2O_4.

For a total pressure of one atm, and with the total amount of material fixed at the equivalent of one mole of N_2O_4, the results of the calculations are as depicted in Fig. 8–18.

The value of $\Delta G°$ yields an equilibrium constant of 0.115, from which we calculate that at equilibrium there will be 0.834 moles of N_2O_4 and 0.332 moles of NO_2 present. This point, marked on Fig. 8–18, occurs exactly at the minimum of the free energy curve. The details of this curve need not concern us here, except to note that when $\Delta G°$ for the reaction is quite negative, the equilibrium lies essentially at the point corresponding to pure products, while for a large positive $\Delta G°$, the equilibrium mixture is essentially that of the pure reactants. It is only when the value of $\Delta G°$ for the reaction is not far from zero that major amounts of both products and reactants will coexist at equilibrium.

Thus we see that tabulated standard free energies allow us to predict thermodynamically whether or not a reaction will proceed, remembering always that nothing is said or implied in this treatment about the rate of reaction. Further, even when free energy data are not available, it is generally possible, using methods outlined here and extensions of these methods, to make an educated guess at enthalpies and entropies, and to make at least order-of-magnitude estimates of thermodynamic stabilities or equilibrium constants.

(a) Thermodynamic activity

A close examination of the data of Table 8–1 reveals that, even when random errors are taken into account, there is a distinct downward trend in the value of K_p as the pressure increases. In other words, the equilibrium constant, as formulated in terms of partial pressures according to Eq. (8–11), exhibits a functional dependence on the total pressure. This variation stems from nonideal behavior on the part of the reacting gases, and must be allowed for, if the thermodynamic arguments of this chapter are to be valid when they are applied to real gases.

The difficulty is readily overcome by defining the thermodynamic equilibrium constant in terms of the change in standard free energy according to Eq. (8–59). This may then be expressed as a function of the activity a of each species involved in the equilibrium. That is,

$$K_{th} = \frac{(a_X)^x (a_Y)^y \cdots}{(a_A)^a (a_B)^b \cdots}$$

for the reaction

$$aA + bB + \cdots, \qquad xX + yY + \cdots.$$

The activity of a substance is a function of its pressure (or concentration), but because of intermolecular interactions in real gases the two are not usually equal. On the other hand, as the pressure is reduced, the behavior of a real gas approaches that of an ideal gas, and at infinitely low pressures the activity and partial pressure will be equal. This is conveniently expressed by the relation

$$a = \gamma p,$$

where γ, the *activity coefficient*, is such that

$$\lim_{p \to 0} \gamma = 1.$$

The introduction of activity makes it possible to develop thermodynamics in a completely general way without introducing assumptions as to ideal behavior. We can, for example, rewrite Eq. (8–62) in the form

$$\Delta G = \Delta G° + RT \ln a,$$

for application to real as well as to ideal gases. Note, however, that the standard state will now be defined by unit activity rather than by one atmosphere pressure.

The activity coefficient will obviously be determined by molecular interactions in the gas, and is not properly a thermodynamic quantity at all. From an experimental point of view, it is a measure of the effect of the intermolecular interactions. Theoretically, it is estimated by nonthermodynamic arguments involving kinetic theory and the van der Waals forces operating between the molecules. Fortunately, the effect of these forces is small at reasonable temperatures and pressures, so that the assumption of unit activity coefficient under these conditions does not usually lead to serious errors (almost always less than 10%).

BIBLIOGRAPHY

A

BARROW, G. M., *Physical Chemistry*. New York: McGraw-Hill, 1961.

NASH, L. K., *Elements of Chemical Thermodynamics*. Reading, Mass.: Addison-Wesley, 1962.

WILKS, J., *The Third Law of Thermodynamics*. New York: Oxford, 1961.

B

LEWIS, G. N., and M. RANDALL (revised by K. PITZER and L. BREWER), *Thermodynamics*. New York: McGraw-Hill, 1961.

PRIGOGINE, I., and R. DEFAY, *Chemical Thermodynamics*. London: Longmans-Green, 1954.

WENNER, R. R., *Thermochemical Calculations*. New York: McGraw-Hill, 1941.

PROBLEMS

8-1. From the data given in Appendix II, calculate $\Delta G°$ at 298°K for each of the following reactions, and then decide whether the reactants or products are favored thermodynamically.

  (a) $SiH_4(g) + 2H_2O(l) \rightleftharpoons SiO_2(s) + 4H_2(g)$

  (b) $Hg_2Cl_2(s) \rightleftharpoons Hg(l) + HgCl_2(s)$

  (c) $ZnO(s) + H_2S(g) \rightleftharpoons ZnS(s) + H_2O(l)$

  (d) $SiO_2(s) + 4HF(g) \rightleftharpoons SiF_4(g) + 2H_2O(g)$

8-2. Calculate K_p and $\Delta G°$ for the "water-gas reaction"

$$CO_2(g) + H_2(g) \rightleftharpoons CO(g) + H_2O(g)$$

at 1300°C, from the information that 63% of an equimolar mixture of CO_2 and H_2 is converted into CO and H_2O at equilibrium. Find $\Delta G°$ at 298°K from Appendix II and, assuming that $\Delta H°$ and $\Delta S°$ are independent of temperature, evaluate these latter quantities [use Eq. (8–59)] and compare them with the corresponding values of 298°K found with the data in Appendix II.

8-3. In discussing the temperature dependence of the enthalpy and entropy of a compound, it was pointed out that at the temperature of a phase transition, the enthalpy change for the transition, $\Delta H_i°$, is related to the entropy change, $\Delta S_i°$, through the relation

$$\Delta S_i° = \Delta H_i°/T_i.$$

Discuss the implication of this equation with respect to the free energy change in a phase transition and the equilibrium constant for the transition.

8-4. Estimate the entropy changes for the following reactions under standard conditions, using information such as that available in Appendix II:

  (a) $P_4(g) \rightleftharpoons 2P_2(g)$

  (b) $2POBr_3(g) \rightleftharpoons 2PBr_3(g) + O_2(g)$

  (c) $TiCl_4(g) + 2H_2O(g) \rightleftharpoons TiO_2(s) + 4HCl(g)$

  (d) $Sn(s) + SnCl_4(g) \rightleftharpoons 2SnCl_2(s)$

8–5. Refer back to Problem 4–7. Estimating any entropy values not given in Appendix II, find the entropies of formation of each of the compounds. From these and the previously estimated heats of formation, find the free energies of formation; if required, suitably modify the conclusions reached previously which considered only the enthalpy changes.

8–6. (a) Calculate the standard free energy change and the equilibrium constant for the reaction

$$2Au(s) + Cl_2(g) \rightleftharpoons 2AuCl(s),$$

estimating any thermodynamic data which may be required and which is not given below or in Appendix II. What error in the entropy change would be required to reverse the sign of $\Delta G°$ at 298°K? On this basis, is your conclusion about the thermodynamic stability of AuCl(s) apt to be reliable? (b) Decide whether or not $AuCl_3$(s) would be stable with respect to (1) decomposition into the elements, and (2) disproportionation in the presence of Au(s) into AuCl(s).

$$\Delta H°(AuCl,s) = -8.4 \text{ kcal/mole}$$
$$\Delta H°(AuCl_3,s) = -28.3 \text{ kcal/mole}$$
$$\Delta S°(Au,s) = 11.4 \text{ cal/deg}$$

8–7. As pointed out in Section 8–4(a), the equilibrium constants for the NO_2-N_2O_4 reaction which are given in Table 8–1 exhibit a dependence on total pressure. Illustrate this by plotting the equilibrium constant against total pressure, and indicate how the graph could be used to derive the true thermodynamic equilibrium constant.

8–8. Using Eq. (8–64) to represent the free energy of a mixture of NO_2 and N_2O_4, show that the minimum in the curve of Fig. 8–18 defines the equilibrium constant for the reaction in terms of the difference in standard free energy of NO_2 and N_2O_4. Note that the total amount of gas is equivalent to one mole of N_2O_4, or two moles of NO_2.

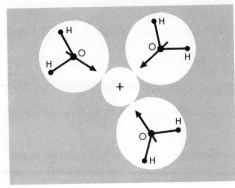

CHAPTER NINE

Solutions of Electrolytes

Historically the study of solutions of electrolytes has played an important role in the development of inorganic chemistry. It is furthermore still a very active field, although the lines of investigation bear little similarity to those which led Arrhenius to propose ionic dissociation in 1887. In part, this interest arises from the prevalence of ionic reactions in inorganic chemistry; but the convenience of the liquid state, in particular the aqueous solution, as a medium for such reactions is undoubtedly an additional factor. Our task is to examine the thermodynamic changes which accompany the dissolution of an electrolyte and to interpret these changes, as far as is possible, in terms of intermolecular forces. This will, of course, involve a close examination of the species actually present in solutions of electrolytes.

9–1. NATURE OF ELECTROLYTIC SOLUTIONS

As their name implies, solutions of electrolytes are characterized by a high electrical conductivity. However, in contrast to metallic conduction through electrons, electrolytic conductivity is ascribed to the presence in solution of mobile, positively and negatively charged ions. Thus a salt such as sodium chloride is commonly said to dissociate in aqueous solution according to the equation

$$NaCl \rightarrow Na^+ + Cl^-.$$

At the same time, the dissolution and ionic dissociation of the salts are obviously

316

a result of interaction with the solvent. This process, termed *hydration*, *aquation* or, more generally, *solvation* is more clearly indicated if we rewrite the equation for dissociation in the form

$$NaCl(solid) \rightarrow Na^+(aq) + Cl^-(aq).$$

We are thus reminded that in solution we are dealing with solvated rather than free species.

That equilibria involving ions may be established in electrolytic solutions is undoubtedly already known to the student. These may be treated thermodynamically in a manner similar to the analogous gas-phase equilibria, but the presence of the solvent introduces a number of complications. Equilibrium constants, for example, usually vary with the properties of the solvent. Formic acid, although only slightly ionized in aqueous solution, is completely so in liquid ammonia. Some care must be employed, then, in the use of the terms "weak" and "strong" to designate partially and completely ionized electrolytes. Even if the solvent is specified, the difference is only one of degree and varies with concentration.

(a) Ionic equilibria and activity

The principles with which we shall be concerned in our treatment of ionic equilibria are essentially those already discussed in Chapter 8. Thus we shall begin with the application of the Law of Mass Action to the equilibria involving ions in aqueous solution.

It was pointed out previously in dealing with gaseous equilibria [Section 8–4(a)] that the formulation of the equilibrium constant in terms of concentration or pressure involves assumptions as to ideal behavior. That an analogous situation exists with regard to ionic equilibria may be conveniently demonstrated by a study of the weak electrolyte, acetic acid. In aqueous solution, acetic acid dissociates according to the equation

$$HAc \rightleftharpoons H^+ + A^-,$$

and the equilibrium constant in terms of molar concentrations will be

$$K_a' = \frac{[H^+][Ac^-]}{[HAc]}. \tag{9–1}$$

Alternatively, K_a' may be expressed as a function of the degree of dissociation α and the concentration c, in moles/liter.

$$K_a' = \frac{\alpha^2 c}{(1 - \alpha)c}.$$

This form is particularly convenient for the study of the acid equilibrium because

TABLE 9–1

DISSOCIATION CONSTANT OF ACETIC ACID
(at 298°K)

c (millimoles/liter)	α	$K_a' \times 10^5$
0.02801	0.5393	1.768
0.11135	0.3277	1.779
0.21844	0.2477	1.781
1.02831	0.1238	1.797
2.41400	0.08290	1.809
5.91153	0.05401	1.823
9.8421	0.04222	1.832
20.000	0.02987	1.840
52.303	0.01865	1.854

α is readily obtainable from conductance measurements. Data obtained in this way are listed in Table 9–1 and plotted in Fig. 9–1.

Clearly the equilibrium constant, as expressed in Eq. (9–1), is a function of concentration. We can, however, employ the procedure of Section 8–4(a) and define a thermodynamic equilibrium constant in terms of activities. Then

$$K_a = \frac{a_{\mathrm{H}^+} \cdot a_{\mathrm{Ac}^-}}{a_{\mathrm{HAc}}} = \frac{\gamma_+[\mathrm{H}^+]\gamma_-[\mathrm{Ac}^-]}{\gamma_{\mathrm{HAc}}[\mathrm{HAc}]} = K_a' \frac{\gamma_+\gamma_-}{\gamma_{\mathrm{HAc}}}. \tag{9–2}$$

The problem of nonideal behavior is thereby eliminated from the thermodynamic argument. As the concentration approaches zero, the activity coefficient term in Eq. (9–2) approaches unity, and in the limit $K_a = K_a'$, that is,

$$\lim_{c \to 0} \left(\frac{\gamma_+\gamma_-}{\gamma_{\mathrm{HAc}}}\right) = 1.$$

Furthermore, at low concentrations $\log K_a'$ is found to be a linear function of $\sqrt{\alpha c}$ (Debye-Hückel limiting law), so that K_a is conveniently determined by extrapolation to zero concentration. When plotted, as in Fig. 9–1, the data gives

$$-\log K_a = 4.7564$$

so that

$$K_a = 1.752 \times 10^{-5}.$$

The quantity αc is the value, in this particular case, of the ionic strength I. Defined more generally by the equation

$$I = \tfrac{1}{2} \sum_i z_i^2 c_i,$$

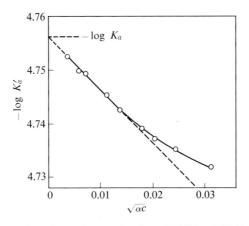

Fig. 9–1. Concentration dependence of $K'_a = [H^+][Ac^-]/[HAc]$ in dilute aqueous solutions of acetic acid. Extrapolation to zero ionic strength (αc) gives the value of K_a, the thermodynamic dissociation constant.

where c_i is the concentration of ion i with net charge z_i, the ionic strength is an important parameter in electrolytic solution theory.

From a practical point of view, the situation is further complicated by the fact that the activity coefficient is a function of the total ionic concentration of the solution, and not just the concentration of the species involved in the equilibria. This is conveniently demonstrated by considering the solubility of AgCl in aqueous solutions of nitric acid. Assuming the AgCl to be completely dissociated in solution, the equilibrium

$$AgCl(s) \rightleftharpoons Ag^+(aq) + Cl^-(aq)$$

is characterized by the expression

$$K_{sp} = a_{Ag^+} \cdot a_{Cl^-} = \gamma_+[Ag^+]\gamma_-[Cl^-] = S^2\gamma_+\gamma_-,$$

where S is the solubility of the AgCl.

In this case, as Fig. 9–2 shows, $\log S$ is a linear function of $\sqrt{I}$, and the thermodynamic or true K_{sp} may be determined by extrapolation to zero ionic strength. Ignoring a negligible concentration of hydroxyl ions, the ionic strength is simply

$$I = c + S$$

where c is the concentration of the nitric acid. The intercept of the extrapolated straight line yields

$$-\tfrac{1}{2}\log K_{sp} = 4.895,$$

so that $K_{sp} = 1.621 \times 10^{-10}$.

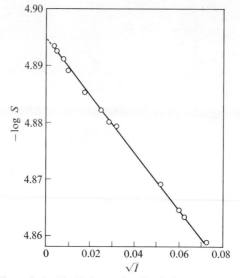

Fig. 9-2. Solubility of AgCl (S in moles/liter) in aqueous nitric acid solutions. Extrapolation to zero ionic strength (I) gives the value of the thermodynamic K_{sp}.

For emphasis, it is worth mentioning again that the role of the activity coefficient in thermodynamics is largely one of convenience. The activity coefficient comes into its own in theories of the structure of solutions which attempt to relate it to inter-ionic interactions. By expressing equilibrium constants in terms of activities, it is possible to develop thermodynamics in a rigorous manner without regard for nonideal behavior. The general expression for an equilibrium constant is then

$$K = \frac{\prod a_{\text{products}}}{\prod a_{\text{reactants}}}.$$

This expression may be applied to the four basic types of ionic equilibria with which we shall be concerned:

(1) the ionic dissociation of a sparingly soluble salt, such as

$$\text{AgCl(s)} \rightleftharpoons \text{Ag}^+(\text{aq}) + \text{Cl}^-(\text{aq}),$$

$$K_{sp} = a_{\text{Ag}^+} + a_{\text{Cl}^-} = [\text{Ag}^+][\text{Cl}^-]\gamma_{\text{Ag}^+}\gamma_{\text{Cl}^-};$$

(2) the ionic dissociation of a weak acid or base, such as

$$\text{HAc(aq)} \rightleftharpoons \text{H}^+(\text{aq}) + \text{Ac}^-(\text{aq}),$$

$$K_a = \frac{a_{\text{H}^+}a_{\text{Ac}^-}}{a_{\text{HAc}}} = \frac{[\text{H}^+][\text{Ac}^-]}{[\text{HAc}]} \frac{\gamma_{\text{H}^+}\gamma_{\text{Ac}^-}}{\gamma_{\text{HAc}}};$$

(3) the dissociation of a complex ion, such as

$$Ag(NH_3)_2^+(aq) \rightleftharpoons Ag^+(aq) + 2NH_3(aq),$$

$$K = \frac{a_{Ag^+}a_{NH_3}^2}{a_{Ag(NH_3)_2^+}} = \frac{[Ag^+][NH_3]^2}{[Ag(NH_3)_2^+]} \frac{\gamma_{Ag^+}\gamma_{NH_3}^2}{\gamma_{Ag(NH_3)_2^+}};$$

(4) the oxidation-reduction reaction, such as

$$6Fe^{2+}(aq) + Cr_2O_7^{2-}(aq) + 14H^+(aq)$$

$$\rightleftharpoons 6Fe^{3+}(aq) + 2Cr^{3+}(aq) + 7H_2O,$$

$$K = \frac{a_{Fe^{3+}}^6 a_{Cr^{3+}}^2}{a_{Fe^{2+}}^6 a_{Cr_2O_7^{2-}} a_{H^+}^{14}} = \frac{[Fe^{3+}]^6[Cr^{3+}]^2}{[Fe^{2+}]^6[Cr_2O_7^{2-}][H^+]^{14}} \frac{\gamma_{Fe^{3+}}^6 \gamma_{Cr^{3+}}^2}{\gamma_{Fe^{2+}}^6 \gamma_{Cr_2O_7^{2-}} \gamma_{H^+}^{14}}.$$

We shall not be concerned further with activity coefficients and their theoretical interpretation, but the reader will gain some insight into how they may be determined by studying the manner in which the data of Figs. 9–1 and 9–2 have been treated. It is pertinent, however, to examine the error involved in the assumption, often made in practical calculations, that the activity of a species is equal to its concentration. Because the error is a function of both the concentration and the form of the equilibrium constant, generalizations are difficult. It would seem safe to say, however, that the error introduced by such an assumption is rarely greater than 25% in most solutions of practical interest. As Table 9–1 shows, the error may be much less than this in dilute solutions of weak electrolytes. Since order-of-magnitude accuracy is often sufficient in the calculation of ionic concentrations, the assumption is a reasonable one. This is especially true if one considers that the equilibrium constants used are no better than this in some cases. A practical solution to the problem (which is sometimes employed) is to quote a nonthermodynamic equilibrium constant for use in more concentrated solutions.

(b) Thermodynamic properties

In defining the thermodynamic equilibrium constant for an ionic process with reference to an infinitely dilute solution, we have, in essence, defined the *standard state* for solutions of electrolytes. More specifically, the standard state of a solute refers to a hypothetical one-molar solution in which the solute has unit activity. The activity of the real one-molar solution is then just the activity coefficient. This is a particularly convenient reference state for electrolytic solutions for, under these (hypothetical) conditions, there will be no interionic interactions, and the thermodynamic functions of the species in solution will be additive. Thus, the standard free energy of formation of an anion in aqueous solution will be independent of the type of cation present and vice versa. Note, however, that this does not mean that the sum of the standard free energies of the ions is equal to that of the undissociated species. On the contrary, $\Delta G_f^\circ(KCl, aq)$, for example, will be quite different from the sum of $\Delta G_f^\circ(K^+, aq)$ and $\Delta G_f^\circ(Cl^-, aq)$.

TABLE 9-2

THERMODYNAMIC PROPERTIES OF IONS AND MOLECULES IN AQUEOUS SOLUTION

(kcal/mole and cal/mole-deg at 298°K)

	ΔH_f°	ΔG_f°	S°		ΔH_f°	ΔG_f°	S°
H^+	0.00	0.00	0.00	NO_2^-	−25.4	−8.25	29.9
OH^-	−54.96	−37.59	−2.52	NO_3^-	−49.37	−26.43	35.0
F^-	−78.66	−66.08	−2.3	PO_4^{3-}	−306.9	−245.1	−52
HF	−78.66	−70.41	26	HPO_4^{2-}	−310.4	−261.5	−8.6
Cl^-	−40.02	−31.35	13.2	$H_2PO_4^-$	−311.3	−271.3	21.3
ClO_2^-	−17.18	2.74	24.1	H_3PO_4	−308.2	−274.2	42.1
$HClO_2$	−13.68	0.07	42	$HCOO^-$	−98.0	−80.0	21.9
ClO_3^-	−23.5	−0.6	39	$HCOOH$	−98.0	−85.1	39.1
ClO_4^-	−31.41	−2.47	43.2	CO_3^{2-}	−161.63	−126.22	−12.7
Br^-	−28.90	−24.57	19.29	HCO_3^-	−165.18	−140.31	22.7
I^-	−13.37	−12.35	26.14	H_2CO_3	−167.01	−149.00	45.7
I_3^-	−12.4	−12.31	57.1	CH_3COO^-	−116.84	−89.02	20.8
S^{2-}	7.8	20.6	−4	CH_3COOH	−116.74	−95.51	
HS^-	−4.10	3.00	15.0	CN^-	36.1	39.6	28.2
H_2S	−9.4	−6.54	29.2	HCN	25.2	26.8	30.8
SO_4^{2-}	−216.90	−177.34	4.1	CNO^-	−33.5	−23.6	31.1
HSO_4^-	−211.70	−179.94	30.52	$C_2O_4^{2-}$	−195.7	−159.4	10.6
SO_3^{2-}	−149.2	−118.8	10.4	$HC_2O_4^-$	−195.7	−165.12	
HSO_3^-	−150.09	−126.03	31.64	$H_2C_2O_4$	−195.57	−166.8	
H_2SO_3	−145.5	−128.59	56	Sn^{2+}	−2.39	−5.81	5.1
SeO_4^{2-}	−145.3	−105.42	5.7	Pb^{2+}	0.39	−5.81	5.1
$HSeO_4^-$	−143.1	−108.2	22.0	Tl^+	1.38	−7.76	30.4
NH_4^+	−31.74	−19.00	26.97	Tl^{3+}	46.8	50.0	
NH_3	−19.32	−6.36	26.3	Zn^{2+}	−36.43	−35.18	−25.45

	ΔH°	ΔG_f°	S°
Cd^{2+}	−17.30	−18.58	−14.6
$CdCl^+$		−51.8	5.6
$CdCl_2$		−83.3	17
$CdCl_3^-$		−115.9	50.7
Hg^{2+}	41.59	39.38	−5.4
Hg_2^{2+}		36.35	
$HgBr_4^{2-}$	−99.9	−88.0	84
HgI_4^{2-}	−55.4	−51.15	90
Cu^{2+}	15.39	15.53	−23.6
$CuCl_2^-$	−66.1	−57.9	49.4
Ag^+	25.31	18.43	17.67
$Ag(NH_3)_2^+$	−26.72	−4.16	57.8
$Ag(CN)_2^-$	64.5	72.05	49.0
Ni^{2+}	−15.3	−11.53	33
$Ni(CN)_4^{2-}$	86.9	117.1	
Co^{2+}	−14.2	−12.8	−27
$Co(NH_3)_6^{2+}$		−57.7	
$Co(NH_3)_6^{3+}$		−55.2	
$Co(NH_3)_5H_2O^{3+}$	−192.9	−106.2	73.4
$Co(NH_3)_5Cl^{2+}$	−162.1	−86.2	96.1
Fe^{2+}	−21.0	−20.30	−27.1
Fe^{3+}	−11.4	−2.53	−70.1
$Fe(OH)^{2+}$	−67.4	−55.91	−23.2
$Fe(OH)_2^+$		−106.2	
$FeCl^{2+}$	−42.9	−35.9	−22

	ΔH_f°	ΔG_f°	S°
$FeBr^{2+}$	−34.2	−27.9	−28
$FeNO^{2+}$	−9.7	1.5	−10.6
$Fe(CN)_6^{4-}$	126.7	170.4	68
$Fe(CN)_6^{3-}$		162	
Mn^{2+}	−53.3	−54.4	−20
MnO_4^-	−129.7	−107.4	45.4
Cr^{2+}	−33.2	−42.1	
Cr^{3+}	−61.2	−51.5	−73.5
$Cr_2O_7^{2-}$	−364.0	−315.4	51.1
CrO_4^{2-}	−213.75	−176.1	9.2
$H_2BO_3^-$	−251.8	−217.6	7.3
H_3BO_3	−260.2	−230.2	21.41
BF_4^-	−365	−343	40
Al^{3+}	−125.4	−115.0	−74.9
AlF_6^{3-}		−539.6	
Mg^{2+}	−110.41	−108.99	−28.2
Ca^{2+}	−129.77	−132.18	−13.2
Sr^{2+}	−130.38	−133.2	−9.4
Ba^{2+}	−128.67	−134.0	3
Li^+	−66.55	−70.22	3.4
Na^+	−57.28	−62.59	14.4
K^+	−60.04	−67.46	24.5
Rb^+	−59.4	−67.65	28.7
Cs^+	−62.6	−70.8	31.8

Unfortunately, present-day experimental techniques are incapable of determining absolute thermodynamic data for individual ions. It is necessary, therefore, to make an arbitrary choice for the values for one ion; by convention, the following assignments are made:

$$\Delta G_f^\circ(H^+, aq) = 0.000 \text{ kcal/mole},$$

$$\Delta H_f^\circ(H^+, aq) = 0.000 \text{ kcal/mole},$$

$$S^\circ(H^+, aq) = 0.000 \text{ cal/mole-deg}.$$

A scale formed on this basis is both useful and meaningful as long as the data are used for electrostatically neutral sets of ions. Because of the arbitrary zero, only the differences between the individual values have significance.

The experimental sources of the data in Table 9–2 are rather varied, and depend on the nature of the electrolyte. We shall not go into detail here, but it will be apparent that the temperature dependence of equilibrium constants and the thermal properties of solution (heats of solution, heats of dilution) are important sources of information. Even more useful, perhaps, are measurements of the temperature dependence of electrode potentials (Section 9–6).

For completely dissociated electrolytes, the analysis of the data is quite straight-forward. Experiments on HCl, for example, would provide the data

$$\Delta G_f^\circ(H^+, aq) + \Delta G_f^\circ(Cl^-, aq) = -31.35 \text{ kcal/mole}.$$

With the convention that

$$\Delta G_f^\circ(H^+, aq) = 0,$$

we obtain

$$\Delta G_f^\circ(Cl^-, aq) = -31.35 \text{ kcal/mole}.$$

Combining this with the data for NaCl, that is,

$$\Delta G_f^\circ(Na^+, aq) + \Delta G_f^\circ(Cl^-, aq) = -93.94 \text{ kcal/mole},$$

we find that

$$\Delta G_f^\circ(Na^+, aq) = -62.59 \text{ kcal/mole}.$$

Obviously the process may be continued to build up a set of self-consistent data for ions in solutions.

9–2. HYDRATION

In order that salts and other substances dissolve in polar solvents such as water, there must be strong solute-solvent interactions to overcome the large crystal or bonding forces. The source of this interaction will be ion-dipole forces but, before investigating this aspect further, it is appropriate to use the thermodynamic data given in Table 9–2 to evaluate quantitatively the magnitude of the effect. The evaluation of enthalpies, free energies, and entropies of hydration provides important information on which the detailed model of ions in solution can be based.

(a) Enthalpy of hydration

We are here interested, just as we were in the discussion of crystal enthalpies (in Chapters 2 and 4), in the formation of a system from the free gaseous ions. For sodium chloride, for example, we wish the thermodynamic functions for the reaction

$$Na^+(g) + Cl^-(g) \rightarrow Na^+(aq) + Cl^-(aq).$$

The enthalpy change in this reaction, called the hydration enthalpy, is given by Hess' law as

$$\Delta H^\circ_{hyd} = \Delta H^\circ_f(Na^+, aq) + \Delta H^\circ_f(Cl^-, aq) - \Delta H^\circ_f(Na^+, g) - \Delta H^\circ_f(Cl^-, g),$$

with the last two quantities given by

$$\Delta H^\circ_f(Na^+, g) = \Delta H^\circ_{sub}(Na, s) + \Delta H^\circ_{ion}(Na, g)$$

and

$$\Delta H^\circ_f(Cl^-, g) = \tfrac{1}{2}\Delta H^\circ_{diss}(Cl_2, g) - \Delta H^\circ_{ion}(Cl^-, g).$$

We have in Tables 9–2, 3–2, 3–3 and Appendix II all of the data necessary to calculate this hydration enthalpy, as well the hydration enthalpies of numerous other salts. Some of these are given in Table 9–3, together with the enthalpies of crystallization for purposes of comparison.

TABLE 9–3

SOME ENTHALPIES AND ENTROPIES OF HYDRATION
(298°K)

	ΔH°_{cryst}, kcal/mole	ΔH°_{hyd}, kcal/mole	ΔS°_{hyd}, cal/mole-deg
LiF	−246.7	−240.1	−65.9
NaCl	−186.2	−181.6	−44.3
KF	−194.3	−195.7	−49.5
RbF	−185.4	−189.4	−47.7
SrCl₂	−504.2	−516.6	−95.5
AlF₃	−1467.4	−1472.5	−222.0
AlCl₃	−1303.1	−1379.9	−180.9
AgCl	−219.0	−203.4	−45.6
HCl	—	−346.4	−49.4

The striking thing about these data is the extremely close similarity between the crystal and the hydration enthalpies. Rarely is the *enthalpy of solution* (which is the difference between the enthalpies of hydration and of crystallization) very large numerically, compared with either of the other two quantities. Thus the enthalpies of hydration, like those of crystallization, would seem, at least qualitatively, to depend on ionic radius and charge.

Although on a strict thermodynamic basis it is not possible to define absolute thermodynamic functions for individual ions, there have been numerous attempts to evaluate these quantities. Despite the fact that the values so obtained are only very approximate, they do provide an insight into the problem of hydration. The first estimate, by Bernal and Fowler (1933), was based on the assumption that, since the ionic radii of K^+ and F^- are almost identical (see Table 2–3), their enthalpies of hydration should also be the same. On this basis, then, the total enthalpy of hydration of -195.7 kcal/mole was divided equally between K^+ and

TABLE 9–4

ABSOLUTE THERMODYNAMIC DATA FOR AQUEOUS IONS
(298°K)

Ion	r_{ion}, angstroms	ΔH^*_{hyd}, kcal/mole	ΔS^*_{hyd}, cal/mole-deg	ΔG^*_{hyd}, kcal/mole
H^+	—	-267.9	-29.3	-259.2
F^-	1.33	-113.2	-34.1	-103.1
Cl^-	1.81	-80.9	-20.3	-74.8
Br^-	1.96	-72.7	-16.3	-67.9
I^-	2.19	-62.4	-11.3	-59
Zn^{2+}	0.70	-503.0	-70.5	-482
Cu^{2+}	0.69	-516.4	-72.2	-494.9
Ni^{2+}	0.72	-519.5	-88.1	-491.5
Co^{2+}	0.74	-505	-87.4	-479
Fe^{2+}	0.76	-473.4	-76.7	-450.5
Fe^{3+}	0.64	-1038	-121	-1002
Mn^{2+}	0.80	-455.4	-68.3	-435.1
Cr^{2+}	0.84	-456.6	-43.8	-443.5
Cr^{3+}	0.69	-1044	-127	-1006
Al^{3+}	0.45	-1135.3	-121.1	-1099.2
La^{3+}	1.15	-806.3	-96.6	-777.5
Mg^{2+}	0.65	-473.8	-70.3	-452.9
Ca^{2+}	0.94	-395.1	-56.8	-378.2
Sr^{2+}	1.10	-354.2	-53.1	-338.4
Ba^{2+}	1.29	-326.1	-44.8	-312.7
Li^+	0.68	-130.3	-31.7	-120.8
Na^+	0.98	-104.1	-23.8	-97
K^+	1.33	-84.0	-15.7	-79.3
Rb^+	1.48	-78.0	-12.9	-74.2
Cs^+	1.67	-70.1	-12.2	-66.5

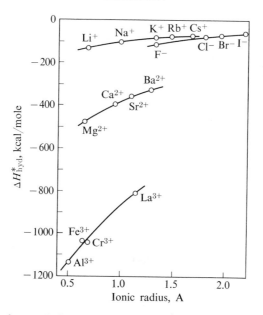

Fig. 9–3.   Absolute enthalpy of hydration (ΔH^*_{hyd}) as a function of ionic radius.

F^-. Once one value has been settled, the other ionic hydration enthalpies can be determined from the data in Table 9–2.

There have been a number of other approaches to the problem of individual ionic enthalpies of hydration, the most recent of which (Noyes, 1962) leads to the values given in Table 9–4. That ionic size and charge have a significant effect on the properties of ions in solution is brought out strikingly in Fig. 9–3, in which some of the hydration enthalpies from Table 9–4 are plotted against the ionic radius. These curves show that the enthalpies involve a dependence on z^2/r, which is similar to that of the enthalpies of crystallization. We shall return to this point in a later section.

Accepting the enthalpy of hydration of the hydrogen ion from Table 9–4 as -267.9 kcal/mole, we can calculate its enthalpy of formation by

$$\Delta H^*_{\text{hyd}}(\text{H}^+, \text{aq}) = \Delta H^*_f(\text{H}^+, \text{aq}) - \Delta H^\circ_f(\text{H}^+, \text{g}),$$

in which the asterisk superscript is used to denote these "absolute" hydration enthalpies. Therefore we find

$$\Delta H^*_f(\text{H}^+, \text{aq}) = 99.1 \text{ kcal/mole}.$$

However, if we look in detail at the chemical reaction involved in the formation of $\text{H}^+(\text{aq})$,

$$\tfrac{1}{2}\text{H}_2(\text{g}) \rightarrow \text{H}^+(\text{aq}) + \text{e}^-(\text{g}),$$

we see that we still have not escaped the inevitable problem of the electron, which, according to this equation, would be left behind in the gas phase. Nevertheless, this result provides an interesting comparison with the convention used in thermodynamics which assigns the value zero to $\Delta H_f^\circ(H^+, aq)$, the standard enthalpy of formation of the aquated hydrogen ion.

(b) Entropy of hydration

The entropies of hydration of neutral sets of ions can be calculated as the difference between the entropies of the ions in the gas phase and in aqueous solution. The latter have been tabulated in Table 9–2. The former are rarely given as such, but, for closed-shell configurations of monatomic ions, may be calculated by the Sackur-Tetrode equation (see Chapter 8) as

$$S^\circ = \tfrac{3}{2}R \ln M + 25.992 \qquad (9\text{–}3)$$

at 298°K under standard conditions. Thus all that is required for many gaseous ions is the molecular (atomic) weight, M. The problem is more complex for transition metal ions, for which the entropy contributed by the electronic structure must be included. More advanced works must be consulted for details of these calculations.

As an example, let us calculate the entropy of hydration of AlF_3. The appropriate chemical equation is

$$Al^{3+}(g) + 3F^-(g) \rightarrow Al^{3+}(aq) + 3F^-(aq).$$

The entropy of the gaseous Al^{3+} ion is 35.81 cal/mole-deg, and that of the gaseous F^- ion is 34.77 cal/mole-deg, both from Eq. (9–3), since they have inert-gas or closed-shell electron configurations. The entropies of Al^{3+} and F^- in aqueous solution are given in Table 9–2 as: −74.9 and −2.3 cal/mole-deg, respectively. The entropy change we require is then

$$\Delta S^\circ_{hyd} = S^\circ(Al^{3+}, aq) - S^\circ(Al^{3+}, g) + 3S^\circ(F^-, aq) - 3S^\circ(F^-, g),$$

and therefore has the value −222.0 cal/mole-deg. Some data on entropies of hydration are presented in Table 9–3.

The entropy change associated with the solution in water of monatomic neutral gases (e.g., the inert gases) is about the same order of magnitude as the entropy of vaporization, but of opposite sign, roughly −22 cal/mole-deg. We can therefore make a comparison between an entropy change of $-22n$ with the ionic entropies of hydration, in which n is the number of ions per molecule. For the most part we find a more negative entropy change for pairs of ions compared with pairs of neutral atoms, particularly when small, highly charged ions are considered. On the other hand, the entropy change for a pair of large ions, such as Rb^+ and I^-, is not as negative as the −44 cal/mole-deg with which it can be compared. The interpretation of these effects, however, is best left until we have an estimate of entropies of hydration of individual ions.

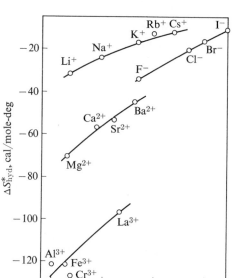

FIG. 9–4.   Absolute entropies of hydration (ΔS^*_{hyd}) as a function of ionic radius.

The problem of the determination of individual values of ionic entropies poses much the same difficulties as ionic enthalpies, but the distribution of the total entropy of hydration between the cation and anion can be done somewhat more reliably. A reasonable set of values is that given by Noyes (1962), some parts of which are listed in Table 9–4. The entropy of hydration of the hydrogen ion, that is, for the process

$$H^+(g) \rightarrow H^+(aq),$$

is -29.3 cal/mole-deg, on this "absolute" basis. From this the absolute entropy of the hydrogen ion in aqueous solution can be found from the equation

$$S^*(H^+, aq) = \Delta S^*_{hyd} + S^\circ(H^+, g).$$

Equation (9–3) supplies the entropy of the gaseous hydrogen ion, 26.0 cal/mole-deg; therefore we find

$$S^*(H^+, aq) = -3.3 \text{ cal/mole-deg.}$$

It is doubtful that this value can be more than one or two units in error. Thus the arbitrary choice of zero for the standard entropy of the hydrogen ion is conveniently close to the "true" value.

That the entropy of hydration largely results from coulombic interaction between the ion and the solvent is shown in Fig. 9–4. Here we see illustrated clearly the dependence of the entropy of hydration on both ionic radius and charge.

Comparison of the curves for univalent cations and anions shows that even the sign of the charge has an important effect. Although K^+ and F^- have the same ionic radii, the entropy of hydration of the latter is about twice as negative as that of the former.

(c) Theoretical treatment of hydration

It is apparent from the polar nature of electrolyte solvents and the data of Figs. 9–3 and 9–4 that ion-dipole interactions are responsible for ionic dissociation. Since enthalpies of crystallization are so successfully interpreted in terms of coulombic interactions of ions (see Chapters 2 and 7), it would be logical to assume that the same approach might work in the case of electrolytic solutions. To some extent this is true, but the approach has been far less successful than in the case of crystalline solids.

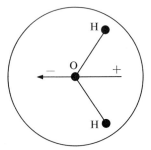

FIG. 9–5. Idealized model of the polar water molecule employed in theoretical hydration studies. The arrow indicates the direction of the dipole (1.84 debyes).

One of the problems concerns the uncertain structure of the solvent in the immediate vicinity of the ion. Assuming, for the water molecule, a model of the type illustrated in Fig. 9–5, it is to be expected that solute ions are surrounded by oriented water molecules in one or more layers, as shown in Fig. 9–6. The number of water molecules in a layer and the number of layers would depend on the charge

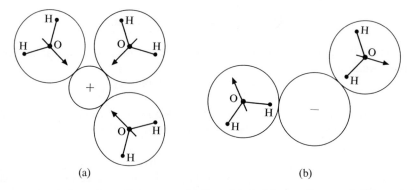

(a)   (b)

FIG. 9–6. Orientation of water molecules about (a) a cation, and (b) an anion.

and the size of the ion. This concept has been employed to explain solvent effects in a number of physical phenomena, including conductance, volume change on solution, specific heat, etc., and each application is capable of yielding a value for the *hydration number*. Unfortunately, the experimental values for the number of water molecules "associated" with an ion in solution tend to depend on the method used to evaluate them. This is perhaps not surprising, since the question of association is really one of degree.

TABLE 9–5

HYDRATION NUMBERS

Li^+	5 ± 1
Na^+	5 ± 1
K^+	4 ± 2
Rb^+	3 ± 1
F^-	4 ± 1
Cl^-	1 ± 1
Br^-	1 ± 1
I^-	1 ± 1
Mg^{2+}	15 ± 2
Ba^{2+}	12 ± 4
Al^{3+}	26 ± 5

From the summary of the available data given in Table 9–5, it is apparent that the hydration number of univalent ions, particularly anions, is small. Around a small, highly charged ion such as Al^{3+}, the influence of the ion must be strong over several layers of water molecules, and the hydration number is quite large. The water molecules in the hydration sphere of an ion are generally in rapid dynamic equilibrium with the water molecules in the bulk of the solvent. However, there are specific examples, such as $Cr(H_2O)_6^{3+}$, in which the innermost layer is quite firmly bonded, so that the water molecules exchange with other solvent molecules only very slowly. An ion such as this would have still more solvent in its outer hydration sphere. In these cases, it is probably more realistic to consider the aquated ion as a complex ion, that is, a specific entity itself.

Special considerations would also apply in the case of the ions H_3O^+ and OH^- as a result of hydrogen bonding. Although it is not possible to assign an unambiguous formula to these hydrated ions, Eigen has proposed that the dominant species are $H_9O_4^+$ and $H_7O_4^-$, as shown in Fig. 9–7. The approximately tetrahedral coordination around the central oxygen atom is similar to that in ice, with the exception that only three hydrogen bonds are formed because of the overall net charge. Thus H_3O^+ bonds only through its own hydrogens and OH^- only through the hydrogens of the coordinating water molecules.

Born (1920) approached the problem by calculating the free energy change associated with the process in which an ion of radius r is transferred from the gas phase to a solvent, considered to be a continuous medium, of dielectric constant

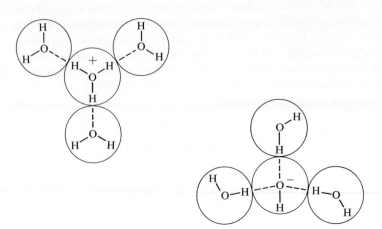

FIG. 9-7. Hydration models of the proton and of the hydroxyl ion in aqueous solution.

D. The resulting expression,*

$$\Delta G_{\text{hyd}} = -\frac{Nz^2e^2}{2r}\left(1 - \frac{1}{D}\right),\tag{9-4}$$

gives results in error by as much as a factor of two, in most cases. For example, from the data in Table 9-4, the free energy of hydration can be calculated according to:

$$\Delta G^*_{\text{hyd}} = \Delta H^*_{\text{hyd}} - T\,\Delta S^*_{\text{hyd}}.$$

For the ions, Na^+, Ca^{2+}, Al^{3+}, and F^-, we find ΔG^*_{hyd} to be: -97.0, -378.2, -1099.2 and -103.1 kcal/mole, respectively. In the Born equation, if we substitute the dielectric constant of water, 78.3, the appropriate ionic radii, and a conversion factor to give

$$\Delta G_{\text{hyd}} = -163.9\, z^2/r \text{ kcal/mole,}$$

we find for the calculated free energies of hydration: -167, -698, -2950 and -123 kcal/mole, respectively, for the same series of ions. Although these calculations at least give the correct sign and the correct order of magnitude, there is considerable error.

---

* The reader is referred to physics textbooks for the electrostatic derivation of this equation. From a chemical point of view, it is more interesting to note that, because of the use of the macroscopic dielectric constant in the calculation, the appropriate quantity for comparison is ΔG rather than ΔU. The calculation of crystal energies (in Section 2-4) involved only molecular parameters; hence the crystal energies were compared with the change in internal energy, ΔU.

The principal defect in the direct application of Eq. (9–4) is that the dielectric constant of the solvent near an ion must be considerably less than that in the bulk of the solvent. The reason for this effect is that the water molecules in the hydration layers are more or less fixed in position, and are oriented with respect to the ion by its intense electric field. The effect of a reduced dielectric constant in Eq. (9–4) would be to reduce numerically the free energy of hydration, bringing the results in closer agreement with experiment. The error in the computed free energy of hydration is least for the monovalent anions (small charge and large radius) and largest for trivalent cations (large charge and small radius).

On a semi-empirical basis, Latimer, Pitzer, and Slansky (1939) noted that if an effective radius were used instead of the ionic radius, the calculated free energies of hydration could be brought into agreement with experiment. They found the best fit to the data by adding 0.75 A to the ionic radii of cations and 0.10 A to those of anions. A rationalization of the effective radii is that one should consider the ion and its first hydration layer as an entity to go into the Born equation. This cannot, of course, be correct in principle, for it neglects completely the interaction between an ion and the first hydration layer, which is, in fact, the most important contribution to the total free energy of hydration.

Recognizing that the dielectric constant must be appreciably smaller than the macroscopic value around an ion, Noyes (1962) turned the Born equation around and calculated an effective average dielectric constant of the solvent for each ion from its ionic radius and experimental free energy of hydration (corrected for the free energy of hydration of a neutral atom). There results the interesting correlation between the effective dielectric constants and the ionic radii of cations which have an inert gas electron configuration:

$$D_{eff} = 1 + 1.376\, r_{ionic}, \tag{9–5}$$

which is independent of the charge of the cation. The reader may verify that if Eq. (9–5) is substituted in Eq. (9–4), the result is essentially the same as the empirical increase of the cation radius. However, the use of a reduced dielectric constant is intuitively more plausible than that of effective radii. The effective dielectric constants calculated for anions and for cations other than those with closed electronic shells do not fit Eq. (9–5). In the latter case, the dielectric constant is smaller than predicted, because there may be an appreciable contribution of covalent bonding between the ion and the first hydration layer. Why it does not fit the data for anions is less certain. However there are too few monatomic anions in aqueous solution to carry out extensive correlations of this type.

Calculations based on the detailed structure of the solvent around an ion have met with only limited success. Bernal and Fowler (1933) broke the calculation down into several parts. The interaction of the ion with the first layer of water molecules is given by a term

$$-\frac{Nnze\mu}{(r_{ionic} + r_w)^2}, \tag{9–6}$$

in which n is the number of water molecules with dipole moment μ and radius

TABLE 9–6

THEORETICALLY ESTIMATED ENTHALPIES OF HYDRATION

Ion	Eley and Evans	Verwey
F$^-$	-91	-122*
Cl$^-$	-59	
Br$^-$	-52	-72*
I$^-$	-45	
Li$^+$	-133	
Na$^+$	-115	
K$^+$	-90	-75†
Rb$^+$	-81	
Cs$^+$	-73	-53†
Al^{3+}	-1010	
La^{3+}	-708	

* Ionic radius of 1.36 A assumed.
† Ionic radius of 2.00 A assumed.

r_w (1.38 A) in the layer. It was then assumed that the Born equation would apply outside this hydration layer, therefore they added the term

$$\frac{Nz^2e^2}{2(r_{\mathrm{ionic}} + 2r_w)}\left(1 - \frac{1}{D}\right). \tag{9–7}$$

The final term is that of a water molecule whose place is taken up in the solution by the ion, although the repulsion between the ion and its immediate neighboring water molecules should also be considered.

Eley and Evans (1938) considered a more detailed cyclic process, in which they summed the energy terms for removal of five water molecules as a unit from the bulk of the solvent, dissociated them into molecules, associated four of them with the gaseous ion, and returned this complex to the cavity in the solvent. Verwey (1942) used a more complex model for the interaction of the ion with water molecules in the first hydration layer, and calculated the enthalpy of hydration of cations and anions with radii of 1.36 and 2.00 A. Table 9–6 compares the results of these theoretical treatments in terms of enthalpies of hydration, and shows that, although a considerable improvement over the Born equation is obtained, the problem is by no means solved.

There is definitely a relationship between the enthalpies and entropies of hydration, as we can see by a comparison of Figs. 9–3 and 9–4. The same factors that lead to a large negative enthalpy of hydration, i.e., high charge and small radius, also lead to a large negative entropy of hydration. The orientation of one or more layers of water molecules around an ion restricts their motion compared with their freedom in the bulk of the solvent. It is this ordering process around an ion that largely determines the entropy change. On the other hand, large monovalent ions, such as Cs^+ and I^-, have more positive entropies than would be expected. From the magnitude of these entropy changes, it can be deduced that these ions cause a breakdown in the structure of liquid water. This effect is probably present with other ions, but is overshadowed by the strong orienting effect of high charge and small size.

The theories which have been developed to permit the calculation of entropies of hydration are more complex than those required for the enthalpy or free energy. However, the theoretical results of Eley and Evans (1938) are in reasonable agreement with the experimental values.

9–3. ACIDS AND BASES

The investigation of the nature of acids and bases ranks as one of the earliest preoccupations of chemistry. With the advancement of science, attempts to define an acid on a phenomenological basis gave way to definitions based on composition, and finally with the discovery of electrolytic dissociation came the association of an acid with the hydrogen ion or proton. The most widely accepted present-day definition is that due to Brønsted, who defined an acid as a species having a tendency to lose a proton. Thus the dissociation of an acid A according to the reaction

$$A \rightleftharpoons B + H^+$$

produces a proton and the conjugate base B.

When we consider an actual acid-base reaction, we find that the general scheme

$$A_1 + B_2 \rightleftharpoons B_1 + A_2$$

always applies. That is, in order for an acid A_1 to give up a proton and form its conjugate base B_1, there must also be a base B_2 which accepts the proton, and is converted thereby into its conjugate acid A_2. Thus, according to the Brønsted idea, the dissociation of HCN would be represented by

$$HCN(aq) + H_2O \rightleftharpoons CN^-(aq) + H_3O^+(aq). \qquad (9\text{--}8)$$

Here the acid HCN becomes its conjugate base CN^- when it loses a proton to the base H_2O, converting the latter to its conjugate acid H_3O^+. A reaction similar to that of Eq. (9–8) is the equilibrium between sodium cyanide and water,

$$CN^-(aq) + H_2O \rightleftharpoons HCN(aq) + OH^-(aq). \qquad (9\text{--}9)$$

In this example, however, water acts as an acid and becomes, on giving up a proton to the base CN^-, the conjugate base OH^-. This versatility of a protonated solvent molecule to act as both an acid and a base is common.

Water, for example, dissociates to a slight extent according to

$$2H_2O \rightleftharpoons H_3O^+(aq) + OH^-(aq). \qquad (9\text{--}10)$$

Other solvents exhibit similar equilibria, in which one solvent molecule acts as an acid and donates a proton to another solvent molecule. Thus we have, in liquid ammonia,

$$2NH_3 \rightleftharpoons NH_4^+(sol) + NH_2^-(sol),$$

and in anhydrous sulfuric acid,

$$2H_2SO_4 \rightleftharpoons H_3SO_4^+(sol) + HSO_4^-(sol).$$

Whether we write the formula of the hydrated proton as $H^+(aq)$, $H_3O^+(aq)$, or $H_{2n+1}O_n^+(aq)$ does not really matter, except that, for purposes of thermodynamic calculations, only the first of these is significant. For example, we may calculate the free energy change in the reaction

$$H_2O(l) \rightleftharpoons H^+(aq) + OH^-(aq)$$

to be $+19.10$ kcal, which corresponds to

$$K_w = \frac{a_{H^+}a_{OH^-}}{a_{H_2O}} = 10^{-14}.$$

With the approximation of unit activity coefficients for the ions and unit activity for the water (i.e., extremely dilute solution), this equation reduces to

$$K_w = [H^+][OH^-], \tag{9-11}$$

a common approximation. Notice that if we used Eq. (9–10) to calculate the free energy change, we would get an incorrect answer unless we chose $\Delta G_f^\circ(H_3O^+, aq) = -56.69$ kcal/mole. Even though $H_3O^+(aq)$ and $H^+(aq)$ are to be regarded as the same species, care must be exercised in thermodynamic calculations to ensure that the manner in which a formula is written in a chemical equation is consistent with that used in the tabulation of thermodynamic data.

(a) Acid and base strength

An acid such as hydrochloric acid, when dissolved in water, reacts essentially completely according to

$$HCl(g) + H_2O(l) \rightarrow H_3O^+(aq) + Cl^-(aq),$$

while HCN reacts only partially in water, so that the major fraction of the solute is in the form of molecular HCN. In this sense we distinguish between these acids by stating that HCl is a stronger acid than $H_3O^+(aq)$, but that HCN is a weaker acid than $H_3O^+(aq)$. If we now compare the behavior of HCl with that of perchloric acid, $HClO_4$, we find that it also is a stronger acid than H_3O^+. In fact, the strongest acid in the Brønsted sense that can exist in appreciable concentration in water is H_3O^+. There is, then, a leveling effect, in which all acids stronger than H_3O^+ react with the solvent to give this acid. Solutions called hydrochloric acid, perchloric acid, etc., are essentially solutions containing in common H_3O^+, together with the appropriate anion.

From this discussion it is apparent that we cannot designate the strength of an acid on an absolute basis. It can only be determined relative to some other acid. The common way to do this is to use the solvent itself as a reference. This works well, provided that the acid considered is a weaker acid than the protonated solvent. Thus, for the equilibrium of HCN with water, Eq. (9–8), the K_a provides a measure of the acid strength of HCN compared with that of H_3O^+. Since the equilibrium constants cover a vast numerical range, it is convenient to make use of the definition

$$pK_a = -\log_{10} K_a.$$

Then for HCN, $pK_a = 9.32$ ($K_a = 4.8 \times 10^{-10}$). Table 9–7 lists the pK_a values for a number of weak acids in water. These could be calculated from the data

TABLE 9–7

pK_a VALUES FOR SOME WEAK ACIDS IN AQUEOUS SOLUTION (298°K)

Acid	pK_a	Acid	pK_a
H_3AsO_3	9.2	HNO_2	3.3
H_3AsO_4	2.3	NH_4^+	9.2
$H_2AsO_4^-$	7.0	$CH_3NH_3^+$	10.7
$HAsO_4^{2-}$	11.5	$(CH_3)_2NH_2^+$	11.0
H_3BO_3	9.2	$(CH_3)_3NH^+$	9.9
$HBrO$	8.7	$N_2H_3^+$	8.0
H_2CO_3	6.4	$HONH_3^+$	5.0
HCO_3^-	10.3	H_2O_2	11.8
$HOOCH$	3.7	H_3PO_2	2.0
$HOOCCH_3$	4.7	H_3PO_3	1.8
HCN	9.3	$H_2PO_3^-$	6.7
$HOCN$	3.7	H_3PO_4	2.1
$HClO$	7.2	$H_2PO_4^-$	7.2
$HClO_2$	2.0	HPO_4^{2-}	12.0
$HCrO_4^-$	6.5	H_2S	7.0
HF	3.3	HS^-	12.9
HIO	10.0	H_2SO_3	1.9
H_5IO_6	1.6	HSO_3^-	7.2
$H_4IO_6^-$	8.4	HSO_4^-	1.9
$H_3IO_6^{2-}$	15.0	H_2Se	3.8
HN_3	4.7	HSe^-	11.0
$H_2N_2O_2$	7.1	H_2Te	2.6
$HN_2O_2^-$	11.0	HTe^-	11

in Table 9–2, but the pK_a's are more precise because they are obtained directly and do not depend on the more difficult determination of a free energy of formation of each species in the equilibrium.

If a different solvent is chosen, then the acid strengths will be different. Thus in strongly acid solvents such as sulfuric acid, the normally strong, i.e., completely dissociated, acids, perchloric and hydrochloric, are not as strong as the acid $H_3SO_4^+$, and hence have pK_a values in sulfuric acid greater than unity. The pK_a value for perchloric acid is about $+4$, whereas in aqueous solution its pK_a is about -10, a difference of fourteen powers of ten in K_a. In a more basic solvent such as liquid ammonia, there is a much greater leveling effect, and even a weak acid such as formic acid, HCOOH, with $pK_a = 3.68$ in water, acts as a strong acid:

$$HCOOH(sol) + NH_3(l) \rightarrow NH_4^+(sol) + HCOO^-(sol).$$

The leveling effect on acids in liquid ammonia occurs for acids with a pK_a (in water) less than about four. Unfortunately, the relative strengths are not exactly the same from solvent to solvent, although they are nearly so for acids of the same type, e.g., the series HF to HI or the homologous series of monocarboxylic acids.

The same effect is noted on the basic side. Just as H_3O^+, $H_3SO_4^+$, and NH_4^+ are the strongest acids that can exist in water, anhydrous H_2SO_4 and anhydrous NH_3, so also the strongest bases in such systems are OH^-, HSO_4^-, and NH_2^-, respectively. The bases O^{2-} and NH_2^- are stronger bases than OH^-; hence if Na_2O or $NaNH_2$ are dissolved in water, the reactions

$$O^{2-}(aq) + H_2O \rightarrow 2OH^-(aq)$$

and

$$NH_2^-(aq) + H_2O \rightarrow NH_3(aq) + OH^-(aq)$$

go essentially to completion. Other bases, such as CN^-, NH_3, $HCOO^-$, etc., exist in aqueous solution in equilibrium with a solvent, according to Eqs. (9–9), (9–12), and (9–13).

$$NH_3(aq) + H_2O \rightleftharpoons NH_4^+(aq) + OH^-(aq), \qquad (9\text{--}12)$$

$$HCOO^-(aq) + H_2O \rightleftharpoons HCOOH(aq) + OH^-. \qquad (9\text{--}13)$$

The equilibrium constants for these latter reactions are necessarily related to the K_a values of the corresponding conjugate acids. To see this, we write the base equilibrium constant expression of CN^- as

$$K_b = \frac{a_{HCN}a_{OH^-}}{a_{CN^-}a_{H_2O}}. \qquad (9\text{--}14)$$

If we formulate the ratio K_w/K_b, combining Eqs. (9–11) and (9–14), we find

$$\frac{K_w}{K_b} = \frac{a_{H^+}a_{CN^-}}{a_{HCN}},$$

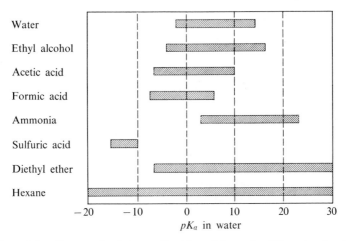

FIG. 9–8.   Range of existence of acids and bases in different solvents.

which is just K_a for the acid HCN, conjugate to the base CN⁻. As a general principle, then, the sum of pK_a and pK_b for a conjugate acid-base pair must be equal
to 14 in aqueous solution:

$$pK_a + pK_b = pK_w = 14 \text{ (aqueous)}.$$

In the more general case, the sum of the pK_a and pK_b in any solvent must be equal
to the pK for the dissociation of that solvent, provided that there are no complications. For example, H_2SO_4 dissociates in two distinct ways, to give $H_3SO_4^+$
and HSO_4^-, and also H_3O^+ and $HS_2O_7^-$.

  The situation with regard to leveling effects is summed up in Fig. 9–8 for a
number of solvents. The shaded areas span the pK_a (in water) values, for which
the equilibrium between the conjugate acid-base pair and the solvent is measurable. This range is quite small in sulfuric acid; although sulphur trioxide is a strong
acid in this medium,

$$SO_3(\text{sol}) + 2H_2SO_4 \rightarrow H_3SO_4^+(\text{sol}) + HS_2O_7^-(\text{sol}); \qquad (9\text{–}15)$$

water acts as a strong base:

$$H_2O(\text{sol}) + H_2SO_4 \rightarrow H_3O^+(\text{sol}) + HSO_4^-(\text{sol}). \qquad (9\text{–}16)$$

Note that in Eq. (9–15), the solvated proton (i.e., acid) is $H_3SO_4^+$, but that in
Eq. (9–16) the base is HSO_4^-. Although ether and hexane have wide pK_a limits,
acid-base equilibria in these solvents tend to be complicated because of the low
dielectric constant. In many cases the equilibria have been found to involve ion
pairs and low polymers.

(b) Trends in acidities

There are trends in the acid strength of various compounds with which the molecular structures of the appropriate species can be correlated. One of the most straightforward series is that of the hydrogen halides, HF, HCl, HBr, and HI. In water the last three members of this series are strong acids, completely dissociated according to the leveling effect of the solvent, but HF is a weak acid with $pK_a = 3.25$. In more acid solvents such as anhydrous formic acid, dissolved hydrochloric acid is weak. Vapor pressure data on HCl, HBr, and HI over aqueous solutions can be used to estimate roughly the pK_a's, and these are found to be -6, -8, and -9, respectively. We can also calculate the pK_a's from thermodynamic free energy data, provided only that an estimate can be made of the free energy of solution of the undissociated molecules of the last three members of the series.

The requisite data have been collected in Table 9–8, in which we have broken down the process

$$HX(aq) \rightleftharpoons H^+(aq) + X^-(aq)$$

into detailed steps of an alternate path. The $\Delta G°$ values for the reaction

$$HX(aq) \rightleftharpoons HX(g)$$

are estimated [Bell (1959)]. Since the equations in Table 9–8 have been arranged so that they may be added directly, we can see at a glance the effect of any one step on the final answer. Thus the factors that contribute to a positive pK_a are: a large bond dissociation (free) energy of HX(g), a small ionization (free) energy of X^-(g), and a (numerically) small free energy of hydration. The dominant effect in this series lies in the bond dissociation energies, while the hydration energies oppose this trend. It is interesting to note that if the bond dissociation energy

TABLE 9–8

FREE ENERGY CHANGES FOR DISSOCIATION OF HYDROGEN
HALIDES IN AQUEOUS SOLUTION

($\Delta G°$ in kcal/mole, 298°K)

Hydrogen Halides	HF	HCl	HBr	HI
$HX(aq) = HX(g)$	5.7	-1	-1	-1
$HX(g) = H(g) + X(g)$	127.8	96.5	81.0	65.0
$H(g) = H^+(g) + e$	315.3	315.3	315.3	315.3
$X(g) + e = X^-(g)$	-83.0	-87.6	-82.5	-75.3
$H^+(g) + X^-(g) = H^+(aq) + X^-(aq)$	-361.5	-332.8	-325.7	-317.7
$HX(aq) = H^+(aq) + X^-(aq)$	4.3	-10	-13	-14
pK_a	3.3	-7	-9.5	-10

TABLE 9–9

pK_a VALUES FOR SOME HYDRIDES IN AQUEOUS SOLUTION (298°K)

CH$_4$ 58	NH$_3$ 35	H$_2$O 16	HF 3.2
	PH$_3$ 27	H$_2$S 7	HCl −7
		H$_2$Se 4	HBr −9
		H$_2$Te 3	HI −10

of HF were smaller by 10 kcal/mole and all other quantitites were kept constant, HF would also be a strong acid. The same general trend of acidities of hydrides is found with the elements of Group VI; the pK_a values are 16, 7, 4, and 3, for H$_2$O, H$_2$S, H$_2$Se and H$_2$Te, respectively. Note that, in this series also, there is a large jump between the pK_a's of the first and second members, again arising predominantly from the large decrease in bond dissociation energy from water to hydrogen sulfide.

Table 9–9 summarizes the data on the pK_a's of some hydrides. The pK_a for NH$_3$ is that for its reaction as an acid, that is,

$$NH_3 + H_2O \rightleftharpoons H_3O^+ + NH_2^-,$$

rather than its normal reaction in aqueous solution as a weak base. Although there is a paucity of data for extremely weak acids, the trend across a period is clear. Since information on ionization, hydration, etc., is not available, it is not possible to correlate the trend with detailed thermodynamic data. Contrary to

TABLE 9–10

pK_a'S FOR SOME INORGANIC OXYACIDS IN AQUEOUS SOLUTION (298°K)

Acid	pK_a	Acid	pK_a	Acid	pK_a	Acid	pK_a
Cl(OH)	7.2	NO(OH)	3.3	NO$_2$(OH)	−1.4	ClO$_3$(OH)	(−10)
Br(OH)	8.7	ClO(OH)	2.0	ClO$_2$(OH)	−1		
I(OH)	10.0	CO(OH)$_2$	3.9*	IO$_2$(OH)	0.8		
B(OH)$_3$	9.2	SO(OH)$_2$	1.9	SO$_2$(OH)$_2$	(−3)		
As(OH)$_3$	9.2	SeO(OH)$_2$	2.6	SeO$_2$(OH)$_2$	(−3)		
Sb(OH)$_3$	11.0	TeO(OH)$_2$	2.7				
Si(OH)$_4$	10.0	PO(OH)$_3$	2.1				
Ge(OH)$_4$	8.6	AsO(OH)$_3$	2.3				
Te(OH)$_6$	8.8	IO(OH)$_5$	1.6				
		HPO(OH)$_2$	1.8				
		H$_2$PO(OH)	2.0				

* This is the true value for H$_2$CO$_3$, which takes into account the H$_2$CO$_3$-CO$_2$ equilibrium.

what might be expected, however, the decreasing acidity parallels a similar trend in bond energy. There must therefore be an opposing trend in some other property, likely the electron affinity, which more than offsets the change in bond energy.

A third general trend in acidity concerns oxyacids of nonmetals having the general formula $XO_n(OH)_m$. The relevant data in Table 9–10, taken from a summary by Bell (1959), show that, when these acids are grouped with common values of n, the pK_a values within a group are similar in magnitude. Very roughly, the pK_a of a neutral oxyacid is given by $8 - 5n$. This phenomenon, like those discussed above, arises primarily as an enthalpy effect, since all simple neutral acids have in common an entropy of dissociation of about -20 cal/mole-deg. There have been several interpretations of this trend, based on the number of equivalent oxygen atoms in the anion, which is $n + 1$. The increase of acidity with n is attributed to an increased stability of the anion, either by resonance in the anion or by spreading of the negative charge over the equivalent oxygens. In a restricted sense, the acidity of a series of oxyacids of a particular element increases with increasing oxidation number of the element, e.g., the chlorine series; however, where there is a radical change in structure type, this is not so. [Compare $Te(OH)_6$ with $TeO(OH)_2$.]

The last general trend concerns the increase in acidity on successive removal of protons from a polyprotic acid, such as H_3PO_4, $H_2PO_4^-$, HPO_4^{2-}, and PO_4^{3-}. A selection of pK_a's is given in Table 9–11 to illustrate this point. We have

TABLE 9–11

SUCCESSIVE pK_a's OF SOME POLYPROTIC ACIDS IN AQUEOUS SOLUTION (298°K)

Class I	pK_1	pK_2	pK_3	ΔpK_{12}	ΔpK_{23}
H_2CO_3	3.88	10.32	—	6.4	—
H_5IO_6	1.64	8.36	15.0	6.7	6.6
H_3PO_3	2.00	6.70	—	4.7	—
H_2S	7.00	12.92	—	5.9	—
H_3PO_4	2.12	7.21	12.0	5.1	4.8
H_2SO_3	1.76	7.21	—	5.5	—
H_2Se	3.80	11.0	—	7.2	—

Class II	pK_1	pK_2	pK_3	pK_4	ΔpK_{12}	ΔpK_{23}	ΔpK_{34}
$H_4P_2O_6$	2.2	2.81	7.27	10.03	0.6	4.5	2.8
$H_4P_2O_7$	0.85	1.96	6.54	8.46	1.1	4.6	1.9
Citric acid	3.13	4.75	6.39	—	1.6	1.6	—
$(COOH)_2$	1.23	4.19	—	—	3.0	—	—
$CH_2(COOH)_2$	2.83	5.69	—	—	2.9	—	—
$(CH_2)_2(COOH)_2$	4.19	5.48	—	—	1.3	—	—
$(CH_2)_3(COOH)_2$	4.34	5.27	—	—	0.9	—	—
$(CH_2)_7(COOH)_2$	4.55	5.41	—	—	0.9	—	—

separated these acids into two groups, in the first of which the pK_a increases by four to seven units on removal of a proton. In the second group, the change in pK_a is smaller, of the order of one to three. There is a clear distinction in structure between these two groups, for in the first, the oxygen atoms that give up protons are bonded to the same atom, while in the second group these oxygen atoms are separated by two or more atoms. This distinction is marked in the two inorganic acids in the second part. The difference in the pK_a's for removal of the first and second protons is small, because the protons are removed from oxygen atoms as far from each other as possible. But when the third proton is removed, the corresponding ΔpK_a is of the same magnitude as those acids of the first group. The dibasic acids listed have successively more atoms between the protonated oxygen atoms. As this number increases, ΔpK_a decreases. In the limit of very long chain dibasic acids, the difference between pK_1 and pK_2 would be expected to be 0.6.

Qualitatively, the successive pK_a's of a polyprotic acid should increase as the protons are removed, simply on a charge basis. Thus it is much more difficult to pull a proton away from a negatively charged HPO_4^{2-} ion than from a neutral H_3PO_4 molecule. This effect is very nearly constant for the acids of Class I.

Again qualitatively, when successive protons are removed from different ends of a complex molecule, this charge effect should decrease with an increase in the distance between the proton sites, as is found in Class II acids. The series of dicarboxylic acids, $HOOC(CH_2)_nCOOH$, provide the interesting trends shown in Fig. 9–9. The change in pK_1 is often attributed to an inductive effect of one COOH group on the other, in that the carboxyl group is said to pull electrons in the bonds toward itself, making the opposite proton more acidic. That the chlorine atom has just about the same effect is illustrated in Fig. 9–9 for the acids $Cl(CH_2)_nCOOH$. The pK_a's for these two series are almost identical for $n = 0$, 1, and 2. On the other hand, the inductive effect of the COO^- group is small, hence the pK_2 values of the dicarboxylic acids do not vary greatly. These effects and others relating to organic acids are discussed fully in most advanced organic chemistry texts.

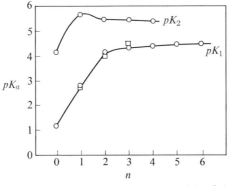

FIG. 9–9.   Dissociation constants of organic acids of the formulas
$HOOC(CH_2)_nCOOH$ (○) and $Cl(CH_2)_nCOOH$ (□).

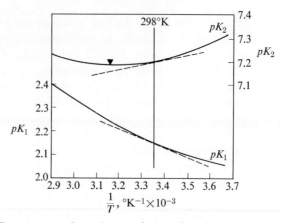

FIG. 9–10. Temperature dependence of the dissociation constants of phosphoric acid. The triangle denotes the minimum in the pK_2 curve.

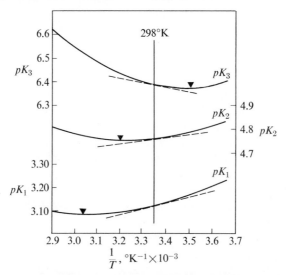

FIG. 9–11. Temperature dependence of the dissociation constants of citric acid. The triangles denote the minima in the curves.

The phenomena can be treated on a thermodynamic basis also. Normally, as pointed out in Chapter 8, the enthalpy change in a reaction can be determined as the slope of the line, $\log K$, versus $1/T$. Provided that the enthalpy change is large (either positive or negative) the slight curvature of this line introduces only a small uncertainty in the enthalpy data. In the case of the equilibria of weak acids in water, the reactions are very near to being thermoneutral; hence, as shown in Fig. 9–10 for H_3PO_4, and in Fig. 9–11 for citric acid, the curvature actually changes the sign of ΔH. The curves shown have minima (except for pK_1 of H_3PO_4), because ΔH decreases with increasing temperature; that is, there is a large negative

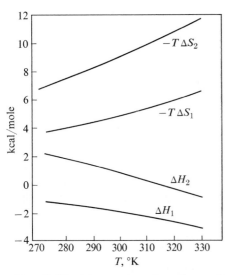

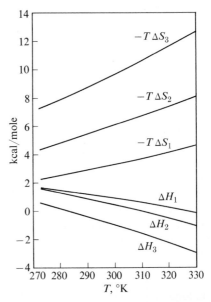

FIG. 9–12. Temperature dependence of ΔH and $T \Delta S$ for the ionic dissociation of H_3PO_4.

FIG. 9–13. Temperature dependence of ΔH and $T \Delta S$ for the ionic dissociation of citric acid.

heat capacity change of the order of -50 cal/deg for these reactions. Thus all three dissociations of citric acid are endothermic below 11°C, and all three are exothermic above about 55°C. Figures 9–12 and 9–13 show the variation with temperature of ΔH and $-T \Delta S$ for phosphoric and citric acids, respectively. Consideration of the data for phosphoric acid shows that both the enthalpy and entropy changes contribute to the large differences in the successive pK_a values. In the case of citric acid, however, the enthalpy changes become more negative as protons are removed; hence the enthalpy changes oppose the effect of entropy, although the latter dominates. It would be interesting to examine this point further, but there are insufficient thermodynamic data to explore these effects in other acids of interest.

(c) Aprotic acids and bases

The Brønsted concept of acids and bases obviously cannot be applied to solvents which do not contain bound hydrogen. Nevertheless, some of the general features of acid–base theory find analogies in other solvents such as BrF_3, SO_2, and N_2O_4. Each of these solvents is a conductor of electricity, the ions arising from the self-ionization of the solvents

$$2BrF_3 \rightleftharpoons BrF_2^+ + BrF_4^-,$$
$$2SO_2 \rightleftharpoons SO^{2+} + SO_3^{2-},$$
$$N_2O_4 \rightleftharpoons NO^+ + NO_3^-.$$

Carrying the analogy further, the cations correspond to acids while the anions are bases. Thus, in BrF_3, silver fluoride is a strong base and SbF_5 is a strong acid, leading to the following:

$$AgF + BrF_3 \rightleftharpoons Ag^+ + BrF_4^-,$$

$$SbF_5 + BrF_3 \rightleftharpoons BrF_2^+ + SbF_6^-.$$

Similarly, $SOCl_2$ and Cs_2SO_3 are acidic and basic in SO_2, although $SOCl_2$ apparently does not ionize to give SO^{2+} to any large extent. Sulphur atoms exchange between thionylchloride and the solvent SO_2 only very slowly. Compounds which contain the sulfite ion do, however, exchange rapidly.

A more general acid–base concept, due to Lewis (1923), considers acids and bases as electron acceptors and donors, respectively. Not, however, in the sense of oxidation and reduction, but rather in the formation of covalent bonds. The classical example is the reaction of BF_3 (a *Lewis acid*) with NH_3 (a *Lewis base*):

$$NH_3 + BF_3 \rightleftharpoons H_3NBF_3. \tag{9-17}$$

The lone pair of electrons on the nitrogen atom of ammonia forms a bond using the unoccupied orbital of the boron atom in BF_3. A Lewis acid is often described as an *electrophilic* reagent (electron-loving) and a base as a *nucleophilic* reagent. These terms, however, are more common to descriptions of the mechanism of reactions (see Chapter 10).

Unfortunately, Lewis' definition is so general that it includes reactions which are often more usefully considered from different standpoints. For example, along with such reactions as that of Eq. (9–17), the following have been considered as examples of reactions of Lewis acids and bases:

$$\begin{matrix} \text{Acid} & & \text{Base} & & \\ Ag^+ & + & 2NH_3 & \rightleftharpoons & Ag(NH_3)_2^+, \end{matrix}$$

$$\begin{matrix} \text{Acid} & & \text{Base} & & \\ H_2CO & + & H^- & \rightleftharpoons & CH_3O^-, \end{matrix}$$

although they are better described in terms of complex formation and oxidation-reduction respectively.

9–4. COMPLEX IONS

In Chapter 6, we considered the nature of the bonding in complex ions. Our concern now is to examine some of the equilibria that are established among these complexes, various ligands and a solvent. The formation of complex ions represents the association of a cation (usually) with either anions, neutral molecules or both. In a very real sense, it is not possible, except in very special circumstances such as in the gas phase, to have cations which are not associated in this way. Thus the concept of hydration of ions, that is, of the first or inner co-ordination sphere of water molecules, embodies the same principle as the formation of other complexes. Unfortunately there is a tendency, particularly in textbooks, to ignore the fact that an equilibrium written as

$$Ag^+(aq) + 2NH_3(aq) \rightleftharpoons Ag(NH_3)_2^+(aq)$$

is first a stepwise process and second a replacement of water ligands by ammonia ligands:

$$Ag(H_2O)_2^+(aq) + NH_3(aq) \rightleftharpoons Ag(H_2O)(NH_3)^+(aq) + H_2O,$$

$$Ag(H_2O)(NH_3)^+(aq) + NH_3(aq) \rightleftharpoons Ag(NH_3)_2^+(aq) + H_2O.$$

These equilibria are very much analogous to those in acid–base reactions, where only the relative, but not the absolute, acidities can be measured. With complex ions, stabilities again cannot be determined on any absolute basis; they are compared with the solvated ion itself. Thus the equilibrium constant which is quoted refers to a competition between ligand and solvent for coordination positions. At the same time, it is convenient not to be too specific about the nature of the hydrated ion. Instead we shall be content with writing formulas such as $Al^{3+}(aq)$.

There is an abundance of experimental data on the stability of complex ions, but, for either very strong or very weak complexes, information other than that of a qualitative nature is often lacking. The reason for this lies in the experimental difficulties which are usually encountered when a number of simultaneous equilibria are involved. Further, very strong complexes are frequently inert (see Chapter 10) and equilibrium is consequently difficult to achieve.

A careful nomenclature system for the equilibrium constants must be used in order to avoid confusion. We shall use the system given in detail in "Stability Constants" (see Bibliography).

The reactions are always taken, by convention, as complex formations. Thus the reaction (charges are omitted here)

$$M(aq) + X(aq) \rightleftharpoons MX(aq)$$

has a *formation constant*, K_1, which gives the ratios of the appropriate activities:

$$K_1 = \frac{a_{MX}}{a_M a_X}.$$

This must not be confused with the solubility product for the reaction

$$MX(s) \rightleftharpoons M(aq) + X(aq),$$

where

$$K_{sp} = \frac{a_M a_X}{a_{MX}} = a_M a_X.$$

That is, we must be careful to distinguish uncharged species in solution, $MX(aq)$, from solids, $MX(s)$, having the same empirical formula.

For the reaction

$$MX_{n-1}(aq) + X(aq) \rightleftharpoons MX_n(aq),$$

the *stepwise formation constant* K_n, where n can be any integer from one to the maximum coordination number, is given by

$$K_n = \frac{a_{MX_n}}{a_{MX_{n-1}}a_X}.$$

It is often convenient to consider the *overall formation constants* for the reaction,

$$M(aq) + nX(aq) \rightleftharpoons MX_n(aq),$$

for which the symbol is β_n, with

$$\beta_n = \frac{a_{MX_n}}{a_M \cdot a_X^n}.$$

It follows, of course, that $\beta_n = K_1 K_2 \ldots K_n$. For purposes of tabulation, the logarithms of the formation constants are usually quoted, since they will otherwise be, in general, inconveniently large numbers.

Polynuclear complexes are given overall formation constants, β_{nm}, for the reaction

$$mM(aq) + nX(aq) \rightleftharpoons M_mX_n(aq).$$

A comprehensive survey of the data up to 1956 is tabulated in "Stability Constants," by J. Bjerrum, G. Schwarzenbach, and L. G. Sillén. Some of the data are given in the discussion below, but these represent only a very small fraction of the total.

In general, the determination of the stepwise constants is complicated. For example, with a complex ion of coordination number six, at least eight different species are involved in the equilibrium. For this reason a considerable amount of the data have been obtained in solutions of constant ionic strength, often adjusted with $NaClO_4$, since neither Na^+ nor ClO_4^- show any great tendency to form complexes. The equilibrium constants so obtained, unless corrected or extrapolated to zero ionic strength, do not represent thermodynamic equilibrium constants. This is probably not an important point because the uncertainty, as judged by the scatter in the data from different laboratories, often exceeds the correction required, except for complexes of low coordination number [such as $Ag(NH_3)_2^+$] which have been very carefully studied.

(a) Trends in stability

Certain trends in the stability of complexes can be clearly discerned; others, because of the gaps in the experimental data, are less certain. Most of the information concerns the equilibrium constants; only in a very few cases have the studies

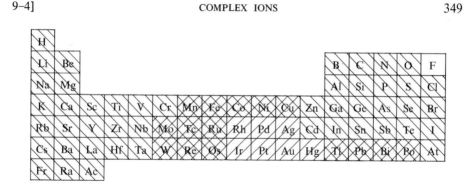

FIG. 9–14. Periodic table, showing classification of the elements according to the stability of their complexes: \\\\Class *a*,////Class *b*, and⬚⬚intermediate.

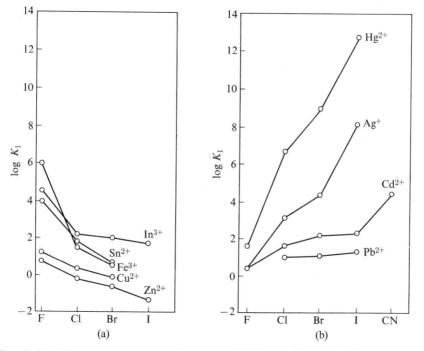

FIG. 9–15. Formation constants for some halide complexes, showing typical behavioral trends of the Class-*a* and Class-*b* elements (see Fig. 9–14).

been extended to the determination of enthalpy and entropy changes, because of the involved nature of the equilibria. There is, however, considerable research activity in this field.

It was demonstrated by Chatt and his coworkers (1958) that the metallic elements forming the central atoms of complexes can be divided roughly into two classes, according to trends in stability of their complexes with different ligand atoms. The larger group, the *a*-elements, form their strongest complexes with or through the most electronegative elements, F, O, and N. Ions having an inert gas (closed-shell) electron configuration belong to this class. In these complexes the bonding is mainly electrostatic in nature. A relatively small number of b-elements grouped around Pt in the periodic table (see Fig. 9–14) form their strongest complexes with I, S and P as the donor atom in the ligand. These complexes are characterized by relatively low oxidation state and filled or nearly filled d-orbitals of the b-element. These are just the conditions which promote the formation of bonds by donation of electrons from the metal d-orbitals (e.g., in octahedral complexes) to empty orbitals of the ligand of π-symmetry (see Chapter 6).

This behavior is brought out most clearly in a comparison of the halide complexes. The log K_1 values for a number of complex ions are shown in Fig. 9–15. The species Hg(II) and Fe(III) provide the most clear-cut examples of the difference in pattern of stabilities, while for Zn(II) and Pb(II), the difference is slight. These classifications are by no means rigid. Thus, one of the characteristics of a b-element is the formation of a strong complex with cyanide, yet $Fe(CN)_6^{3-}$ is a very stable complex. This effect can probably be traced to ligand-field stabilization and π-bonding, since the cyanide complex of Fe(III) has a spin-paired configuration, while the halide complexes are spinfree.

The data given in Table 9–12 show similar trends in the relative stability of oxygen and sulfur complexes. The data needed to define unambiguously the same trends for the elements of Group V of the periodic table are insufficient. However, the general overall trends in stability are the following:

$$a\text{-elements:}\quad O > F > N > P > S,$$

$$b\text{-elements:}\quad P > S \approx I > N > O,$$

although the order depends somewhat on the character of the ligand. In a more specific sense, the following order provides a criterion of a- or b-element classification:

$$a\text{-elements:}\quad OH^- > F^- \gg NH_3 \approx H_2O \approx I^-,$$

$$b\text{-elements:}\quad CN^- > I^- > OH^- > NH_3 \approx Br^-.$$

TABLE 9–12

STABILITY OF COMPLEXES WITH GROUP VI LIGANDS
(log K_1)

	$O(CH_2CO_2^-)_2$	$S(CH_2CO_2^-)_2$
Ca^{2+}	3.4	1.4
Zn^{2+}	3.6	3.0
Co^{2+}	2.7	3.4
Ni^{2+}	2.8	4.1
Cu^{2+}	3.9	4.5

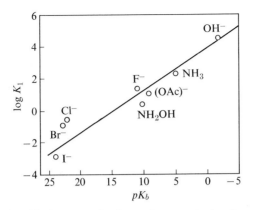

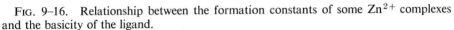

FIG. 9–16. Relationship between the formation constants of some Zn^{2+} complexes and the basicity of the ligand.

It is interesting to note that the proton acts as an element of class a, that is, the order of increasing basicity of a ligand approximately matches that of increasing stability of its complexes with a given class-a element (Fig. 9–16).

With regard to trends in stability when a central atom in a complex is changed, the greatest effects are associated with charge and size, particularly for the a-elements. The trivalent lanthanides provide the clearest example of the size effect. In this case, $\log K_1$ for the EDTA complexes increases linearly with the

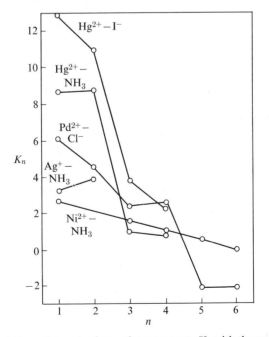

FIG. 9–17. Variation of stepwise formation constants K_n with the number of ligands n.

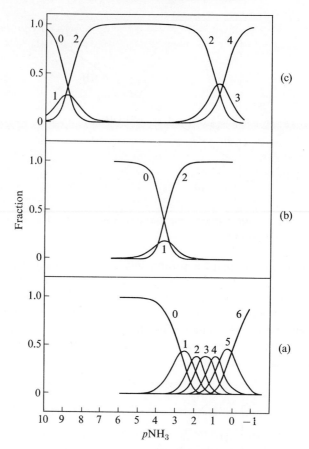

Fig. 9–18. Distribution curves for ammine complexes of (a) Ni(II); (b) Ag(I), and (c) Hg(II), in aqueous solution as a function of NH_3 concentration. The numbers appended to the curves designate the number of ligands, while the curves themselves give the fraction of metal ion present, as the species indicated.

reciprocal of the ionic radius. Such series as Na^+, Ca^{2+}, Y^{3+}, Th^{4+}, or K^+, Sr^{2+}, La^{3+}, in which the size is approximately constant, show the expected increase in stability of their complexes with increasing charge; however, this is not so for b-elements.

The sequence of stabilities for the complexes of the divalent ions of the first transition series, found by Irving and Williams in 1948, is generally

$$Cr > Mn < Fe < Co < Ni < Cu > Zn.$$

This trend results from differences in ligand-field stabilization (see Chapters 6 and 7) between the aquated and complexed ions. The ionic radii follow a similar but reciprocal pattern.

Specific effects often cause reversal of the expected stabilities. Thus some ligands, such as orthophenanthroline and dipyridyl, form complexes with Fe(II) more stable than those with Fe(III), despite the higher charge of the latter. The added stability of these Fe(II) complexes is also a result of ligand-field stabilization, since, unlike the paramagnetic aquated Fe(II) ion, the orthophenanthroline and dipyridyl complexes are diamagnetic (spin-paired).

The successive stepwise formation constants K_n of a complex generally decrease as the number of ligands increases. Where there are no specific effects the change is regular, as is shown for the ammine complexes of Ni(II) in Fig. 9–17. The large decrease from K_2 to K_3 for the Hg(II) complexes is associated with the unusual stability of linear coordination (see Chapter 5). This also accounts for the increase of K_2 over K_1 for the ammines of both Hg(II) and Ag(I). Similarly the marked tendency of Pd(II) to form four coordinated square planar complexes results in a large decrease in K_5 and K_6 from K_4.

In Fig. 9–18 are shown the calculated fractions (assuming that the activity coefficients are all unity) of each species present for the ammine complexes of Hg(II), Ag(I), and Ni(II) as a function of ammonia concentration. For both Hg(II) and Ag(I), the two-coordinated complex is the dominant form over a wide range of concentrations, while for Ni(II) there is no ammonia concentration above 10^{-4} molal at which a single species is predominant.

(b) Chelates

In general, complexes formed with polydentate ligands (see Chapter 6) are more stable than those with monodentate ligands. The values of K_1 increase in the series NH_3, en, den, etc., that is, as the coordination number of the ligand increases (Fig. 9–19). However, a better comparison would be β_2, β_3, and β_6 of ammine

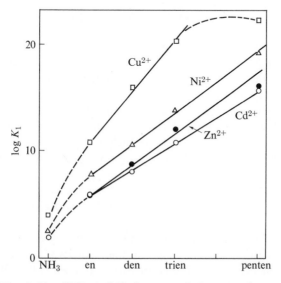

FIG. 9–19. Values of K_1 for some chelate complexes.

TABLE 9–13

COMPARISON OF CHELATE AND NONCHELATE COMPLEXES

	Co^{2+}	Ni^{2+}	Cu^{2+}	Zn^{2+}	Cd^{2+}
$\log \beta_2$ (NH$_3$)	3.7	5.0	7.7	4.8	4.5
$\log K_1$ (en)	6.0	7.9	10.8	6.0	5.7
$\log \beta_3$ (NH$_3$)	4.8	6.7	10.6	7.3	5.8
$\log K_1$ (den)	8.1	10.7	16.0	8.9	8.4
$\log \beta_6$ (NH$_3$)	4.4	7.9	8.9	—	—
$\log K_1$ (penten)	15.8	19.3	22.4	16.2	16.8
$\log \beta_2'$ (NH$_3$)	7.2	8.5	11.2	8.3	8.0
$\log K_1'$ (en)	7.7	9.6	12.5	7.7	7.4
$\log \beta_3'$ (NH$_3$)	10.0	11.9	15.8	12.5	11.0
$\log K_1'$ (den)	9.8	12.4	17.7	10.6	10.1
$\log \beta_6'$ (NH$_3$)	14.8	18.3	19.3	—	—
$\log K_1'$ (penten)	17.5	21.1	24.1	17.9	18.5

complexes with the K_1 values for en, den and penten, respectively, as has been done in Table 9–13. Although there are still appreciable differences, these are, in part, related to the particular choice of concentration units in that the standard state of the solute (1 molal) is different from that of the solvent (pure liquid). The part of the equilibrium constant that depends on the choice of units can be removed by formulating the equilibrium constants as

$$\beta_n' = \frac{[M][X]^n}{[MX_n][H_2O]^n} = \frac{\beta_n}{55.8^n},$$

putting the water concentration in molal units. This means that if we add $1.74n$ to each of the $\log \beta_n$ values and 1.74 to the $\log K_1$ values in Table 9–13, we shall have the part of the equilibrium constants, independent of concentration units. This has been done in the lower half of Table 9–13, and the stability of the ammine and the polydentate ligand complexes are seen to be about the same. This means that the enthalpy and entropy change differences, computed in this form, would be not far from zero. Nevertheless, a given concentration of a polydentate ligand will have a lower concentration of aquated metal ion in equilibrium with it than would be the case with a chemically similar monodentate ligand of the same concentration. Thus, as normally formulated, there will be a more positive entropy change associated with the formation of a chelate complex than with one that is not chelated.

There is, in addition, some evidence that the enthalpy changes associated with chelation are somewhat more exothermic than otherwise. This effect, however, is certainly not of major importance in what has been called the chelate effect. In general, chelates involving five-membered rings are more stable than chemically similar complexes with six-membered rings. This is probably associated with ring strain in a six-membered ring where (for an octahedral complex) one angle will be fixed close to 90°. On the other hand, when the ring formed is part of a ligand in which extensive delocalization of electrons occurs, the six-membered ring is often more stable than the five.

9–5. HYDROLYTIC EQUILIBRIA

Most cations form strong complexes with hydroxyl as a ligand. These may be cationic, such as $Fe(OH)^{2+}$(aq), or anionic, such as $(HO)_2VO_2^-$. Much of the early work of the effect of acidity on metal ions in solution was concerned with solubility products of their hydroxides, as in the equilibrium

$$Fe(OH)_3(s) \rightleftharpoons Fe^{3+}(aq) + 3OH^-(aq),$$

but the situation is scarcely this simple. Table 9–14 shows some of the known equilibria in this system deduced by Hedstrøm (1953). (Note that the formation constants are written $^*K_n$ when a hydrogen ion is released on formation of the complex.) In more basic solutions, no doubt large polynuclear complexes are formed as an immediate precursor to the formation of a solid phase, which is best termed a hydrous oxide rather than ferric hydroxide.

The equilibrium of Hg(II) is particularly interesting in that for the reactions

$$Hg^{2+}(aq) + H_2O \rightleftharpoons HgOH^+(aq) + H^+(aq); \log {}^*K_1 = -3.7,$$

$$HgOH^+(aq) + H_2O \rightleftharpoons Hg(OH)_2(aq) + H^+(aq); \log {}^*K_2 = -2.6,$$

the second acidity constant is more positive than the first. Other polyprotic acids, such as H_3PO_4, show the reverse behavior, with each succeeding constant decreasing by about five.

Although we cannot give a comprehensive coverage of the field of hydrolytic equilibria, it is interesting to look at some of the polynuclear species that have been found in relatively high concentrations. In the case of bismuth, it is not the bismuthyl ion (BiO^+) that occurs, but rather $BiOH^{2+}$ and $Bi_6(OH)_{12}^{6+}$. Similarly, both Be_2OH^{3+} and $Be_3(OH)_3^{3+}$ were found by Sillén (1956), with the latter stable over a wide range of acidity. A good many other systems have been studied, with indications that complexes of the general formula $M[M(OH)_t]_n$ occur, with t a constant integer and with a range of values for n.

TABLE 9–14

EQUILIBRIA IN THE Fe(III) − OH⁻ SYSTEM

$Fe^{3+}(aq) + H_2O \rightleftharpoons FeOH^{2+}(aq) + H^+(aq); \log^* K_1 = 3.05$
$FeOH^{2+}(aq) + H_2O \rightleftharpoons Fe(OH)_2^+(aq) + H^+(aq); \log^* K_2 = 3.26$
$2Fe^{3+}(aq) + 2H_2O \rightleftharpoons Fe_2(OH)_2^{4+} + 2H^+(aq); \log^* \beta_{22} = -2.91$

TABLE 9–15

ANIONIC HYDROLYTIC EQUILIBRIA

Molybdates:

$$MoO_4^{2-}(aq) + H^+(aq) \rightleftharpoons HMoO_4^-; \log K = 4.08$$
$$7MoO_4^{2-}(aq) + 8H^+(aq) \rightleftharpoons Mo_7O_{24}^{6-}(aq) + 4H_2O; \log K = 57.7$$
$$Mo_7O_{24}^{6-}(aq) + H^+(aq) \rightleftharpoons HMo_7O_{24}^{5-}(aq); \log K = 4.33$$

Vanadates:

$$10VO_2^+(aq) + 8H_2O \rightleftharpoons H_2V_{10}O_{28}^{4-} + 14H^+; \log K = 6.75$$
$$H_2V_{10}O_{28}^{4-}(aq) \rightleftharpoons HV_{10}O_{28}^{5-}(aq) + H^+(aq); \log K = 3.6$$
$$HV_{10}O_{28}^{5-}(aq) \rightleftharpoons V_{10}O_{28}^{6-}(aq) + H^+(aq); \log K = 5.8$$
$$3HVO_4^{2-}(aq) + 3H^+(aq) \rightleftharpoons V_3O_9^{3-}(aq) + 3H_2O; \log K = 30.7$$

Polynuclear complexes in hydrolytic anionic systems (such as those of the tungstates and molybdates and vanadates) have been known for many years, but details of the equilibria have only recently become available. The involved nature of these systems is well illustrated in the examples of Table 9–15.

9–6. OXIDATION AND REDUCTION

The type of reaction known as an oxidation-reduction or redox reaction can be considered, at least on a formal basis, as one in which one or more electrons are transferred from one chemical species to another. In many respects these reactions are analogous to acid-base reactions in which a proton is transferred. Just as there must be, in the latter systems, two conjugate acid-base pairs, so also in redox systems there must be two conjugate oxidation-reduction pairs:

$$\text{acid}_1 + \text{base}_2 \rightleftharpoons \text{base}_1 + \text{acid}_2$$
$$\text{red}_1 + \text{ox}_2 \rightleftharpoons \text{ox}_1 + \text{red}_2.$$

In neither case can we attribute more than formal significance to part reactions involving a proton or an electron:

$$\text{acid}_1 \rightleftharpoons \text{base}_1 + H^+$$
$$\text{red}_1 \rightleftharpoons \text{ox}_1 + e.$$

Just as an acid is a proton donor, a reducing agent (red) is an electron donor. In this analogy, then, an acid corresponds to a reducing agent and a base to an oxidizing agent (ox).

It was pointed out in Section 9–3 that the strength of an acid can be measured only relative to that of some other acid, usually that present in the solvent (H_3O^+ in water, for example). In redox systems the same restriction applies, and it is convenient to refer the strength of a reducing agent in some way to that of the solvent. In each case using water as a solvent, the formal reference reactions are:

$$H_3O^+(aq) \rightleftharpoons H_2O + H^+ \qquad \text{(acid-base)}$$

$$\tfrac{1}{2}H_2(g) \rightleftharpoons H^+(aq) + e \qquad \text{(redox)}.$$

The thermodynamic properties of acid-base reactions are usually measured in terms of concentrations of species present, hence the equilibrium constant is determined directly and the quantity pK_a is most convenient. However, in redox systems, by arranging experimentally for the electrons to be transferred through an external electrical system, the free energy change for the redox reaction is itself measured directly, usually in volts. In practice, an electrochemical system is measured, not at chemical equilibrium, but with the driving force of the reaction just balanced by an opposing electrical force. A measurement of the latter can then be converted to a free energy change through the relation

$$\mathcal{E} = -\frac{\Delta G}{\mathfrak{F}n}, \qquad (9\text{--}18)$$

where $\mathfrak{F}$ is the Faraday constant and n is the number of equivalents of electrons passed in the reaction as written. Clearly the behavior of oxidation-reduction systems is closely allied with that of electrochemical cells. We shall therefore look into the latter in more detail.

(a) Electrochemical cells

Let us consider the properties of the cell illustrated in Fig. 9–20 and represented schematically as

$$Pt|H_2(g)|HCl(aq)|AgCl(s)|Ag. \qquad (9\text{--}19)$$

By convention, the reduced form of the left electrode is written as a reactant and the reduced form of the right electrode as a product; hence the reaction associated with the cell is

$$\tfrac{1}{2}H_2(g) + AgCl(s) \rightleftharpoons H^+(aq) + Cl^-(aq) + Ag(s). \qquad (9\text{--}20)$$

Experimentally, the prime requirement of the device used for measuring cell emf's is that it draw little or no current. If current does flow through the cell, then the measurement is complicated by two effects: (1) the internal resistance of the cell will lower the measured emf; (2) chemical reactions may occur at the electrodes, changing their character and the emf. Precise measurements are carried out with a millivolt potentiometer, but routine laboratory measurements are often made with a high-resistance vacuum tube voltmeter (pH meter). Such a device, when used to measure the emf of a cell of the type of Eq. (9–19), for which $p_{H_2} = 1$ atm and $c_{HCl} = 0.05$ molar, will show that the silver electrode is positive by about 0.23 v. By convention the *cell* emf takes the sign of the right-hand electrode; thus $\mathcal{E}_{cell}$ is $+0.23$ v.

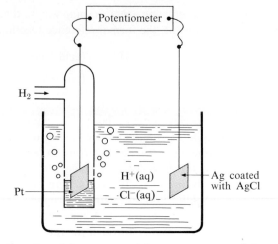

FIG. 9–20. Experimental arrangement for measurement of the emf of the cell
$Pt|H_2(g)|HCl(aq)|AgCl(s)|Ag$.

When c_{HCl} is small, the concentration dependence of the cell emf may be represented by an equation of the type

$$\mathcal{E}_{cell} = \mathcal{E}^\circ_{cell} - \frac{RT}{\mathcal{F}} \ln \frac{[H^+][Cl^-]}{p_{H_2}^{1/2}} \tag{9–21}$$

where R is the gas constant, T the temperature in °K, and $\mathcal{F}$ the Faraday constant. For large concentrations, Eq. (9–21) will no longer be accurate because of nonideal behavior of the solution; but, as before, such difficulties can be eliminated by employing activities. Then Eq. (9–21) becomes

$$\mathcal{E}_{cell} = \mathcal{E}^\circ_{cell} - \frac{RT}{\mathcal{F}} \ln \frac{a_{H^+} a_{Cl^-}}{a_{H_2}^{1/2}}. \tag{9–22}$$

For practical purposes, p_{H_2} differs insignificantly from a_{H_2} so that, to a good approximation, we may write

$$\mathcal{E}_{cell} = \mathcal{E}^\circ_{cell} - \frac{RT}{\mathcal{F}} \ln \frac{a_{H^+} a_{Cl^-}}{p_{H_2}^{1/2}}.$$

Also, since $a_{H^+} = \gamma_{H^+} c_{HCl}$ and $a_{Cl^-} = \gamma_{Cl^-} c_{HCl}$ (assuming complete dissociation of the HCl), the emf of the cell is given by

$$\mathcal{E}_{cell} = \mathcal{E}^\circ_{cell} - \frac{RT}{\mathcal{F}} \ln \frac{\gamma_{H^+} \gamma_{Cl^-} c_{HCl}^2}{p_{H_2}^{1/2}}$$

$$= \mathcal{E}^\circ_{cell} - \frac{RT}{\mathcal{F}} \ln c_{HCl}^2 - \frac{RT}{\mathcal{F}} \ln \gamma_{H^+} \gamma_{Cl^-} + \frac{RT}{\mathcal{F}} \ln p_{H_2}^{1/2}. \tag{9–23}$$

TABLE 9–16

ELECTROMOTIVE FORCE OF THE CELL
$Pt|H_2(g)|HCl(aq)|AgCl(s)|Ag$
$(T = 298°K, p_{H_2} = 1.000 \text{ atm})$

c_{HCl}, moles/liter	$\mathscr{E}_{cell}$, volts	$\mathscr{E}'$, volts
0.003564	0.51527	0.22566
0.004488	0.50384	0.22608
0.006239	0.48747	0.22663
0.008636	0.47135	0.22722
0.011195	0.45861	0.22775
0.01710	0.43783	0.22879
0.02563	0.41824	0.23000
0.05391	0.38222	0.23218

Rearranging Eq. (9–23), we obtain

$$\mathscr{E}' = \mathscr{E}_{cell} + \frac{RT}{\mathscr{F}} \ln c_{HCl}^2 - \frac{RT}{\mathscr{F}} \ln p_{H_2}^{1/2} = \mathscr{E}_{cell}^{\circ} - \frac{RT}{\mathscr{F}} \ln \gamma_{H^+}\gamma_{Cl^-}, \qquad (9\text{–}24)$$

where all of the quantities on the left-hand side are measurable. Furthermore, at infinite dilution the right-hand side will reduce to $\mathscr{E}_{cell}^{\circ}$. Thus, by plotting $\mathscr{E}'$ as a function of c_{HCl} and extrapolating to $c_{HCl} = 0$, we may obtain the standard cell emf, $\mathscr{E}_{cell}^{\circ}$.

Data for the cell of Eq. (9–19) are given in Table 9–16 for $T = 298.15°K$ and $p_{H_2} = 1.000$ atm. Under these conditions Eq. (9–24) becomes

$$\mathscr{E}' = \mathscr{E}_{cell} + 0.1183 \log c_{HCl}$$
$$= \mathscr{E}_{cell}^{\circ} - 0.05915 \log \gamma_{H^+}\gamma_{Cl^-},$$

and $\mathscr{E}'$, when plotted as in Fig. 9–21, gives $\mathscr{E}_{cell}^{\circ} = 0.222$ v at 298°K. In practice, a modified form of Eq. (9–24), which permits a linear extrapolation, is usually employed. (See Problem 9–9.) Note also that, once $\mathscr{E}_{cell}^{\circ}$ has been obtained, the data of Table 9–16 may also be used to determine values of the *mean activity coefficient*, $\gamma_{\pm} = \sqrt{\gamma_{H^+}\gamma_{Cl^-}}$.

The general form of Eq. (9–22), given by

$$\mathscr{E}_{cell} = \mathscr{E}_{cell}^{\circ} - \frac{RT}{n\mathscr{F}} \ln Q, \qquad (9\text{–}25)$$

is known as the *Nernst equation*. Here Q is the ratio

$$Q = \frac{\Pi a_{products}}{\Pi a_{reactants}},$$

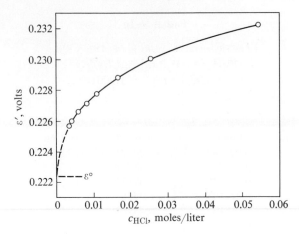

FIG. 9–21. Determination of $\mathcal{E}°$ for the cell of Fig. 9–20 by extrapolation of Eq. (9–24) to infinite dilution (p_{H_2} = 1 atm; T = 298°K).

and the remaining constants are as specified above. At 298°K with the emf in volts, Eq. (9–25) becomes

$$\mathcal{E}_{cell} = \mathcal{E}°_{cell} - \frac{0.05915}{n} \log Q. \qquad (9\text{–}26)$$

Clearly, when a state of chemical equilibrium obtains (i.e., the cell has run down), $\mathcal{E}_{cell} = \Delta G = 0$, and $Q = K$, the equilibrium constant. Thus

$$\mathcal{E}°_{cell} = \frac{RT}{\mathcal{F}} \ln K \qquad (9\text{–}27)$$

and

$$\Delta G° = -n\mathcal{F}\mathcal{E}°_{cell}. \qquad (9\text{–}28)$$

A measurement of the standard cell potential thus provides values for the standard free energy change and for the equilibrium constant. Note that a positive cell emf corresponds to a negative free energy change and a spontaneous chemical reaction. For the example we have been discussing, $\mathcal{E}°$ = 0.222 v; hence

$$\Delta G° = -10.25 \text{ kcal} \qquad \text{and} \qquad K = 3.24 \times 10^7.$$

(b) Electrode potentials

Consider the following three electrochemical cells:

$$Pt|H_2(g)|HCl(aq)|\ |CuSO_4(aq)|Cu; \qquad \mathcal{E}°_{cell} = 0.337 \text{ v}, \qquad (9\text{–}29)$$

$$Pt|H_2(g)|HCl(aq)|\ |ZnSO_4(aq)|Zn; \qquad \mathcal{E}°_{cell} = -0.763 \text{ v}, \qquad (9\text{–}30)$$

$$Zn|ZnSO_4|\ |CuSO_4|Cu; \qquad \mathcal{E}°_{cell} = 1.100 \text{ v}. \qquad (9\text{–}31)$$

Experimentally these differ from the cell previously discussed in having a *liquid*

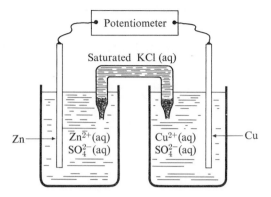

FIG. 9–22. Experimental arrangement of the Daniell cell, showing the salt bridge or liquid junction.

junction, as represented by the double vertical line (Fig. 9–22). Although they are necessary experimentally, such junctions are often a problem because it is not always possible to estimate accurately the potential drop across the junction. These difficulties can be overcome in the above cases, however, and the standard cell emfs are as listed above.

It can be seen that the Daniell cell of Eq. (9–31) employs one electrode from each of the two preceding cells. Furthermore, the emf of the Daniell cell is the algebraic difference of the emf's of these cells. This important observation carries with it the implication that we can assign potentials to the individual electrodes. Thus the emf's of the cells of Eqs. (9–29), (9–30), and (9–31) may be written

$$\mathcal{E}^{\circ}_{\text{cell}} = \mathcal{E}^{\circ}(\text{Cu}^{2+}/\text{Cu}) - \mathcal{E}^{\circ}(\text{H}^{+}/\text{H}_2) = 0.337 \text{ v,}$$

$$\mathcal{E}^{\circ}_{\text{cell}} = \mathcal{E}^{\circ}(\text{Zn}^{2+}/\text{Zn}) - \mathcal{E}^{\circ}(\text{H}^{+}/\text{H}_2) = -0.763 \text{ v,}$$

and

$$\mathcal{E}^{\circ}_{\text{cell}} = \mathcal{E}^{\circ}(\text{Cu}^{2+}/\text{Cu}) - \mathcal{E}^{\circ}(\text{Zn}^{2+}/\text{Zn}) = 1.100 \text{ v,}$$

respectively.

It is immediately apparent that electrochemical measurements can provide us only with differences in these electrode potentials. We must therefore make an arbitrary assignment of one electrode potential. By convention, a value of zero is given to the emf of the hydrogen electrode so that we immediately obtain

$$\mathcal{E}^{\circ}(\text{Cu}^{2+}/\text{Cu}) = 0.337 \text{ v,} \qquad \mathcal{E}^{\circ}(\text{Zn}^{2+}/\text{Zn}) = -0.763 \text{ v,}$$

and of course $\mathcal{E}^{\circ}(\text{H}^{+}/\text{H}_2) = 0$. These are termed *standard electrode potentials*, and associated with them are the half-reactions,

$$\text{Cu}^{2+} + 2\text{e} = \text{Cu}, \quad \text{Zn}^{2+} + 2\text{e} = \text{Zn}, \quad \text{and} \quad \text{H}^{+} + \text{e} = \tfrac{1}{2}\text{H}_2,$$

respectively.

TABLE 9–17

SELECTED STANDARD ELECTRODE POTENTIALS

Half-reaction	$\mathcal{E}°$, volts
$Ag^+ + e = Ag$	$+0.799$
$AgCl + e = Ag + Cl^-$	$+0.222$
$AgBr + e = Ag + Br^-$	$+0.071$
$AgI + e = Ag + I^-$	-0.152
$Al^{3+} + 3e = Al$	-1.66
$As_2O_3 + 6H^+ + 6e = 2As + 3H_2O$	$+0.234$
$H_3AsO_4 + 2H^+ + 2e = HAsO_2 + 2H_2O$	$+0.56$
$AuCl_2^- + e = Au + 2Cl^-$	$+1.12$
$Au(CN)_2^- + e = Au + 2CN^-$	-0.61
$AuCl_4^- + 3e = Au + 4Cl^-$	$+0.99$
$H_3BO_3 + 3H^+ + 3e = B + 3H_2O$	-0.87
$Ba^{2+} + 2e = Ba$	-2.90
$Be^{2+} + 2e = Be$	-1.85
$BiO^+ + 2H^+ + 3e = Bi + H_2O$	$+0.32$
$Br_2 + 2e = 2Br^-$	$+1.087$
$2CO_2 + 2H^+ + 2e = H_2C_2O_4$	-0.49
$Ca^{2+} + 2e = Ca$	-2.87
$Cd^{2+} + 2e = Cd$	-0.402
$Ce^{4+} + e = Ce^{3+}$	-1.70
$Cl_2 + 2e = 2Cl^-$	$+1.359$
$HClO + 2H^+ + 2e = \frac{1}{2}Cl_2 + 2H_2O$	$+1.63$
$HClO_2 + 2H^+ + 2e = HClO + H_2O$	$+1.64$
$ClO_4^- + 2H^+ + 2e = ClO_3^- + H_2O$	$+1.19$
$Co^{2+} + 2e = Co$	-0.28
$Co^{3+} + e = Co^{2+}$	$+1.82$
$Cr^{3+} + 3e = Cr$	-0.74
$Cr^{3+} + e = Cr^{2+}$	-0.41
$Cr_2O_7^{2-} + 14H^+ + 6e = 2Cr^{3+} + 7H_2O$	$+1.33$
$Cs^+ + e = Cs$	-2.952
$Cu^+ + e = Cu$	$+0.521$
$Cu^{2+} + 2e = Cu$	$+0.337$
$F_2 + 2e = 2F^-$	$+2.87$
$Fe^{2+} + 2e = Fe$	-0.440
$Fe^{3+} + e = Fe^{2+}$	$+0.771$
$[Fe(CN)_6]^{3-} + e = [Fe(CN)_6]^{4-}$	$+0.356$
$Ga^{3+} + 3e = Ga$	-0.56
$H_2 + 2e = 2H^+$	$+0.0000$
$Hg_2^{2+} + 2e = 2Hg$	$+0.792$
$2Hg^{2+} + 2e = Hg_2^{2+}$	$+0.907$
$I_2 + 2e = 2I^-$	$+0.536$

(*Continued*)

TABLE 9–17 (*continued*)

SELECTED STANDARD ELECTRODE POTENTIALS

Half-reaction	$\mathcal{E}°$, volts
$HIO + H^+ + 2e = I^- + H_2O$	$+0.99$
$2IO_3^- + 12H^+ + 10e = I_2 + 6H_2O$	$+1.19$
$H_5IO_6 + H^+ + 2e = IO_3^- + 3H_2O$	$+1.6$
$K^+ + e = K$	-2.925
$La^{3+} + 3e = La$	-2.52
$Li^+ + e = Li$	-3.03
$Mg^{2+} + 2e = Mg$	-2.37
$Mn^{2+} + 2e = Mn$	-1.190
$MnO_2 + 4H^+ + 2e = Mn^{2+} + 2H_2O$	$+1.23$
$MnO_4^- + 8H^+ + 5e = Mn^{2+} + 4H_2O$	$+1.51$
$HNO_2 + H^+ + e = NO + H_2O$	$+0.99$
$N_2O_4 + 2H^+ + 2e = 2HNO_2$	$+1.07$
$NO_3^- + 3H^+ + 2e = HNO_2 + H_2O$	$+0.94$
$Na^+ + e = Na$	-2.698
$Ni^{2+} + 2e = Ni$	-0.23
$H_2O_2 + 2H^+ + 2e = 2H_2O$	$+1.77$
$O_2 + 4H^+ + 4e = 2H_2O$	$+1.229$
$O_2 + 2H^+ + 2e = H_2O_2$	$+0.69$
$O_3 + 2H^+ + 2e = O_2 + H_2O$	$+2.07$
$H_3PO_3 + 2H^+ + 2e = H_3PO_2 + H_2O$	-0.50
$H_3PO_4 + 2H^+ + 2e = H_3PO_3 + H_2O$	-0.276
$Pb^{2+} + 2e = Pb$	-0.126
$PbO_2 + H_2O + 2e = PbO + 2OH^-$	$+0.28$
$PdCl_4^{2-} + 2e = Pd + 4Cl^-$	$+0.623$
$PdCl_6^{2-} + 2e = PdCl_4^{2-} + 2Cl^-$	$+1.29$
$PtCl_4^{2-} + 2e = Pt + 4Cl^-$	$+0.73$
$PtCl_6^{2-} + 2e = PtCl_4^{2-} + 2Cl^-$	$+0.79$
$Rb^+ + e = Rb$	-2.93
$S + 2H^+ + 2e = H_2S$	$+0.14$
$SO_4^{2-} + 4H^+ + 2e = H_2SO_3 + H_2O$	$+0.17$
$Sn^{2+} + 2e = Sn$	-0.140
$Sr^{2+} + 2e = Sr$	-2.89
$Tl^+ + e = Tl$	-0.336
$Tl^{3+} + 2e = Tl^+$	$+1.28$
$V^{2+} + 2e = V$	-1.2
$V^{3+} + e = V^{2+}$	-0.265
$VO^{2+} + 2H^+ + e = V^{3+} + H_2O$	$+0.34$
$VO_2^+ + 2H^+ + e = VO^{2+} + H_2O$	$+0.999$
$Zn^{2+} + 2e = Zn$	-0.763

More than a little confusion exists over the conventions and nomenclature used in electrochemistry. The emf's quoted here (Table 9–17) are the most recent ones adopted by the International Union of Pure and Applied Chemistry (IUPAC), and they define the electrode potential for the electrode reaction written as a reduction process.   It is still common practice, however, to list the electrode potentials with reversed sign as *oxidation potentials*, and either sign may be found in tabulations of redox potentials.   The student should note, however, that it is really only the terminology which is confusing.   If the emf is always paired with a written half-reaction, then there is no ambiguity or confusion.

An oxidation-reduction reaction is usually composed of two half-reactions. Any two such half-reactions may be combined by subtraction in such a way as to cancel the electrons, to yield a complete reaction that corresponds to a cell reaction.   The cell emf is then the algebraic difference between the electrode potentials.   Consider, for example, the half-reactions

$$Fe^{2+}(aq) + 2e = Fe(s); \qquad \mathcal{E}°(Fe^{2+}/Fe) = -0.440 \text{ v}, \qquad (9\text{--}32)$$

and

$$Fe^{3+}(aq) + e = Fe^{2+}(aq); \qquad \mathcal{E}°(Fe^{3+}/Fe^{2+}) = 0.771 \text{ v}. \qquad (9\text{--}33)$$

Multiplying Eq. (9–33) by two and subtracting Eq. (9–32) from it gives the overall reaction

$$Fe(s) + 2Fe^{3+}(aq) = 3Fe^{2+}(aq); \qquad \mathcal{E}°_{cell} = 1.211 \text{ v}.$$

Note that doubling the quantities in the second half-reaction does not affect the electrode potential although it will double the free energy change.   Thus for the half-reactions of Eqs. (9–32) and (9–33), the standard free energy changes are

$$\Delta G°(Fe^{2+}/Fe) = -2\mathcal{F}\mathcal{E}°(Fe^{2+}/Fe)$$

and

$$\Delta G°(Fe^{3+}/Fe^{2+}) = -\mathcal{F}\mathcal{E}°(Fe^{3+}/Fe^{2+}),$$

respectively.   The overall standard free energy change is given by

$$\Delta G° = -2\mathcal{F}\mathcal{E}°_{cell} = \Delta G°(Fe^{2+}/Fe) - 2\,\Delta G°(Fe^{3+}/Fe^{2+})$$
$$= -2\mathcal{F}[\mathcal{E}°(Fe^{2+}/Fe) - \mathcal{E}°(Fe^{3+}/Fe^{2+})].$$

Thus

$$\mathcal{E}°_{cell} = \mathcal{E}°(Fe^{2+}/Fe) - \mathcal{E}°(Fe^{3+}/Fe^{2+}).$$

A different situation arises when the half-reactions of Eqs. (9–32) and (9–33) are combined to form a new half-reaction.   Thus adding them together gives the half-reaction

$$Fe^{3+}(aq) + 3e = Fe(s).$$

The change in standard free energy for this reaction is

$$\Delta G^\circ(\text{Fe}^{3+}/\text{Fe}) = \Delta G^\circ(\text{Fe}^{2+}/\text{Fe}) + \Delta G^\circ(\text{Fe}^{3+}/\text{Fe}^{2+})$$
$$= -2\mathcal{F}\mathcal{E}^\circ(\text{Fe}^{2+}/\text{Fe}) - \mathcal{F}\mathcal{E}^\circ(\text{Fe}^{3+}/\text{Fe}^{2+})$$
$$= -3\mathcal{F}\mathcal{E}^\circ(\text{Fe}^{3+}/\text{Fe}).$$

Thus we have

$$\mathcal{E}^\circ\ (\text{Fe}^{3+}/\text{Fe}) = \frac{2\mathcal{E}^\circ(\text{Fe}^{2+}/\text{Fe}) + \mathcal{E}^\circ(\text{Fe}^{3+}/\text{Fe}^{2+})}{3}.$$

Returning to the electrode potentials given in Table 9–17, we can make the generalization that the reducing power of a reducing agent increases as the electrode potential of the couple decreases. Conversely, the oxidizing power of an oxidizing agent increases as the electrode potential increases. Just as a strong acid is associated with a weak conjugate base, and vice versa, so also in redox systems the oxidizing agent conjugate to a strong reducing agent has only weak oxidizing power, and vice versa. When the electrode reactions are tabulated in order of increasing electrode potentials, it follows that a reducing agent can react spontaneously with any oxidizing agent above it in the series. The difference in electrode potentials gives the value of the equilibrium constant via Eq. (9–27).

(c) Concentration dependence of electrode potentials

The reducing or oxidizing power, as measured by the electrode potential, is a function of the activities of the oxidized and reduced species, as well as of any other species required for a balanced chemical equation. Thus the half-reaction

$$\text{Fe}^{3+}(\text{aq}) + \text{e} \rightleftharpoons \text{Fe}^{2+}(\text{aq})$$

has the electrode potential

$$\mathcal{E} = \mathcal{E}^\circ - 0.059 \log \frac{a_{\text{Fe}^{2+}}}{a_{\text{Fe}^{3+}}},$$

while for the half-reaction

$$\text{Cr}_2\text{O}_7^{2-}(\text{aq}) + 14\text{H}^+(\text{aq}) + 6\text{e} \rightleftharpoons 2\text{Cr}^{3+}(\text{aq}) + 7\text{H}_2\text{O},$$

the electrode potential is

$$\mathcal{E} = \mathcal{E}^\circ - \frac{0.059}{6} \log \frac{a_{\text{Cr}^{3+}}^2}{a_{\text{Cr}_2\text{O}_7^{2-}} a_{\text{H}^+}^{14}}.$$

Hence the electrode potential (but not the standard electrode potential) of the $\text{Fe}^{3+}/\text{Fe}^{2+}$ couple depends on the ratio of the activity of $\text{Fe}^{2+}(\text{aq})$ to that of $\text{Fe}^{3+}(\text{aq})$. The electrode potential of the second couple depends not only on the activities of $Cr^{3+}(aq)$ and $Cr_2O_7^{2-}(aq)$, but also on a high power of the activity of $H^+(aq)$. It is obvious then that the addition or removal of any of these species will have a direct effect on the oxidizing power of the couple in question. More interesting still are those cases where the addition of another ionic species leads to the establishment of an equilibrium involving the species of the couple.

Consider, for example, the following half-reaction:

$$Ag^+(aq) + e \rightleftharpoons Ag(s); \qquad \mathcal{E}^\circ = +0.799 \text{ v.} \qquad (9\text{--}34)$$

The standard electrode potential refers to $a_{Ag^+} = 1$. Now consider the effect of adding chloride ions to this system. Since solid AgCl will be formed, we can write reaction (9–34) as

$$AgCl(s) + e \rightleftharpoons Ag(s) + Cl^-(aq). \qquad (9\text{--}35)$$

The standard electrode potential for the reaction in Eq. (9–35) requires that $a_{Cl^-} = 1$. However, the activities of $Cl^-(aq)$ and $Ag^+(aq)$ are not independent but are related, at equilibrium, by the solubility product

$$K_{sp} = a_{Ag^+} a_{Cl^-}.$$

Thus when $a_{Cl^-} = 1$, $a_{Ag^+} = K_{sp}$. If we apply the Nernst equation [Eq. (9–25)] to the electrode potential for Eq. (9–34), we have

$$\mathcal{E} = \mathcal{E}^\circ \ (Ag^+/Ag) - 0.059 \log \frac{1}{a_{Ag^+}}.$$

If we substitute $a_{Ag^+} = K_{sp}$ into this equation, there results

$$\mathcal{E}^\circ(AgCl/Ag) = \mathcal{E}^\circ(Ag^+/Ag) + 0.059 \log K_{sp} = +0.222 \text{ v.}$$

In this way, we could find $\mathcal{E}^\circ(AgCl/Ag)$ from measurements of $\mathcal{E}^\circ(Ag^+/Ag)$ and K_{sp}. Alternatively, K_{sp} could be evaluated from the two standard electrode potentials.

In general, normal complex-ion formation stabilizes a higher oxidation state of an element more than it does a lower. Therefore, the standard electrode potential of a conjugate redox pair usually becomes more negative when complexed, and hence the lower oxidation state increases in reducing power.

When the reducing agent is a metal, the standard electrode potential in the presence of a complexing agent is

$$\mathcal{E}^\circ_{complexed} = \mathcal{E}^\circ - \frac{0.059}{n} \log \beta_n.$$

When a sparingly soluble product represents the oxidized form, the standard

TABLE 9–18

STANDARD ELECTRODE POTENTIALS FOR THE Ag^+/Ag SYSTEM

Couple	$\mathcal{E}°$, volts
$Ag^+(aq)/Ag$	0.799
$Ag(NH_3)_2^+/Ag$	0.371
$AgCl(s)/Ag$	0.222
$AgSCN(s)/Ag$	0.089
$AgBr(s)/Ag$	0.071
$AgI(s)/Ag$	−0.152
$Ag(CN)_2^-/Ag$	−0.376

electrode potential also decreases according to

$$\mathcal{E}°_{solid} = \mathcal{E}° + \frac{0.059}{n} \log K_{sp}.$$

The difference in sign in these equations reflects the definition of solubility as a dissociation and complexing as a formation. This behavior is amply illustrated by the data in Table 9–18 for the Ag^+/Ag system.

In Table 9–19 are given some of the standard electrode potentials relating to the Fe(III)-Fe(II) system. Consider the first pair listed in this table, the ortho-phenanthroline (phen) complexes. The half-reaction is

$$Fe(phen)_3^{3+} + e \rightleftharpoons Fe(phen)_3^{2+}.$$

The basic electrode potential for this system is

$$\mathcal{E} = \mathcal{E}°(Fe^{3+}/Fe^{2+}) - 0.059 \log \frac{a_{Fe^{2+}}}{a_{Fe^{3+}}}. \tag{9–36}$$

TABLE 9–19

STANDARD ELECTRODE POTENTIALS OF SOME Fe(III)-Fe(II) COUPLES

Couple	$\mathcal{E}°$, volts	$\dfrac{\beta_n^{III}}{\beta_n^{II}}$
$[Fe(phen)_3]^{3+}/[Fe(phen)_3]^{2+}$	+1.12	1.2×10^{-6}
$[Fe(dipy)_3]^{3+}/[(Fe(dipy)_3]^{2+}$	+1.10	2.6×10^{-6}
$Fe^{3+}(aq)/Fe^{2+}(aq)$	+0.77	—
$[Fe(CN)_6]^{3-}/[Fe(CN)_6]^{4-}$	+0.36	8.5×10^6
$[Fe(C_2O_4)_3]^{3-}/[Fe(C_2O_4)_3]^{4-}$	+0.02	4.8×10^{12}
$Fe(OH)_3(s)/Fe(OH)_2(s)$	−0.56	3.0×10^{22}*

* Ratio of solubility products ($a_{OH^-} = 1$).

However, when each complex ion has unit activity, the ratio of the activity of Fe^{2+}(aq) to that of Fe^{3+}(aq) is just given by

$$\frac{a_{Fe^{2+}}}{a_{Fe^{3+}}} = \frac{\beta_3^{III}}{\beta_3^{II}},$$

where β_3^{II} is the overall formation constant for the reaction

$$Fe^{2+}(aq) + 3 \, phen \rightleftharpoons Fe(phen)_3^{2+},$$

and β_3^{III} is that for:

$$Fe^{3+}(aq) + 3 \, phen \rightleftharpoons Fe(phen)_3^{3+}.$$

Therefore Eq. (9–36) becomes

$$\mathcal{E}^\circ_{complex} = \mathcal{E}^\circ \, (Fe^{3+}/Fe^{2+}) - 0.059 \log \frac{\beta_3^{III}}{\beta_3^{II}}.$$

Similar considerations apply to the other couples listed in Table 9–19, except that for the last one we have

$$\frac{a_{Fe^{2+}}}{a_{Fe^{3+}}} = \frac{K_{sp}^{II}}{K_{sp}^{III}} a_{OH^-}.$$

With $a_{OH^-} = 1$ for the standard electrode potential, this ratio reduces to just K_{sp}^{II}/K_{sp}^{III}, the ratio of the solubility products. Complexing can thus have a profound effect on the oxidizing or reducing power of a substance; for example, $Fe(C_2O_4)_3^{2+}$ is a good reducing agent, while $Fe(phen)_3^{3+}$ is a very good oxidizing agent. These data also provide an insight into the relative stabilities of the complexes. Thus orthophenanthroline and dipyridine complex more strongly with Fe(II) than with Fe(III), while the reverse is true with cyanide and oxalate as ligands.

The usual decrease of electrode potentials on complex formation is of considerable importance in stabilizing high oxidation states of elements which, in aquated form, are unstable with respect to their reduction by the solvent. Thus Co^{3+}(aq) and Ag^{2+}(aq),

$$Co^{3+}(aq) + e \rightleftharpoons Co^{2+}(aq); \quad \mathcal{E}^\circ = +1.82 \, v,$$

$$Ag^{2+}(aq) + e \rightleftharpoons Ag^+(aq); \quad \mathcal{E}^\circ = +1.98 \, v,$$

can and do oxidize water to oxygen:

$$O_2 + 4H^+ + 4e \rightleftharpoons 2H_2O; \quad \mathcal{E}^\circ = +1.229 \, v.$$

Most complexing agents form very strong complexes with Co(III), much stronger than with Co(II), which makes it possible to prepare Co(III) complexes in aqueous media. In fact the standard preparation is to make a Co(II) complex and then use only a mild oxidizing agent to carry out the conversion to the Co(III) complex. The standard electrode potentials in the presence of ammonia and cyanide are 0.00 and -0.84 v, respectively. It is possible for Ag(II) to be stabilized through formation of either the dipyridyl or the phenanthroline complexes.

An interesting example of the effect of pH on electrode potentials concerns the systems

$$H_2O_2(aq) + 2H^+(aq) + 2e \rightleftharpoons 2H_2O; \qquad \mathcal{E}° = +1.77 \text{ v,}$$

$$2H^+(aq) + O_2 + 2e \rightleftharpoons H_2O_2(aq); \qquad \mathcal{E}° = +0.682 \text{ v.}$$

These potentials tell us that in acid solution, hydrogen peroxide is a very good oxidizing agent but a rather poor reducing agent. In basic solution, the potentials decrease by $0.059\, pK_w$:

$$H_2O_2(aq) + 2e \rightleftharpoons 2OH^-(aq); \qquad \mathcal{E}_b° = +0.94 \text{ v,}$$

$$2H_2O + O_2 + 2e \rightleftharpoons H_2O_2(aq) + 2OH^-(aq); \qquad \mathcal{E}_b° = -0.146 \text{ v.}$$

Under these conditions, then, hydrogen peroxide is an excellent reducing agent, but only a moderately strong oxidizing agent. In either case, the overall decomposition reaction, obtained by combining these two reactions,

$$2H_2O_2(aq) \rightleftharpoons 2H_2O + O_2; \qquad \mathcal{E}° = +1.09 \text{ v,}$$

is thermodynamically favored to the same extent. In the absence of catalysts, however, the decomposition of hydrogen peroxide solutions is slow (see Chapter 10).

Examination of the balanced half-reactions in Table 9–17 shows that wherever H^+ appears in these equations it is found on the left-hand side, with the oxidized form of the couple. This is simply a reflection of the increase of acidity with increase in oxidation number. In practice this means that in all those systems in which H^+ appears specifically (and in some in which it does not), the electrode potentials are decreased in going from an acidic to a basic solution.

There are a number of observations that can be made on the relation of the standard electrode potentials in Table 9–17 to the position of elements in the periodic table. One such relation, illustrated in Fig. 9–23, shows the electrode potentials of the first transition series. In general these increase in a period with increasing atomic number. There are several anomalies, particularly the low values for Mn(II)–Mn(s), Fe(III)–Fe(II), and Zn(II)–Zn(s) and the high value for Mn(III)–Mn(II). All of these involve one ion with either a d^5 or d^{10} electron configuration [Mn(II), Fe(III) and Zn(II)], for which the ligand-field stabilization is zero. The low value for Cr(III)–Cr(II) and the high value for Cu(II)–Cu(s) are, at least in part, a result of the large ligand-field stabilization of Cr(III) and Cu(II).

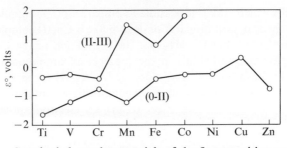

FIG. 9–23.   Standard electrode potentials of the first transition metal series.

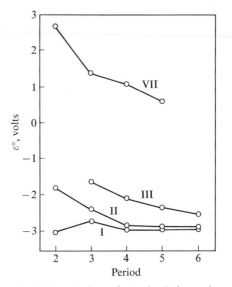

FIG. 9–24.   Periodic variation of standard electrode potentials:

Group I   (Li to Cs), $M^+ + e = M$,

Group II   (Be to Ba), $M^{2+} + 2e = M$,

Group III (Al, Sc, Y, La), $M^{3+} + 3e = M$,

Group VII (F to I), $\frac{1}{2}X_2 + e = X^-$.

Some of the trends found in groups of the periodic table are regular (Fig. 9–24). These can be interpreted principally by the ramifications of increasing size with atomic number within any one group. Other correlations are not as clear cut as these, particularly among the oxyacids of the nonmetallic elements.

BIBLIOGRAPHY

A

Barrow, G. M., *Physical Chemistry*. New York: McGraw-Hill, 1961.

Bell, R. P., *Acids and Bases*. London: Methuen, 1952.

Day, M. C., and J. Selbin, *Theoretical Inorganic Chemistry*. New York: Reinhold, 1962.

Heslop, R. B., and P. L. Robinson, *Inorganic Chemistry*. Amsterdam: Elsevier, 1960.

Ketelaar, J. A. A., *Chemical Constitution*. Amsterdam: Elsevier, 1958.

B

Bell, R. P., *The Proton in Chemistry*. Ithaca, New York: Cornell, 1959.

Bjerrum, J., G. Schwarzenbach, and L. G. Sillén, *Stability Constants*. London: Chemical Society, 1958.

Bockris, J. O'M., and B. E. Conway, *Modern Aspects of Electrochemistry*. London: Butterworth, 1954.

Butler, J. N., *Ionic Equilibria*. Reading, Mass.: Addison-Wesley, 1963.

Latimer, W. M., *The Oxidation States of the Elements and their Potentials in Aqueous Solution*. Englewood Cliffs, N. J.: Prentice-Hall, 1952.

Lewis, G. N., and M. Randall (revised by K. Pitzer and L. Brewer), *Thermodynamics*. New York: McGraw-Hill, 1961.

Robinson, R. A., and R. H. Stokes, *Electrolyte Solutions*. London: Butterworth, 1959.

Sillén, L. G., "Quantitative Studies of Hydrolytic Equilibria," *Quart. Rev.*, **13**, 146 (1959).

PROBLEMS

9–1. Using Eq. (9–2), calculate the activity coefficient term $\gamma_{H^+}\gamma_{Ac^-}/\gamma_{HAc}$ for the series of solutions listed in Table 9–1. Plot log $(\gamma_{H^+}\gamma_{Ac^-}/\gamma_{HAc})$ as a function of $\sqrt{\alpha c}$.

9–2. Calculate the standard entropy changes for the following reactions:

$$CdCl^+(aq) \rightleftharpoons Cd^{2+}(aq) + Cl^-(aq),$$

$$FeCl^{2+}(aq) \rightleftharpoons Fe^{3+}(aq) + Cl^-(aq).$$

Comment on the results.

9–3. Thermodynamic data are given in the tables that permit the calculation of the enthalpy and entropy changes in reactions of the type

$$HX^{(1-n)+}(aq) \rightleftharpoons H^+(aq) + X^{-n}(aq),$$

with n taking values from zero to three. Calculate ΔH and ΔS for some representative examples, and comment on any regularities observed.

9–4. Make a list of the principal species to be expected in solutions of the following solutes in (a) water, (b) anhydrous sulfuric acid, and (c) anhydrous liquid ammonia:

$$NaOH, \quad SO_3, \quad (NH_4)_2SO_4, \quad H_2O.$$

9-5. The values of pK_2 for H_2CrO_4 and $H_2Cr_2O_7$ are 6.5 and 1.6, respectively. Estimate pK_1 for each of these. Compare the acidity of H_2CrO_4 with that of H_2SO_4 in aqueous solution, and suggest reasons for the difference.

9-6. The following complexes are found in the Ag(I)—ethylenediamine(en) system:

$$Ag(en)^+ \qquad \log K_1 = 4.7$$
$$Ag(en)_2^+ \qquad \log \beta_2 = 7.7$$
$$Ag_2(en)^{2+} \qquad \log \beta_{12} = 1.8$$
$$Ag_2(en)_2^{2+} \qquad \log \beta_{22} = 13.2$$

Recalling that Ag(I) preferentially tends to linear coordination, suggest structures for these complexes which are consistent with the formation constants.

9-7. Using the data given in Section 9-4 on aqueous solutions of Hg(II), plot a graph showing the fraction of Hg(II) present as Hg^{2+}, $HgOH^+$, and $Hg(OH)_2$ as a function of pH.

9-8. Using the data of Table 9-11 for aqueous solutions of H_3PO_4, plot a graph showing the fraction of PO_4 present as PO_4^{3-}, HPO_4^{2-}, $H_2PO_4^-$, and H_3PO_4 as a function of pH.

9-9. According to the Debye-Hückel theory of activity coefficients in dilute solutions, the mean ionic activity coefficient for a 1-1 electrolyte can be represented by the equation

$$\log \gamma_\pm = -0.509\sqrt{I}.$$

Employ this expression to replace $\log \gamma_\pm$ in Eq. (9-24) and, assuming $\gamma_{HCl} = 1$ and $p_{H_2} = 1$ atm, rearrange the equation so that $\mathcal{E}^\circ_{cell}$ may be determined from a linear extrapolation. Use the data of Table 9-16 to prepare the graph, and derive a value for $\mathcal{E}^\circ_{cell}$.

9-10. For the following oxidation-reduction reactions, find the standard potentials from the tables of electrode potentials (Table 9-17). Check these results by calculating the standard free energy changes from the free energies of formation, and converting ΔG° to $\mathcal{E}^\circ$:

$$\text{(a) } 2Fe^{2+} + I_2 = 2Fe^{3+} + 2I^-$$
$$\text{(b) } 2Ag^+ + Cu = 2Ag + Cu^{2+}.$$

9-11. The electrode potential for the half-reaction

$$SO_4^{2-} + 4H^+ + 2e = H_2SO_3 + H_2O$$

is $+0.17$ volts. Calculate the electrode potential for the same system in basic solution, i.e., for

$$SO_4^{2-} + H_2O + 2e = SO_3^{2-} + 2OH^-.$$

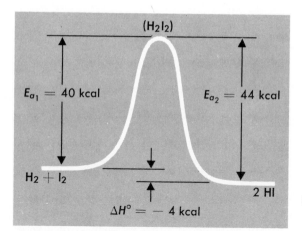

(H_2I_2)

$E_{a_1} = 40$ kcal $E_{a_2} = 44$ kcal

$H_2 + I_2$

2 HI

$\Delta H° = -4$ kcal

CHAPTER TEN

Rates and

Mechanisms of Reactions

In the preceding chapters we have dealt with the structure of molecules and crystals, and with the equilibrium aspects of their reactions. Even an introduction to physical inorganic chemistry such as this cannot be concluded without a discussion of the rates at which reactions occur, and of the detailed path by which they proceed. These two subjects are intimately connected, for the principal source of information about the mechanisms comes from rate data. Conversely, in order to make even the crudest guess at the rate of an unknown reaction, the approach must be made in terms of a mechanism.

10–1. REACTION KINETICS

The rate of a chemical reaction may be affected by temperature, by the concentrations of reactants (and sometimes of the products), by the presence of catalysts or inhibitors, as well as by many other more subtle factors. The great diversity of variables in kinetic systems makes their experimental study difficult and far less accurate than the corresponding thermodynamic measurements. From the standpoint of the determination of the mechanism of a reaction, the temperature and the concentration dependence of the rate are by far the most significant variables, provided that at the same time all other parameters are kept as constant as possible.

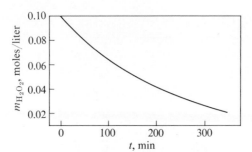

FIG. 10–1.   Decrease with time in the molality of hydrogen peroxide at 313°K.

Experimentally the concentration of one or more (ideally all) of the reactants or products in the reaction is determined as a function of time, i.e., as the reaction proceeds. This determination may be achieved either by analysis of a series of reaction mixtures quenched at different times, or by a physical analysis which does not disturb the course of the reactions. In either case the result is similar to that illustrated in Fig. 10–1, where the decreasing concentration of hydrogen peroxide in the solution reaction

$$2H_2O_2 \rightarrow 2H_2O + O_2$$

is plotted against time. The rate of the reaction is given by a time differential of concentration,

$$\text{Rate} = \frac{d[H_2O_2]}{dt}, \tag{10–1}$$

which is just the slope of the line in Fig. 10–1 at any point (it changes with time). By measuring this slope at various times, we can then find the variation of the rate with either time or concentration. The latter rate variation is the one of interest, for it has been found experimentally (see Fig. 10–2) that the rate of reaction is proportional to the remaining concentration of hydrogen peroxide. We can formulate this by the mathematical equation

$$\frac{d[H_2O_2]}{dt} = -k[H_2O_2], \tag{10–2}$$

in which k is called the *specific rate constant*. This equation may be integrated to the form

$$[H_2O_2] = [H_2O_2]_0 e^{-kt}$$

to give the concentration of hydrogen peroxide at time t in terms of the initial concentration $[H_2O_2]_0$, which is the curve of Fig. 10–1.

It is a feature common to many (but not all!) reactions that the rate of reaction is proportional to some power of the concentrations of reactants. For the

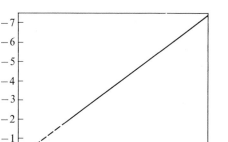

FIG. 10–2. Rate data for hydrogen peroxide decomposition, showing first-order dependence of the rate law.

general reaction

$$aA + bB + \cdots \rightarrow \text{Products},$$

the rate may be of the form

$$\text{Rate} = k[A]^m[B]^n \ldots.$$

The powers m, n, etc., are not necessarily integral, and certainly may bear no relation to the stoichiometric factors a, b, etc. The *overall order* of a reaction is the sum $m + n + \ldots$, while the *order* with respect to A is m, to B is n, etc. The order of a reaction is an experimental quantity that is, in general, not predictable from a balanced chemical equation. Some examples follow to illustrate this point.

The reaction of hydrogen and iodine at high temperatures to form hydrogen iodide,

$$H_2(g) + I_2(g) \underset{2}{\overset{1}{\rightleftharpoons}} 2HI(g), \tag{10–3}$$

is a second-order reaction; but the reverse reaction (also second-order) complicates the expression for the rate of disappearance of hydrogen:

$$\text{Rate} = -k_1[H_2][I_2] + k_2[HI]^2. \tag{10–4}$$

The rate of reaction of hydrogen with bromine, which has the same stoichiometry as Eq. (10–3),

$$H_2(g) + Br_2(g) \rightarrow 2HBr(g), \tag{10–5}$$

has an entirely different and complex dependence on concentrations:

$$\text{Rate} = -\frac{k[H_2][Br_2]^{1/2}}{1 + k'[HBr]/[Br_2]}. \tag{10–6}$$

The substitution reaction in aqueous solution,

$$Pt(NH_3)_2Cl_2 + NH_3 \rightarrow Pt(NH_3)_3Cl^+ + Cl^-, \tag{10-7}$$

is first-order in concentration of the platinum complex, but independent of the concentration of ammonia:

$$\frac{d[Pt(NH_3)_2Cl_2]}{dt} = -k[Pt(NH_3)_2Cl_2]. \tag{10-8}$$

Each of Eqs. (10–2), (10–4), (10–6), and (10–8) represents the *rate law* for the corresponding chemical reaction.

Continuing with direct experimental observations, it is found that the specific rate constants usually vary with temperature in much the same way as do equilibrium constants. Thus when the logarithm of k is plotted against the reciprocal of the absolute temperature, a reasonably good straight line is found. By analogy with the thermodynamic relation between the equilibrium constant and the enthalpy and entropy change in a reaction, an *enthalpy of activation* and an *entropy of activation* may be assigned, according to the temperature dependence of the rate constant. *These are not thermodynamic functions*, but we shall see that it is possible to make a quasi-thermodynamic interpretation of them. However, we may note here that with only a few exceptions, rates of chemical reactions increase with temperature, which means that the enthalpy of activation is generally a positive quantity.

(a) Mechanisms of reaction

The interpretation of experimental rate laws requires a detailed consideration of the way in which the reactants interact and of the various transient species involved in the reaction. A mechanism comprises a series of elementary reactions, each of which can be interpreted on a molecular basis as involving one or more molecules, atoms, or ions. The rate law found by experiment will provide clues to a mechanism but almost never in an unambiguous sense. From a comparison of Eqs. (10–4) and (10–6), it must be concluded that the mechanism of the hydrogen-iodine reaction is quite different in character from that of the hydrogen-bromine reaction, yet these rate laws, particularly the latter, indicate only in a superficial way what form the mechanism must take. Other considerations must be brought to bear on the problem. On the other hand, a postulated mechanism must yield, through mathematical analysis, a rate law in agreement with experiment. Such a mechanism or mechanisms then often provide new criteria and suggest new experiments to test the mechanism. Even then, a reaction mechanism can rarely be considered to be proved.

There are three basic types of elementary reaction, according to whether there are one, two, or three reactant species. These are termed *unimolecular*, *bimolecular*, and *termolecular*, respectively. True termolecular reactions are rare, and no examples have been found in which four or more species react together in the sense of an elementary reaction. The rate laws for these elementary reactions can be written down directly as

$$Rate = k[C]; \qquad\qquad unimolecular,$$

$$Rate = k[C_1][C_2]; \qquad\qquad bimolecular,$$

$$Rate = k[C_1][C_2][C_3]; \qquad termolecular,$$

and are first, second, and third order, respectively. For reasons involving energy transfer, unimolecular reactions of simple molecules in the gas phase approach second order at low pressures, while bimolecular association reactions under the same conditions approach third order.

In order to show how an overall rate law is obtained from a mechanism, we shall consider two typical simple examples. For the first, the overall reaction

$$A + B = C + D \tag{10–9}$$

might be represented by the following sequence of elementary reactions:

$$A + B \overset{1}{\to} X, \tag{10–10}$$

$$X \overset{2}{\to} A + B, \tag{10–11}$$

$$X \overset{3}{\to} C + D. \tag{10–12}$$

In this scheme the species X is supposed to be a *reactive intermediate* of very low concentration. The complete rate equation that can be derived from this mechanism is

$$Rate = \frac{k_1 k_3 [A][B]}{k_2 + k_3}, \tag{10–13}$$

showing the reaction to be second-order, first-order with respect to each of A and B. An experimental rate law of this type cannot be distinguished kinetically from that obtained, assuming that the reaction goes in one step, e.g., that Eq. (10–9) represents an elementary reaction, for the rate law then would be:

$$Rate = k[A][B] \tag{10–14}$$

which has the same form as Eq. (10–13). If B represents a solvent molecule in a solution reaction, then its concentration would remain fixed through the course of reaction, and Eq. (10–13) becomes effectively first-order,

$$Rate = k'[A], \tag{10–15}$$

where $k' = k_1 k_3 [B]/(k_2 + k_3)$. In such a case the reaction is said to be *pseudo first-order*.

A second mechanism applies to the same overall reaction [Eq. (10–9)]:

$$A \xrightarrow{1} C + Y, \tag{10–16}$$

$$C + Y \xrightarrow{2} A, \tag{10–17}$$

$$Y + B \xrightarrow{3} D. \tag{10–18}$$

The overall rate (with Y as a reactive intermediate) is:

$$\text{Rate} = \frac{k_1' k_3' [A][B]}{k_2' [C] + k_3' [B]}. \tag{10–19}$$

Here the reaction is first-order because of the concentration dependence in the denominator. This becomes clear if we assume that the third reaction [Eq. (10–18)] is very much faster than the second. Then the rate becomes

$$\text{Rate} = k_1' [A]. \tag{10–20}$$

There are several circumstances in which these mechanisms become indistinguishable. The first is apparent from comparison of Eqs. (10–15) and (10–20), that is, if B represents a solvent molecule and the inhibiting effect of C in the second mechanism is small. A second case would be that in which C is a solvent molecule and $k_2'[C] \gg k_3'[B]$ in the second mechanism. Both mechanisms then predict a second-order reaction. Of course, many other mechanisms could apply to the reaction of Eq. (10–9), and there will usually be several plausible ones for any experimental order of reaction.

In either of the reaction mechanisms discussed above, if the rate of the second reaction is very much faster than that of the third, then a pre-equilibrium is established, with the concentration of the transient intermediates given by

$$[X] = K[A][B], \qquad \text{(first mechanism)},$$

$$[Y] = K'[A]/[C], \qquad \text{(second mechanism)}.$$

The rates of reaction then become

$$\text{Rate} = kK[A][B], \qquad \text{(first mechanism)},$$

and

$$\text{Rate} = k_3'K'[A][B]/[C], \qquad \text{(second mechanism)}.$$

This is a fairly common situation, particularly in solution reactions.

(b) Temperature dependence of the rate constant

The overall temperature dependence of the rate of reaction is a function of the temperature dependences of the elementary reactions. The reaction of hydrogen and iodine is a convenient one to examine in this context, since the overall reaction is certainly an elementary bimolecular reaction. Further, it is one in which the forward and reverse reaction and the equilibrium have been studied in detail.

The rate constants have the form originally suggested by Arrhenius in 1889, which is formally analogous to that for an equilibrium constant [see Eq. (8–23)]. The *Arrhenius equation* can be cast in the equivalent forms

$$\frac{d \ln k}{d (1/T)} = -E_a/R, \tag{10–21}$$

$$\ln k = -\frac{E_a}{RT} + \text{const}, \tag{10–22}$$

in which k is the rate constant and E_a the experimental energy of activation. Equation (10–22) applies to both the forward and reverse reactions in the hydrogen-iodine system; but, of course, with different values of k, E_a, and the constant term.

When hydrogen, iodine, and hydrogen iodide reach equilibrium, we know that the concentrations are related by the equilibrium constant

$$K_{eq} = \frac{[HI]^2}{[H_2][I_2]}. \tag{10–23}$$

Equilibrium implies that in Eq. (10–4), the net rate of reaction is zero; therefore

$$-k_1[H_2][I_2] + k_2[HI]^2 = 0, \tag{10–24}$$

and rearranging gives

$$\frac{k_1}{k_2} = \frac{[HI]^2}{[H_2][I_2]}. \tag{10–25}$$

Thus we see that for these elementary reactions the ratio of the forward and reverse rate constants is just the equilibrium constant,

$$K_{eq} = \frac{k_1}{k_2}. \tag{10–26}$$

We now take the derivative of the logarithm of both sides of Eq. (10–26) with respect to $1/T$ and find

$$\frac{d \ln K_{eq}}{d(1/T)} = -\frac{\Delta H}{R} = -\frac{E_{a_1}}{R} + \frac{E_{a_2}}{R} = \frac{d \ln k_1}{d (1/T)} - \frac{d \ln k_2}{d (1/T)}. \tag{10–27}$$

From this result we see that the difference between the energies of activation of the forward and reverse reactions is just the thermodynamic enthalpy change (Fig. 10–3). The situation illustrated is typical of kinetic systems; that is, there is an energy barrier between the reactants and products. The higher this barrier, the slower the reaction is. In fact, it is just this effect that makes the nonequilibrium state extant. There is no completely general relation between the height of this

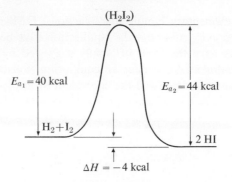

FIG. 10-3. Schematic energy diagram showing activated complex relative to reactants and products in the H_2-I_2 reaction.

barrier and the thermodynamic properties, except that in Eq. (10-27). For some special reactions, there is reason to believe that one of the activation energies is zero or nearly so; in such cases, the other activation energy is just equal to the endothermicity of the reaction.

The *Arrhenius factor*, $e^{-E_a/RT}$, has a profound effect on the rate constant. This factor is tabulated for different activation energies and temperature in Table 10-1.

TABLE 10-1

DEPENDENCE OF THE ARRHENIUS FACTOR $e^{-E_a/RT}$ ON E_a AND T

T, °K \ E_a	10 kcal	20 kcal	40 kcal
298	4.7×10^{-8}	2.2×10^{-15}	4.8×10^{-30}
400	3.4×10^{-6}	1.2×10^{-11}	1.3×10^{-22}
600	2.3×10^{-4}	5.3×10^{-8}	2.8×10^{-15}
800	1.8×10^{-3}	3.4×10^{-6}	1.2×10^{-11}

(c) Theoretical treatment of rate constants

Although a considerable amount of effort has been directed toward the theoretical treatment of reaction rates, the problem is so complicated that only semiempirical theories have had much success, except for some atomic and diatomic reactants. The absolute-rate theory of Eyring and coworkers (1935) can be formulated as

$$k_{\text{rate}} = \left(\frac{kT}{h}\right) e^{\Delta S^{\ddagger}/R} e^{-\Delta H^{\ddagger}/RT} \qquad (10-28)$$

in which the factor kT/h (k and h here are Boltzmann's and Planck's constants, respectively; see Appendix I) is about $6 \times 10^{12} \sec^{-1}$ at room temperature. The *entropy of activation*, $\Delta S^{\ddagger}$, and the *enthalpy of activation*, $\Delta H^{\ddagger}$, refer to a particular standard state, i.e., unit concentration in whatever units the rate constant is given. Strictly speaking, activities rather than concentrations should be used in rate expressions. This becomes an important factor only in solution, but especially so in electrolytic solutions.

Just as outlined in the previous section, the enthalpies of activation in the forward and reverse direction for a reversible elementary reaction are related to the standard enthalpy change as follows:

$$\Delta H^{\circ} = \Delta H_1^{\ddagger} - \Delta H_2^{\ddagger}.$$

The same is true for the entropies of activation,

$$\Delta S^{\circ} = \Delta S_1^{\ddagger} - \Delta S_2^{\ddagger},$$

provided that these all refer to the same standard state.

The absolute-rate theory postulates an activated complex for an elementary reaction as an association of the reactants with an enthalpy greater than $\Delta H^{\ddagger}$ with respect to the reactants. The entropy of activation is then the entropy change required in the formation of the activated complex, although it is not a strictly thermodynamic quantity. Despite the fact that Eq. (10–28) by no means represents an accurate or complete treatment of the rate constants, a great deal can be learned about the mechanism from the magnitude of $\Delta H^{\ddagger}$ and $\Delta S^{\ddagger}$.

A second approach, particularly applicable to bimolecular reactions, is to consider the rate at which molecules collide according to kinetic theory. The *collision number Z* is then modified by a factor $e^{-E_a/RT}$ and a *steric term p*, to give an effective collision frequency, i.e., the bimolecular rate constant. In the gas phase, Z is of the order of $9 \times 10^9 T^{1/2}$ liter/mole-sec, but depends on the size and molecular weight of the colliding molecules. Thus the rate constant is given by:

$$k = 9 \times 10^9 T^{1/2} p e^{-E_a/RT} \text{ liter/mole-sec.} \tag{10–29}$$

The factor p, which is supposed to be unity or less, takes account of all limitations on the effective collision rate except energy. If we make the approximate identification between $\Delta H^{\ddagger}$ of Eq. (10–28) and E_a of Eq. (10–29), we find (at $T = 298°K$) that

$$e^{\Delta S^{\ddagger}/R} \approx \frac{p}{40}.$$

Thus the maximum value of $p = 1$ corresponds to an entropy of activation of -6 cal/deg, while $p = 10^{-3}$ corresponds to $\Delta S^{\ddagger} = -21$ cal/deg (based on a standard state of one mole/liter).

These ideas apply to solution reactions and to gas reactions equally well, with one interesting exception with regard to the collision theory. In the gas phase, when two reactant molecules collide but do not react, they separate again and each goes its separate way. However, in solution, two reactant molecules that meet will be held by the surrounding solvent molecules so that they undergo multiple collisions. We therefore need to distinguish between the average collision frequency, which is that given in Eq. (10–29), and the *encounter frequency*, at which pairs of reactants first meet in a solvent "cage." The ratio of the collision frequency to the encounter frequency represents the average number of collisions the pair makes in the solvent cage. This factor, in typical solvents such as water, will be of the order of 100, but increases with increasing viscosity of the solvent. This *cage effect* is unimportant for slow bimolecular reactions, since the average collision frequency is unaffected. But the rate of a fast bimolecular reaction ($E_a \approx 0$, $p \approx 1$) is determined by the encounter frequency rather than by the collision frequency; thus it will be slower in water than is predicted by Eq. (10–29) by, for example, a factor of 100. Such reactions are said to be diffusion-controlled, and have bimolecular rate constants of the order of 10^9 liter/mole-sec, which, incidentally, makes them too fast to measure by any but the most refined technique.

10–2. GAS-PHASE REACTIONS

The number of inorganic gaseous systems whose rates have been measured is somewhat limited, certainly so compared with organic systems. A number of these gas-phase reactions are listed in Table 10–2, together with their entropies and enthalpies of activation, calculated from Eq. (10–28). These reactions are all thought to be elementary ones. A number of the reactions occur as part of the postulated mechanism of various overall reactions, some of which are detailed below.

Unimolecular reactions and bimolecular association reactions are often found to undergo an increase in the order of the reaction as the total pressure or concentration is decreased. This behavior is understandable on the following basis. For a unimolecular reaction to occur, molecules must acquire an energy greater than or equal to the activation energy. The only way they can do this is by collision with other molecules. Thus for the detailed way in which the reaction occurs, we write the mechanism

$$A + M \xrightarrow{1} A^* + M,$$

$$A^* + M \xrightarrow{2} C + M^*,$$

$$A^* \xrightarrow{3} \text{Products},$$

in which A* refers to a reactant molecule A, with sufficient energy to decompose. It will either lose its energy again, by collision with another molecule M, or decompose. The overall rate is given by the expression:

$$\text{Rate} = \frac{k_1 k_3 [A][M]}{k_2[M] + k_3}.$$

Qualitatively we can see that should $k_2[M]$ be much greater than k_3 (expected at high pressure) the overall rate would be first-order, while at low pressure, if

TABLE 10–2

ENTROPIES AND ENTHALPIES OF REACTION FOR GAS-PHASE REACTIONS

Gas phase reactions	$\Delta S^{\ddagger}$, cal/mole-deg	$\Delta H^{\ddagger}$, kcal/mole
Unimolecular		
$F_2O_2 \rightarrow F_2 + O_2$	0	17
$N_2O_4 \rightarrow 2NO_2$	16	13
$N_2O_5 \rightarrow NO_2 + NO_3$	11	21
cyclo $C_4F_8 \rightarrow 2C_2F_4$	16	74
cyclo $C_3H_6 \rightarrow C_3H_6$	10	65
Bimolecular		
$H_2 + I_2 \rightarrow 2HI$	-8	41
$2HI \rightarrow H_2 + I_2$	-7	46
$2NO_2 \rightarrow 2NO + O_2$	-13	27
$NO + O_3 \rightarrow NO_2 + O_2$	-16	2.3
$H + Br_2 \rightarrow HBr + Br$	-6	0.9
$Br + H_2 \rightarrow HBr + H$	-9	18
$2NO_2 \rightarrow N_2O_4$	-16	0
$2NOCl \rightarrow 2NO + Cl_2$	-7	26
Termolecular		
$2NO + O_2 \rightarrow 2NO_2$	-43	-1
$2NO + Cl_2 \rightarrow 2NOCl$	-39	3.7
$2NO + Br_2 \rightarrow 2NOBr$	-40	0
$I + I + He \rightarrow I_2 + He$	-13	0
$I + I + I_2 \rightarrow 2I_2$	-21	-4

$k_3 \gg k_2[M]$, it is second-order. The pressure region in which this gradual change in order occurs depends on the molecular complexity of the reactant. For a diatomic molecule, k_3 is of the order of 10^{-13} sec^{-1}, hence the unimolecular dissociation is always second-order. Large polyatomic molecules may show first-order dependence even at very low pressures. Similar considerations apply to bimolecular associations, e.g., the mechanism

$$A + B \overset{1}{\rightarrow} (AB)^*,$$

$$(AB)^* \overset{2}{\rightarrow} A + B,$$

$$M + (AB)^* \overset{3}{\rightarrow} AB + M,$$

for which the overall rate expression is

$$\text{Rate} = \frac{k_1 k_3 [A][B][M]}{k_2 + k_3 [M]}.$$

Here the complexity of the product, AB, determines the pressure range over which the reaction changes from second-order to first-order. Association of two atoms (the reverse of the unimolecular dissociation of a diatomic molecule) must always be third-order (see Table 10–2).

Unimolecular reactions generally have entropies of activation of the order of zero or greater, although there is a class of unimolecular isomerizations of organic molecules which have been found to have the equivalent of large negative entropies of activation, but this effect has to be interpreted on a different basis. A zero entropy of activation would be expected in unimolecular reactions in general, because the activated complex, A^*, should not differ greatly from the reactant molecule itself. On the other hand, since the reactant is activated and then has a much greater energy than usual, some entropy increase can be associated with increased motions of the activated molecule.

Bimolecular reactions, at least in the gas phase, should have negative entropies of activation because the formation of the activated complex involves the formation of one molecule from two. That this is so can be seen from the data in Table 10–2. The temperature-independent part of the rate constant for these reactions lies in the range of 10^9 to 10^{11} liter/mole-sec.

For termolecular reactions, those involving nitric oxide in Table 10–2 have quite large negative entropies of activation, while the atom recombinations have smaller (but still negative) entropies of activation. Whether these reactions occur by a true termolecular process, with three molecules forming an activated complex, or by a series of bimolecular reactions is a question that has not been completely resolved, although the available evidence is fairly heavily in favor of the latter alternative. This seems, in fact, to be the only way of explaining the negative activation energies peculiar to these reactions.

10–3. ACID-BASE REACTIONS

The rates of most acid-base reactions in aqueous solution appear to be instantaneous. The only reactions of this type that can be studied by conventional techniques are neutralizations of nitro-paraffins, in which the acidic proton is bonded directly to a carbon atom. The earliest techniques for studying fast reactions, developed by Hartridge and Roughton (1923), utilize a rapid mixing of reagents in a flow system. Such methods are limited in their time resolution to about a millisecond. This means that a second-order rate constant of 10^5 liter/mole-sec can just be measured, whereas diffusion-controlled reactions may have bimolecular rate constants in excess of 10^9 liter/mole-sec.

Simple acid-base reactions often fall in the latter category, and hence are far too fast to measure by any technique that requires a mixing of reagents. These and other very fast reactions can be studied by a relaxation method, pioneered by Eigen and his coworkers during the last decade. In essence, this method involves an equilibrium system perturbed by a sudden (10^{-7} sec) change in temperature, pressure or electrical field. Then the return to equilibrium is followed by observing

TABLE 10–3

RATE CONSTANTS FOR ACID-BASE REACTIONS IN AQUEOUS SOLUTION

Acid-base reactions	k_1, liter/mole-sec	k_2, sec^{-1}
$H^+ + OH^- \rightarrow H_2O$	1.3×10^{11}	2.3×10^{-5}
$H^+ + SO_4^{2-} \rightarrow HSO_4^-$	1×10^{11}	1×10^9
$H^+ + OAc^- \rightarrow HAOc$	4.5×10^{10}	8×10^5
$H^+ + H_2BO_3^- \rightarrow H_3BO_3$	2.5×10^{10}	20
$H^+ + HS^- \rightarrow H_2S$	7.5×10^{10}	9×10^{-3}
$H^+ + [Pt(en)_3]^{3+} \rightarrow [Pt(en)_2H(en)]^{4+}$	1.4×10^9	6×10^{-2}
$NH_3 + H^+ \rightarrow NH_4^+$	4×10^{10}	24
$NH_4^+ + OH^- \rightarrow NH_3 + H_2O$	3×10^{10}	5×10^5
$(CH_3)_3NH^+ + OH^- \rightarrow (CH_3)_3N + H_2O$	1×10^{10}	6×10^5

the change in some physical property of the system, e.g., conductivity. By this means, the mixing problem is avoided completely, and a time resolution of the order of a few microseconds can be reached. The details of these techniques cannot be dealt with here, except to point out that the perturbation can be either a simple pulse or a continuous periodic change, e.g., a sound wave provides a periodic pressure change.

Some of the rate constants for acid-base reactions measured by these relaxation techniques are given in Table 10–3. Combinations of hydrated protons and hydroxide ions with acids and bases are usually diffusion-controlled reactions, and thus have rate constants in the range of 10^9 to 10^{11} liter/mole-sec. The reverse (dissociation) reactions then have rate constants largely determined by the equilibrium constant. Thus the ratio of the rate constants k_2/k_1 for the $H^+ - OH^-$ reaction must be equal to the equilibrium constant which, for water, is 1.8×10^{-16} when the standard state for water is one molar. In the case of water, because of the very small extent of dissociation, the rate constant for the dissociation reaction is very small. Nevertheless, because of the small equilibrium concentrations of H^+ and OH^- (10^{-7} molar), equilibrium in a perturbed pure water system is restored within 10^{-4} sec.

Application of theoretical expressions for the diffusion of ions shows that the effective distance at which proton transfers occur is about 6 to 8 A. This is the equivalent of 2 or 3 hydrogen bond lengths. According to Eigen, the following three phases can be considered in such a process: 1. Formation of a collision complex of acid and base. 2. Combination of a proton from the acid with the base, in which the proton is transferred through the hydration structure of the complex. 3. Breakup of the hydration structure. The first process is the slowest one, and is therefore rate-controlling; it is also the one which is diffusion-controlled. The second and third processes follow very rapidly. The mechanism proposed for these reactions is illustrated in Fig. 10–4.

The process in which a proton migrates through the hydrogen-bonded structure of water accounts for the anomalously high electrical conductivity of H^+ and of

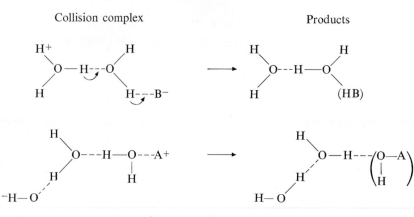

FIG. 10-4.   Combination of H^+(aq) with a base (B^-), or OH^-(aq) with an acid (A^+).

OH^- in aqueous solution, compared with other ions. This mechanism, suggested first by von Grottius in 1805, does not require that a particular proton migrate, but instead implies a series of hops by the proton from one water molecule to the next. Because of the regular hydrogen-bonded structure in ice, the rate at which proton transfer of this type occurs can be measured. The result obtained is that single-proton jumps occur in 10^{-13} to 10^{-14} sec. The relaxation (essential reorientation) of the water structure around the recombined ions occurs in about 10^{-12} sec.

An interesting side issue to acid-base reaction concerns such solutes as NH_3, CO_2, and SO_2, which could exist as the hydrated species NH_4OH, H_2CO_3, and H_2SO_3, respectively. The latter two turn out to have recognizable equilibria of the form

$$H_2CO_3(aq) \rightleftharpoons H_2O + CO_2(aq), \qquad (10\text{-}30)$$

while it appears that NH_4OH as such does not exist. There can be no question that the ammonia molecule in aqueous solution is hydrogen bonded to some of the water molecules surrounding it. Dissociation of the type

$$NH_3(aq) + H_2O \rightarrow NH_4^+(aq) + OH^-(aq)$$

can occur by a proton hop to NH_3 from an adjacent water molecule that is suitably oriented by hydrogen bonding for such a proton transfer.

In the case of the other two systems, CO_2 and SO_2, there must be a fundamental structural change on hydration involving the formation of a covalent bond to oxygen. Thus, for example, the O—C—O skeleton in CO_2 is linear, while the CO_3 skeleton in carbonic acid has approximately trigonal planar symmetry. The equilibrium of Eq. (10-30) has been measured directly, and so have the relevant rate constants. For the equilibrium there results

$$K = \frac{[H_2CO_3]}{[CO_2]} = 0.0037,$$

TABLE 10–4

PROTON EXCHANGE REACTIONS

Reaction	k_1, liter/mole-sec	k_2, liter/mole-sec	$\dfrac{k_2}{k_1}$
$NH_3 + NH_4^+$	10.6×10^8	0.9×10^8	0.09
$CH_3NH_2 + CH_3NH_3^+$	2.5×10^8	3.4×10^8	1.4
$(CH_3)_2NH + (CH_3)_2NH_2^+$	0.4×10^8	5.6×10^8	14
$(CH_3)_3N + (CH_3)_3NH^+$	$<0.3 \times 10^8$	3.1×10^8	>10

while for the rate of dehydration of H_2CO_3, the first-order rate constant is 21 sec^{-1}, hence the (first-order) rate of reaction of $CO_2(aq)$ with water is 0.078 sec^{-1}. The dissociation reactions are measured by flow techniques involving the mixing of hydrochloric acid and bicarbonate solutions. The reaction

$$H^+ + HCO_3^- \rightarrow H_2CO_3$$

is probably diffusion-controlled, hence very rapid on the time scale of a flow reaction. The slower reaction of Eq. (10–30) is followed through the electrical conductivity of the solution. In the case of SO_2, there is evidence that the equilibrium exists but, as yet, neither the equilibrium nor the rate constants have been measured.

Applications of the technique of nuclear magnetic resonance permit the establishment of the rates of symmetric proton exchange reactions. Meiboom (1951) has by this means determined the exchange rate constants for the systems given in Table 10–4. The process for which k_1 is quoted is the direct exchange,

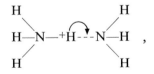

while the column headed k_2 refers to proton transfer through an intervening water molecule:

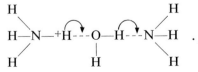

It can be noted that as bulky methyl groups are substituted for hydrogen atoms, the rate of the first process decreases in importance relative to the second.

10–4. SUBSTITUTION REACTIONS

The replacement of one ligand by another in a complex ion exhibits wide variations in rate. An *inert* complex is one in which the substitution occurs slowly enough that the rate can be studied by conventional techniques over periods longer than minutes. The criterion of a *labile* complex implies that its substitution reactions are fast, requiring special techniques for their kinetic study. A clear distinction must be made between stability and inertness because the first is a thermodynamic equilibrium concept while the latter is a kinetic criterion. As to gross connections between the two, extreme stability requires that the complex be inert; however, the converse is not necessarily true. Thus the complex $Co(NH_3)_6^{3+}$ is unstable in acid solution, yet persists unchanged for extended periods. Even the first criterion is subject to some confusion. The complex ion $Hg(CN)_4^{2-}$ is cited as an example of a stable complex ($\log \beta_4 = 41$) which is also labile. However, this is incorrect, since the correct quantity to look at for stability is $\log K_4 = 2.8$, for the reaction

$$Hg(CN)_3^-(aq) + CN^-(aq) \rightleftharpoons Hg(CN)_4^{2-}(aq),$$

rather than the overall formation constant.

Substitution reactions can be classified in a variety of subdivisions which, although involving basically the same type of reaction, have distinguishing features. Exchange reactions that embody no net chemical change, e.g.,

$$Fe(CN)_6^{3-} + C^*N^- \rightarrow Fe(CN)_5(C^*N)^{3-} + CN^-,$$

are studied with isotopically labeled ligands (C^*N). This method is applicable so long as the rate is relatively slow, so that there is sufficient time to physically separate, e.g., by precipitation, one of the products. Recent methods based on magnetic resonance phenomena have been applied to fast exchange reactions. These methods measure essentially the time a particular species spends in an unchanged environment.

Chemical substitution reactions, of the type

$$PtCl_6^{2-} + NO_2^- \rightarrow PtCl_5NO_2^{2-} + Cl^-$$

provide much useful information. Often, however, such reactions may be complicated by hydrolytic equilibria and by unfavorable equilibria. One of the most frequently studied reactions is that of hydrolysis, in which a ligand is replaced by a water molecule. A distinction is made between *acid hydrolysis*,

$$Co(NH_3)_5Cl^{2+} + H_2O \rightarrow Co(NH_3)_5(H_2O)^{3+} + Cl^-$$

in an acid medium, and *base hydrolysis*,

$$Co(NH_3)_5Cl^{2+} + OH^- \rightarrow Co(NH_3)_5OH^{2+} + Cl^-$$

in a basic medium. The classification is based on whether an aquo or a hydroxo complex is the product. Often, however, both may be formed simultaneously, and then we can use only the general term "hydrolysis," unless the reactions are kinetically separable.

The reverse of hydrolysis, i.e., substitution of an aquo ligand by another ligand, has been called *anation:*

$$\mathrm{Cr(H_2O)_6^{3+} + NCS^- \rightarrow Cr(H_2O)_5NCS^{2+} + H_2O}.$$

The rates of these anation reactions can be deduced if the rate of hydrolysis and the equilibrium constant are known.

(a) Mechanisms for hydrolysis reactions

On a theoretical basis there are two principal detailed mechanisms (Ingold, 1935) by which ligand substitution reactions can be expected to occur. The first, called S_N1 (substitution, nucleophilic, unimolecular), goes by a two-step sequence. A heterolytic unimolecular dissociation,

$$\mathrm{MX_n \underset{2}{\overset{1}{\rightleftharpoons}} MX_{n-1} + X},$$

in which an intermediate of $n - 1$ coordination is formed, is followed by rapid attack by a ligand (nucleophilic reagent) at the vacated site:

$$\mathrm{MX_{n-1} + Y \rightarrow MX_{n-1}Y}.$$

The rate law for this mechanism is

$$\mathrm{Rate} = \frac{k_1 k_3 [\mathrm{MX}_n][\mathrm{Y}]}{k_2[\mathrm{X}] + k_3[\mathrm{Y}]}.$$

Provided that the last reaction is indeed fast ($k_3[\mathrm{Y}] \gg k_2[\mathrm{X}]$), this rate law reduces to

$$\mathrm{Rate} = k_1[\mathrm{MX}_n],$$

a simple first-order reaction.

The second classification is S_N2 (substitution, nucleophilic, bimolecular), in which a nucleophilic reagent is expected to displace another ligand in a one-step process:

$$\mathrm{Y + MX \rightarrow MY + X},$$

which would require an activated complex Y—M—X. The rate of reaction here is bimolecular:

$$\mathrm{Rate} = k[\mathrm{MX}][\mathrm{Y}]$$

but, should Y represent the solvent, then the rate law would have the same form and order (pseudo-first order) as that of an S_N1 reaction (first-order). By the same token, if X represents the solvent, then, in an S_N1 mechanism, it is easily possible that $k_2[X] \gg k_3[Y]$ and, on this basis, both S_N1 and S_N2 reactions would be second-order. These consequences are the main disturbing features of hydrolysis and anation reactions, that is, that S_N1 and S_N2 reactions may not be distinguishable on the basis of a rate law.

Just as in many other areas, clear-cut classifications are the exception rather than the rule, there can be expected a gradation from S_N1 to S_N2 reactions. In the rate-determining dissociation step of an S_N1 reaction, ligands Y may have a variable effect on the dissociation rate. In fact, a pure S_N1 reaction would be independent of the nature of the incoming group, if the concentration of the latter were sufficiently high that $k_3[Y] \gg k_2[X]$. However, this behavior has not been found in any series of anation reactions.

A subdivision of S_N1 reactions suggested by Garrick (1937) is that of the S_N1CB reaction (substitution, nucleophilic, unimolecular, conjugate base). The base hydrolysis of $Co(NH_3)_5Cl^{2+}$ is thought to proceed through the series:

$$Co(NH_3)_5Cl^{2+} + OH^- \overset{\text{fast}}{\rightleftharpoons} Co(NH_3)_4(NH_2)Cl^+ + H_2O,$$

$$Co(NH_3)_4(NH_2)Cl^+ \xrightarrow{\text{slow}} Co(NH_3)_4(NH_2)^{2+} + Cl^-,$$

$$Co(NH_3)_4(NH_2)^{2+} + H_2O \xrightarrow{\text{fast}} Co(NH_3)_5(OH)^{2+}.$$

In the first step, a rapid equilibrium, the conjugate base (amido) complex is formed, which is more labile than the original complex. An S_N1 rate-determining dissociation reaction is followed rapidly by the formation of the hydroxo complex. The rate law for such a mechanism is

$$\text{Rate} = k[Co(NH_3)_5Cl^{2+}][OH^-].$$

Of course an S_N2 reaction with attack by hydroxide ion leads to the same rate law, hence considerable effort has been made to distinguish the two. In the absence of an acidic proton on the ligands, an S_N1CB mechanism is not possible. Thus, the complex trans $Co(NO_2)_2 \, dipy_2^{2+}$ undergoes hydrolysis in basic solution at a rate that is independent of hydroxide concentration over a wide range. An S_N2 reaction is ruled out by this rate law (so also is an S_N1CB mechanism); hence the assumption that it is S_N1.

A selection of examples of the rate law constants found in various hydrolysis reactions are displayed in Table 10–5. Some of the general trends are indicated in the following discussion. We might first note the presence in Table 10–5 of only a relatively few ions. The reason for this is that most complexes are so labile that their rates of hydrolysis have not been studied. Thus inert complexes, at least in the first transition series, are largely limited to chelated complexes and complexes of Co(III) and Cr(III) with unidentate ligands.

The cis and trans complexes $M(en)_2Cl_2^+$ for Co(III) and Cr(III) provide an interesting contrast. The rates of acid hydrolysis are almost exactly the same.

TABLE 10–5

HYDROLYSIS RATE CONSTANTS

Complex	k_{acid}, sec^{-1}	T, °K	k_{base}, liter/mole-sec
$[Cr(NH_3)_6]^{3+}$	2.5×10^{-5}	298	
$[Cr(NH_3)_5(H_2O)]^{3+}$	10^{-6}	313	3×10^{-6}
$[Cr(NH_3)_5Cl]^{2+}$	1.0×10^{-5}	298	
$[Cr(NH_3)_5Br]^{2+}$	5×10^{-5}	298	
$[Cr(NH_3)_5I]^{2+}$	2×10^{-4}	273	
$[Cr(NH_3)_5(NCS)]^{2+}$	1×10^{-7}	298	
cis $[Cr(en)_2Cl_2]^+$	3.3×10^{-4}	298	2.8×10^{-2}
trans $[Cr(en)_2Cl_2]^+$	3.8×10^{-5}	298	3.7×10^{-2}
$[Fe(CN)_6]^{4-}$	5×10^{-11}	293	
$[Fe(phen)_3]^{3+}$	1×10^{-4}	298	
$[Fe(phen)_3]^{2+}$	7.2×10^{-5}	298	1.0×10^{-2}
$[Co(NH_3)_6]^{3+}$	Very slow		
$[Co(NH_3)_5(H_2O)]^{3+}$	7×10^{-6}	298	
$[Co(NH_3)_5(NO_3)]^{2+}$	2.7×10^{-5}	298	
$[Co(NH_3)_5(SO_4)]^+$	10^{-6}	298	
$[Co(NH_3)_5Cl]^{2+}$	1.7×10^{-6}	298	
$[Co(NH_3)_5Br]^{2+}$	6.3×10^{-6}	298	
$[Co(NH_3)_5I]^{2+}$	10^{-5}	298	
$[Co(NH_3)_5(NCS)]^{2+}$	3×10^{-9}	298	
cis $[Co(en)_2F_2]^+$	3×10^{-6}	298	
trans $[Co(en)_2F_2]^+$	10^{-5}	298	6.3×10^1
cis $[Co(en)_2Cl_2]^+$	3.5×10^{-4}	298	10^3
trans $[Co(en)_2Cl_2]^+$	3.9×10^{-5}	298	3×10^3
$[Co(phen)_3]^{3+}$	Very slow	298	10^{-5}
$[Co(phen)_3]^{2+}$	2.2×10^{-1}	298	
$[Ni(phen)_3]^{2+}$	8×10^{-6}	298	
$[Cd(CN)_4]^{2-}$	4×10^4	298	

Yet the rates of base hydrolysis for the Cr(III) complexes are about 10^5 times slower than those of the Co(III) complexes. It is unlikely therefore that the hydrolysis mechanisms for Co(III) and Cr(III) are identical.

In general, acid hydrolysis data indicate that the order of decreasing lability of the ligand being replaced, such as in the $Cr(NH_3)_5X$ or $Co(NH_3)_5X$ series, is

$$NO_3^- > I^- > Br^- > Cl^- > F^- > NH_3 > NCS^-,$$

which is approximately the order of the spectrochemical series (Chapter 6) of increasing ligand-field stabilization. There are too few rate constants for base hydrolysis to make any generalizations of this type.

Increased positive charge on a complex ion would be expected to decrease the rate of hydrolysis if an S_N1 mechanism is operative, while base hydrolysis by an S_N2 mechanism (attack by OH$^-$) should be enhanced. The data in Table 10–6

TABLE 10–6

EFFECT OF CHARGE ON HYDROLYSIS RATE

	$\dfrac{k_{acid}\ (a)}{k_{acid}\ (b)}$	$\dfrac{k_{base}\ (a)}{k_{base}\ (b)}$
(a) cis $[Co(en)_2(NH_3)Cl]^{2+}$ (b) cis $[Co(en)_2Cl_2]^+$	1.9×10^{-3}	5.4×10^{-3}
(a) $[Co(NH_3)_5Cl]^{2+}$ (b) trans $[Co(NH_3)_4Cl_2]^+$	9.5×10^{-4}	4.7×10^{-4}
(a) cis $[Pt(NH_3)_2Cl_2]$ (b) $[PtCl_4]^{2-}$	1	1.3

are consistent with S_N1 and S_N1CB mechanisms for acid and base hydrolysis, respectively, for the Co(III) complexes, but not for the Pt(II) complex ions.

Basolo and Pearson (1956) have interpreted the data on Co(III) and Cr(III) in terms of π-repulsion between the ligand p-orbital and the occupied d_{xy} orbital, tending to expel the ligand in an S_N1 mechanism. Further, a trigonal bipyramidal (five-coordinated) intermediate would be stabilized by π-bonding through donation of electrons from the remaining ligand p-orbitals to an empty e_g orbital.

(b) Mechanisms for anation reactions

Second-order kinetics are common to essentially all anation reactions studied, but this does not really provide evidence that the mechanism is S_N2. A second-order rate law for these reactions necessarily follows from the fact that acid hydrolysis reactions are first-order, and that the mass-action law must be obeyed.

In addition to direct S_N2 displacement, the mechanism could include an S_N1 dissociation as a pre-equilibrium:

$$MH_2O \underset{2}{\overset{1}{\rightleftharpoons}} M + H_2O, \qquad M + X \overset{3}{\rightarrow} MX,$$

which also can lead to a second-order rate constant [see Section 10–1(a)]. Thus it is quite difficult to distinguish between the two mechanisms; however, the principle of microscopic reversibility implies that if the hydrolysis of a complex ion occurs via an S_N1 mechanism, then the reverse anation must also. The same, of course, applies to S_N2 reactions. All this really means is that in a reversible reaction, each elementary reaction itself must be reversible; hence the mechanism in one direction fixes the mechanism in the reverse.

(c) Mechanisms for other substitution reactions

When one ligand replaces another, and neither of them is water, the rate law is either first order in the complex ion or else first order in each of the complex and the entering ligand (second order overall). A first-order rate law can follow from an S_N1 dissociation or an S_N2 displacement by water (rate-controlling),

$$MX + H_2O \rightarrow MH_2O + X,$$

followed by a fast displacement of water by the incoming ligand:

$$MH_2O + Y \rightarrow MY + H_2O.$$

Second-order kinetics can arise either from a direct S_N2 displacement by the entering ligand, or from a pre-equilibrium with the aquo complex followed by an S_N2 displacement of water.

Usually such substitution reactions do proceed through the aquo ion; however, in the exchange reaction,

$$Pt(H_2O)Cl_3^- + Cl^{*-} \rightarrow Pt(H_2O)Cl_2Cl^{*-} + Cl^-,$$

the rate law is

$$Rate = k[Pt(H_2O)Cl_3^-],$$

i.e., first order in the complex ion. Since the hydrolysis of $Pt(H_2O)Cl_3^-$ is much slower than its exchange with the chloride ion, this reaction cannot have the aquo ion as an intermediate. Hence the exchange must have an S_N1 mechanism. The same discrimination is not possible in the analogous exchange of $PtCl_4^{2-}$, because the rate of hydrolysis occurs at about the same rate as the exchange.

Because of the prevalence of aquo intermediates, reactions of this type have been studied in methanol. Brown and Ingold (1953) investigated the substitution of chloride in cis $Co(en)_2Cl_2^+$ by the ions: CH_3O^-, N_3^-, NO_2^-, NCS^-, Br^-, Cl^{*-}, and NO_3^-. From the fact that the rate law is first order with a rate constant $(1.4 \times 10^{-4} \ sec^{-1})$ independent of the nature of the incoming ligand for the last four ions, they deduced that these occur via an S_N1 dissociation mechanism with a common rate-determining step

$$cis \ Co(en)_2Cl_2^+ \rightarrow Co(en)_2Cl^{2+} + Cl^-.$$

For the first three ions, the rate law is second order, consistent with an S_N2 displacement. The rate constants increase in the series NO_2^-, N_3^-, CH_3O^-. However, this is also the order of increasing basicity, and it may be that these reactions occur by an S_N1CB mechanism.

The mechanism proposed by Pearson and Basolo (1956) for replacement of Cl^- in a number of four-coordinated square planar Pt(II) complexes, such as $Pt(en)Cl_2$, $Pt(NH_3)_3Cl^+$, etc., by ligands for which the rate law is first order, is a dissociation aided by two solvent molecules approaching along the tetragonal axis forming a five-coordinated square pyramid intermediate in a slow equilibrium process. Such incoming ligands as pyridine, OH^- and Cl^- show this behavior. Second-order kinetics are exhibited with ligands that can stabilize a trigonal bipyramidal intermediate by accepting electrons from the metal to form π-bonds.

10–5. OXIDATION-REDUCTION REACTIONS

The rates of oxidation-reduction reactions also range from those which are diffusion-controlled, therefore extremely fast, to those that, although thermodynamically spontaneous, are immeasurably slow. In order to understand these differences it is necessary to investigate the mechanisms by which such reactions can occur.

Although, in principle, oxidation and reduction reactions can always be represented by processes of electron transfer from a reducing agent to an oxidizing agent, this does not mean that the mechanism must include simple electron transfer reactions as such. The exchange reaction

$$Fe^*(CN)_6^{3-} + Fe(CN)_6^{4-} \rightleftharpoons Fe^*(CN)_6^{4-} + Fe(CN)_6^{3-} \qquad (10\text{--}31)$$

(the asterisk denotes an isotopically distinguishable atom) is, in fact, believed to involve the transfer of an electron from one ion to the other in the activated complex. On the other hand, the redox reaction,

$$NO_2^- + O^*Cl^- \rightarrow NO_2O^{*-} + Cl^-, \qquad (10\text{--}32)$$

can best be described by saying that it involves the transfer of an atom in the transition state. As Eq. (10–32) indicates, the oxygen atom originally in the hypochlorite ion is found quantitatively in the product nitrate ion. The transition state would then be of the form,

$$O_2N^- \text{---} O^* \text{---} Cl^-.$$

A mechanism for a given reaction may be simple to the extent of incorporating a single elementary reaction, as is the case in the reactions mentioned above, or it may involve a series of elementary reactions and equilibria. When elementary reactions themselves can be studied directly there is still the formidable problem of understanding the nature of the activated complex, the role of the solvent, and both the subtle and gross configuration changes of the reactants. To explore these problems, we shall start with some redox reactions in which, hopefully, the experimental data do concern elementary reactions. It is essential to do this in order that more complex reactions may be broken down into elementary steps.

(a) One-electron reactions

The nonmetallic elements form compounds in solution having oxidation states differing by two units, associated with the fact that these compounds rarely have unpaired electrons. On the other hand, the transition elements generally have stable oxidation states differing by one unit. Because these elements also form a variety of complex ions, a great deal of information concerning the details of oxidation and reduction can be gained through a study of their reactions.

The simplest reaction of this type to examine is one involving no net chemical change, such as that of Eq. (10–31). These reactions may be studied by isotopic

TABLE 10–7

SOME EXAMPLES OF OUTER-SPHERE REACTIONS

Reaction	k, liter/mole-sec	T, °K	$\Delta H^{\ddagger}$, kcal/mole	$\Delta S^{\ddagger}$, cal/mole-deg
$[Co(NH_3)_6]^{2+} - [Co(NH_3)_6]^{3+}$	$<10^{-8}$	333		
$[Co(en)_3]^{2+} - [Co(en)_3]^{3+}$	5×10^{-5}	298	13.7	-32
$[Co(phen)_3]^{2+} - [Co(phen)_3]^{3+}$	4.5	293		
$Cr^{2+}(aq) - [Co(NH_3)_6]^{3+}$	9×10^{-5}	298	14.7	-28
$[Cr(dipy)_3]^{2+} - [Co(NH_3)_6]^{3+}$	7.1	281	13.0	-8
$[Cr(dipy)_3]^{2+} - [Co(NH_3)_5H_2O]^{3+}$	6.5×10^2	281		
$[Cr(dipy)_3]^{2+} - [Co(NH_3)_5Cl]^{2+}$	1.0×10^4	281		
$[Cr(dipy)_3]^{2+} - [Co(NH_3)_5Br]^{2+}$	1.6×10^4	281		
$[MnO_4]^- - [MnO_4]^{2-}$	7.1×10^2	273	10.0	-9
$[Fe(CN)_6]^{4-} - [Fe(CN)_6]^{3-}$	3.6×10^2	273	4.1	-32
$[Fe(phen)_3]^{2+} - [Fe(phen)_3]^{3+}$	$>10^5$	273		
$[W(CN)_8]^{4-} - [W(CN)_8]^{3-}$	$>4 \times 10^4$	273		
	$\leq 4 \times 10^8$	293		

labeling, provided that they are only moderately fast, or by any one of a host of recently developed methods, e.g., relaxation, nuclear and electron resonance, etc. Taube (1959) recognizes two general classes of mechanism for redox reactions of transition metal complex ions: outer-sphere and inner-sphere. In the first of these classifications, coordination shells of both reactants remain intact, with transfer of an electron through the ligands. Inner-sphere reactions involve the formation of an activated complex in which one ligand is common to both reactants, and forms a "bridge" between them.

The criterion for outer-sphere reactions is that both reactants be substitution inert, that is, that electron transfer occurs appreciably faster than substitution of a ligand. Although this is a sufficient condition, it is not a necessary one except that, without this condition, a mechanism can be classed as outer-sphere only by analogy. Some reactions that can with some certainty be assigned to this pattern are listed in Table 10–7. It can be seen that there is a wide variation in the rate constants. Those complexes that have easily polarizable ligands or unsaturated ligands exchange rapidly, compared with the aquo and ammine complexes. Further, there are large specific effects connected with the particular transition metal, as, for example, with the phenanthroline complexes of iron and of cobalt. These data by no means give the complete picture. In the case of the manganate–permanganate exchange, which can only be studied in quite basic solutions, the rate constant depends on the particular cation present and on its concentration. The order of increasing effectiveness is $Li^+ \approx Na^+ < K^+ < Cs^+$. Undoubtedly the cation is incorporated into an activated complex, e.g.,

$$MnO^- \text{---} Cs^+ \text{---} OMnO_3^{2-},$$

TABLE 10–8

INNER-SPHERE REACTIONS

Reaction	k, liter/mole-sec	T, °K	$\Delta H^{\ddagger}$, kcal/mole	$\Delta S^{\ddagger}$, cal/mole-deg
$Cr^{2+}(aq) - [Cr(NH_3)_5F]^{2+}$	2.7×10^{-4}	299	13.4	-30
$Cr^{2+}(aq) - [Cr(NH_3)_5Cl]^{2+}$	5.1×10^{-2}	299	11.1	-27
$Cr^{2+}(aq) - [Cr(NH_3)_5Br]^{2+}$	0.32	299	8.5	-32
$Cr^{2+}(aq) - [Cr(NH_3)_5I]^{2+}$	5.5	299	—	—
$Cr^{2+}(aq) - [Co(NH_3)_5H_2O]^{3+}$	0.5	293	2.9	-50
$Cr^{2+}(aq) - [Co(NH_3)_5OH]^{2+}$	1.5×10^6	293	4.6	-15
$Cr^{2+}(aq) - [Co(NH_3)_5Cl]^{2+}$	$>10^3$	293	—	—
$[CuCl_n]^{(n-1)-} - [CuCl_m]^{(m-2)-}$	5×10^7	—	—	—
$[Pt(NH_3)_5Cl]^{3+}$ $- [Pt(NH_3)_4]^{2+} - Cl^-$	$3.9 \times 10^{-2*}$	298	16.1	—

* Third-order rate constant in liter^2/mole^2-sec.

facilitating the transfer of an electron. The opposite effect is observed in the ferrocyanide–ferricyanide exchange, in that, although cations enhance the rate, the order of effectiveness is the reverse: $Cs^+ < K^+ \ll Ba^{2+}$. In fact, for this reaction, the data could just as well be formulated in terms of a third-order reaction with a rate constant of 4×10^4 liter^2/mole^2-sec.

Inner-sphere reactions can be assigned with certainty only to oxidations of the aquated chromous ion. Although Cr(II) is labile to substitution, the product of its oxidation is inert. Thus, when $Cr^{2+}(aq)$ is oxidized by $Co(NH_3)_5Cl^{2+}$, the product is $Cr(H_2O)_5Cl^{2+}$ in which the chloride ligand derives from the original Co(III) complex, not from chloride that may be present in the solution. Therefore it is presumed that the activated complex has the form

$$(H_2O)_5Cr^{2+}---Cl^----Co(NH_3)_5^{2+}.$$

The data for a number of reactions in which $Cr^{2+}(aq)$ is oxidized in an inner-sphere mechanism are given in Table 10–8.

The electron exchange between Cu(I) and Cu(II) in hydrochloric acid is an example of a very fast reaction measured by a nuclear resonance technique. The rate constant quoted probably represents a diffusion-controlled reaction. Whether

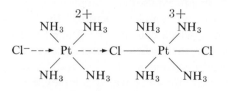

FIG. 10–5. Activated complex in the Cl^- catalyzed exchange of $Pt(NH_3)_5Cl^{3+}$ and $Pt(NH_3)_4^{2+}$.

TABLE 10–9

EXCHANGE REACTIONS OF Fe(II)–Fe(III)

Reaction	T, °K	k, liter/mole-sec	$\Delta H^{\ddagger}$, kcal/mole	$\Delta S^{\ddagger}$, cal/mole-deg
$Fe^{2+}(aq) - Fe^{3+}(aq)$	273	0.87	9.4	−24
$Fe^{2+}(aq) - FeOH^{2+}(aq)$	273	1×10^3	6.9	−19
$Fe^{2+}(aq) - FeF^{2+}(aq)$	273	9.7	8.6	−22
$Fe^{2+}(aq) - FeF_2^{+}(aq)$	273	2.5	9.0	−24
$Fe^{2+}(aq) - FeCl^{2+}(aq)$	273	9.7	8.3	−23
$Fe^{2+}(aq) - FeBr^{2+}(aq)$	273	4.9	8.0	−26
$Fe^{2+}(aq) - FeNCS^{2+}(aq)$	273	1.2×10^{-1}	7.4	−26
$Fe^{2+}(aq) - FeN_3^{2+}(aq)$	273	1.8×10^3	13.2	−5
$Fe^{2+}(aq) - [Fe(phen)_3]^{3+}$	298	3.7×10^4	0.2	−37

it is in fact an inner-sphere reaction is uncertain, however. The last reaction in Table 10–8 represents an exchange of platinum with a chloride ion as a catalyst. The symmetrical activated complex proposed is shown in Fig. 10–5.

Since aquated ions are rarely inert to substitution, the criteria of inner- or outer-sphere reactions cannot usually be applied unambiguously. Indeed, inspection of the data in Table 10–9 for electron transfer between $Fe^{2+}(aq)$ and various Fe(III) complexes show some features not at all common to those of Tables 10–7 and 10–8. Most of these reactions, with some notable exceptions, have about the same exchange rate. This behavior has been interpreted to mean that the activated complex for the exchange is

$$(H_2O)_n Fe^{2+} \overset{\overset{\displaystyle H}{|}}{O} - H --- \overset{\overset{\displaystyle H}{|}}{O} - Fe^{3+}(H_2O)_m X$$
$$\underset{\underset{\displaystyle H}{|}}{}$$

and that whether the ligand X is H_2O, F, Cl, etc., this has little effect on the rate constant. In this reaction, a transfer of a hydrogen atom was proposed, although there is no direct evidence that this is the case, because the products $Fe(OH)^{2+}(aq)$ and $Fe(H_3O)^{3+}(aq)$ would immediately equilibrate with the surroundings. In support of this activated complex (but not of the transfer of the hydrogen atom), the rapid rate of reaction with $Fe(OH)^{2+}$ as the oxidizing agent could be considered to result from the formation of a symmetrical activated complex:

$$(H_2O)_n Fe^{2+} \overset{\overset{\displaystyle H}{|}}{O} - H --- \overset{\overset{\displaystyle H}{|}}{O} - Fe^{3+}(H_2O)_m.$$

Although the reaction of $Fe^{2+}(aq)$ with $FeNCS^{2+}(aq)$ may well proceed via a similar activated complex, the reaction with $FeN_3^{2+}(aq)$ is quite obviously dif-

TABLE 10–10

EXCHANGE REACTIONS OF AQUO IONS

Reaction	k, liter/mole-sec	$\Delta H^{\ddagger}$, kcal/mole	$\Delta S^{\ddagger}$, cal/mole-deg
$V^{2+}(aq) - V^{3+}(aq)$	1×10^{-2}	12.6	-25
$Cr^{2+}(aq) - Cr^{3+}(aq)$	$\leq 2 \times 10^{-5}$	21	-8
$Mn^{2+}(aq) - Mn^{3+}(aq)$	10^2	—	—
$Fe^{2+}(aq) - Fe^{3+}(aq)$	0.87	9.4	-25
$Co^{2+}(aq) - Co^{3+}(aq)$	0.75	12.6	-13

ferent. The formation of an inner-sphere symmetric activated complex,

$$(H_2O)_n Fe^{2+}\text{---}N = N = N - Fe^{2+}(H_2O)_m,$$

is consistent with the data. The π electron system of the bridged ligand then provides a mechanism for fast electron transfer.

In a general sense, there are a number of features of these reactions which provide gross correlations with rates. Thus ligands such a phenanthroline, cyanide, dipyridine, azide ion and carboxylate ions provide an easy path for electron transfer from one complex ion to the other, whether the mechanism requires an inner- or outer-sphere activated complex. Similarly, small polarizable ions such as Br^- as bridged ligands provide a path for electron transfer. Ammonia used as a ligand (since it can only form one bond) results in a slow electron transfer, if the transfer must be through this ligand. Ammonia cannot participate directly in an inner-sphere mechanism.

Exchange reactions where there is no net chemical change, and hence the standard free energy change is zero, have rates which are strongly influenced by the nature of the central metal atoms of the complex ions. The data in Table 10–10 show a large variation in the exchange rates of a number of aquo ions. However, it is difficult to draw any definite conclusions from this information, because in none of these examples is the detailed mechanism known with certainty.

When a net chemical reaction occurs, the rate of reaction may be governed by the free energy change of the reaction. Again it is difficult to find clear-cut experimental evidence for this effect, in the absence of detailed knowledge of mechanisms; however, the oxidation of $Fe^{2+}(aq)$ by Ce(IV) is considerably faster than the exchange reactions of Fe(II)–Fe(III) and of Ce(III)–Ce(IV). There are a number of correlations of rate data with standard free energy data for series in which the ligands are symmetrically varied.

(b) Two-electron reactions

Reactions involving a net two-electron change for each reactant can be considered to be of two types, depending on how drastic a change in coordination is required. The division can be made, essentially, between metallic and nonmetallic elements. Compounds of nonmetallic elements, oxyanions in particular, change oxidation state only in two-electron stages, and the process is associated with a definite change in covalent coordination, such as $ClO_2^- - ClO^-$, while hydrated metal ions undergo a less severe change, although the geometry is certainly changed more than in a one-electron step.

Reactions of the oxyanions of nonmetals have been traced through the technique of isotopic labeling. In the oxidation of the sulfite ion by various halogen acids, the reaction has been demonstrated to involve the transfer of an oxygen atom. Thus with chlorate labeled with O^{18}, the reaction product $(SO_3O^{18})^{2-}$ is formed quantitatively. This strongly suggests an activated complex,

$$O_3S^{2-}\text{---}O^{18} - ClO_2^-,$$

for this reaction. Oxygen from the aqueous solution exchanges only very slowly with the reactants and products, and is not incorporated in either of the products. Essentially the same mechanism applies to the oxidation of sulfite by ClO_2^-, ClO^- and BrO_3^-.

When sulphite is oxidized by nitrite ion, the reaction produces both ammonium and hydroxylammonium ions:

$$NO_2^- + 3SO_3^{2-} + 2H^+ + H_2O \rightarrow NH_4^+ + 3SO_4^{2-}, \qquad (10\text{–}33)$$

$$NO_2^- + 2SO_3^{2-} + 2H^+ + H_2O \rightarrow NH_3OH^+ + 2SO_4^{2-}. \qquad (10\text{–}34)$$

The product sulfate ion is found to have one and only one oxygen atom derived from the water solvent. Taube has isolated the compounds

$$\begin{array}{ccc} \text{OH} & & \text{SO}_3 \\ | & & | \\ O_3S\text{—}N\text{—}SO_3^{2-} & \text{and} & O_3S\text{—}N\text{—}SO_3^{3-}, \end{array}$$

which hydrolyze in acid to give the products in Eqs. (10–33) and (10–34) respectively. Again the sulfate is formed with one oxygen from the solvent. Here, then, the solvent plays a direct part in the reaction, in contrast to those reactions with halogen oxyacids as oxidizing agents.

Complementary reactions involving metallic elements, such as

$$U(IV) + Tl(III) \rightarrow U(VI) + Tl(I)$$

and the Tl(I)–Tl(III) exchange, exhibit second-order kinetics. Although these can be interpreted either by a direct two-electron transfer or by a series of one-electron steps involving intermediate oxidation states, the discrimination between these alternatives is difficult. For the Tl(I)–Tl(III) exchange, the entropy of activation is consistent with the first alternative [compare with the Fe(III)–Tl(I) reaction in the following section].

(c) Noncomplementary reactions

So far we have considered net oxidation-reduction reactions in which the oxidizing and reducing agents match in change of oxidation state. If, however, we consider a reaction such as

$$Tl^{3+}(aq) + 2Fe^{2+}(aq) \rightarrow Tl^{+}(aq) + 2Fe^{3+}(aq),$$

the situation is somewhat different, in that the Tl(I)–Tl(III) is a two-electron transfer, while Fe(II)–Fe(III) involves only one electron. One possibility for this reaction would be a true termolecular reaction as a single elementary process. The rate expression would then be

$$Rate = k[Tl^{3+}][Fe^{2+}]^2.$$

This is not in accord with experiment, however, for the reaction is first order in each of the reactants (second order overall). Further, one of the products, $Fe^{3+}(aq)$, actually inhibits the reaction. There are several mechanisms that could be postulated, but the only one known that fits the experimental data requires the formation of an intermediate oxidation state, Tl(II), in very low concentration. The rate-determining step is, according to the postulated mechanism,

$$Tl^{3+}(aq) + Fe^{2+}(aq) \xrightarrow{1} Tl^{2+}(aq) + Fe^{3+}(aq). \qquad (10\text{--}35)$$

This is followed by the fast reaction,

$$Tl^{2+}(aq) + Fe^{2+}(aq) \xrightarrow{2} Tl^{+}(aq) + Fe^{3+}(aq).$$

When $Fe^{3+}(aq)$ builds up in the course of the reaction, or when it is added initially, the reverse of Eq. (10–35),

$$Tl^{2+}(aq) + Fe^{3+}(aq) \xrightarrow{3} Tl^{3+}(aq) + Fe^{2+}(aq),$$

competes for the $Tl^{2+}(aq)$ formed. The complete rate expression for this mechanism,

$$Rate = \frac{k_1 k_2 [Tl^{3+}][Fe^{2+}]^2}{k_2[Fe^{2+}] + k_3[Fe^{3+}]},$$

is in complete accord with the experimental data. The reactions

$$2Co^{3+}(aq) + Tl^{+}(aq) \rightarrow 2Co^{2+}(aq) + Tl^{3+}(aq),$$

$$2V^{4+}(aq) + Tl^{+}(aq) \rightarrow 2V^{3+}(aq) + Tl^{3+}(aq),$$

have been interpreted by similar mechanisms.

The oxidation of Cr^{2+}(aq) by one-equivalent oxidizing agents leads to mono-nuclear Cr(II) complexes, as has been shown earlier. Two-equivalent oxidizing agents, such as H_2O_2 and Tl^{3+}, yield a binuclear complex, probably with an oxo bridge.

More complex reactions, in which the oxidation state changes by more than two units, almost certainly involve a sequence of reactions of intermediate oxidation states. In the oxidation of Cr(III) to CrO_4^- by Ce(IV), for example, both Cr(IV) and Cr(V) have been postulated as intermediates of low concentration.

(d) Free radical reactions

Some oxidation-reduction reactions, particularly those of peroxides, proceed through free radical intermediates (odd-electron molecules). Thus the decomposition of hydrogen peroxide catalyzed by iron salts is thought to be initiated by an electron-transfer reaction of the type,

$$Fe^{3+} + HO_2^- \rightarrow Fe^{2+} + HO_2;$$

while the reaction between peroxydisulfate and hydrogen peroxide requires the homolytic bond breaking step:

$$S_2O_8^{2-} \rightarrow 2SO_4^-.$$

These free radical intermediates are extremely reactive (they can, for example, readily initiate polymerization reactions) and often the mechanisms proposed involve chain reactions, in which radicals regenerate themselves in the course of the reaction. The presence of a chain reaction implies that appreciable rates of reaction may be obtained even if the initiating reaction is relatively slow.

BIBLIOGRAPHY

A

STEVENS, B., *Chemical Kinetics*. London: Chapman and Hall, 1961.

B

BASOLO, F., and R. G. PEARSON, *Mechanisms of Inorganic Reactions*. New York: Wiley, 1958.

BASOLO, F., and R. G. PEARSON, *Advances in Inorganic and Radiochemistry*, Vol. 3. Ed. by H. J. Emeleus and A. G. Sharpe. New York: Academic Press, 1961.

BENSON, S. W., *The Foundations of Chemical Kinetics*. New York: McGraw-Hill, 1960.

FROST, A. A., and R. G. PEARSON, *Kinetics and Mechanism*. 2nd. ed. New York: Wiley, 1961.

HALPERN, J., "Mechanism of Electron Transfer and Related Processes in Solution," *Quart. Rev.*, Vol. 15 (1961) pp. 207–236.

STRANKS, D. R., *Modern Coordination Chemistry*. Ed. by J. Lewis and R. G. Wilkins. New York: Interscience, 1960.

TAUBE, H., *Advances in Inorganic and Radiochemistry*, Vol. 1. Ed. by H. J. Emeleus and A. G. Sharpe. New York: Academic Press, 1959.

"Oxidation-Reduction Reactions in Ionizing Solvents," *Discussions of the Faraday Society*, Vol. 29, 1960.

International Colloquium on Fast Reactions in Solutions. Z. Elektrochem., Vol. 64 (1960) pp. 1–204.

PROBLEMS

10–1. Even in the absence of specific effects such as ion pairing, "inert" salts affect the rates (in terms of concentration) of reactions in aqueous solutions. According to Brønsted and Bjerrum, the (concentration) rate constant in dilute solution, k, would be given by

$$\log k \approx \log k_0 + 2Az_Az_BI^{1/2},$$

where z_A and z_B are the charges on the reactants in the rate-determining step, i.e., those appearing in the rate law, I is the ionic strength (see Chapter 9) and A a numerical factor in the Debye-Hückel theory of activity coefficients. Predict the effect of increasing ionic strength on each of the following reactions: (a) The electron transfer between Ag(I) and Ag(II). This reaction has a rate which equals $k[Ag(II)]^2$. (b) The base hydrolysis of $Co(NH_3)_5Cl^{2+}$. (c) The acid hydrolysis of $Fe(CN)_6^{4-}$. (d) The oxidation of $Fe^{2+}(aq)$ by $Tl^{3+}(aq)$.

10–2. In Problem 10–1 it was mentioned that the reaction

$$Ag(I) + Ag^*(II) \rightarrow Ag(II) + Ag^*(I)$$

has a rate law second order in Ag(II), independent of the concentration of Ag(I). Suggest a mechanism consistent with these data.

10–3. A mixture of hydrogen and chlorine gases at room temperature reacts only very slowly in the dark. If the mixture is exposed to a bright light, it explodes. (Chlorine gas is known to be dissociated into atoms by light.) Explain in terms of a mechanism, and suggest the reason why the H_2 and Cl_2 ordinarily react so slowly, when the equilibrium is almost completely in favor of the product HCl.

10–4. If the rate law for the bimolecular reaction

$$MX + Y \rightarrow MY + X$$

has the form

$$Rate = k[MX][Y],$$

predict the rate law for the reverse reaction,

$$MY + X \rightarrow MX + Y$$

from considerations of the equilibrium state.

10–5. The rates of reaction of $H^+(aq)$ with various bases seem to be diffusion-controlled reactions (Eigen's rule), and therefore the bimolecular rate constants are, within a factor of about ten, constant. What generalizations can then be made about the order and rate constants for the dissociation of acids? On this basis, arrange the following acids in order of increasing rate of dissociation: (a) HN_3, (b) NH_4^+, (c) HCOOH, (d) H_2S, (e) H_2O, (f) HOI, and estimate the rate constants.

PHYSICAL CONSTANTS

Velocity of light	$c = 2.9979 \times 10^{10}$ cm $\cdot$ sec^{-1}
Avogadro's number*	$N = 6.0232 \times 10^{23}$ mole^{-1}
Electronic charge	$e = 4.8029 \times 10^{-10}$ esu
Mass of electron	$m = 9.1083 \times 10^{-28}$ g
Mass of proton	$M = 1.6724 \times 10^{-24}$ g
Planck's constant	$h = 6.6252 \times 10^{-27}$ erg $\cdot$ sec
Boltzmann's constant	$k = 1.3804 \times 10^{-16}$ erg $\cdot$ deg^{-1}
Gas constant	$R = 1.9872$ cal $\cdot$ deg$^{-1} \cdot$ mole^{-1}
Faraday constant	$\mathfrak{F} = 96{,}496$ coul $\cdot$ equiv^{-1}
Bohr magneton	$BM = 9.2731 \times 10^{-21}$ erg $\cdot$ gauss^{-1}

* The value quoted for Avogadro's number refers to the old chemical scale of atomic weights (O = 16.00000). If the recently adopted carbon-12 scale (C^{12} = 12.00000) is used, then Avogadro's number has the value $N = 6.02296 \times 10^{23}$ mole^{-1}. Strictly speaking, all molar quantities must be adjusted if the newer scale is used (including the appropriate energy conversion factors) but the difference lies in the fifth significant figure and can be ignored in most cases of practical interest.

ENERGY CONVERSION FACTORS

	cm^{-1}	ergs/molecule	kcal/mole	electron volts
1 cm^{-1} =	1	1.9875×10^{-16}	2.8592×10^{-3}	1.2397×10^{-4}
1 erg/molecule =	5.0347×10^{15}	1	1.4396×10^{13}	6.2419×10^{11}
1 kcal/mole =	349.75	6.9468×10^{-14}	1	0.043361
1 electron volt =	8066.0	1.6021×10^{-12}	23.063	1

SELECTED THERMODYNAMIC DATA AT 298.15°K

	ΔH_f°, kcal/mole	ΔG_f°, kcal/mole	S°, cal/mole-deg
Ag(s)	0	0	10.20
Ag(g)	68.4	59.1	41.32
Ag$_2$O(s)	−7.31	−2.59	29.09
AgF(s)	−48.5		
AgF$_2$(s)	−84.6		
AgCl(s)	−30.36	−26.22	22.97
AgBr(s)	−23.78	−22.93	25.60
AgI(s)	−14.91	−15.85	27.3
Ag$_2$S(s)	−7.60	−9.62	34.8
AgNO$_3$(s)	−29.43	−7.69	33.68
Al(s)	0	0	6.77
Al(g)	77.5	67.8	39.30
Al$_2$O$_3$(s)	−400.3	−378.0	12.19
AlF$_3$(s)	−356.3		15.89
AlCl$_3$(s)	−168.6		26.58
Al$_2$Cl$_6$(g)	−307.8		
AlBr$_3$(s)	−132		
AlI$_3$(s)	−75.3		
Al(CH$_3$)$_3$(g)	−12.0		
As(s)	0	0	8.40
As(g)	69.0	59.1	41.61
As$_4$(g)	34.5	22.2	75.0
As$_2$O$_5$(s)	−218.6	−184.6	25.2
As$_4$O$_6$(s)	−313.9	−275.4	51.2
AsH$_3$(g)	41.0		
AsF$_3$(g)	−218.3	−214.7	69.08
B(s)	0	0	1.40
B(g)	135.0	124.0	36.65
B$_2$O$_3$(s)	−305.3	−286.4	12.91
B$_2$H$_6$(g)	7.50		
BF$_3$(g)	−270	−263	51.38
BCl$_3$(g)	−95.7		
Ba(s)	0	0	15.50
Ba(g)	41.74	34.23	40.67
BaO(s)	−133.4	−126.3	16.8
BaF$_2$(s)	−286.9		
BaCl$_2$(s)	−205.6	−193.8	30
BaSO$_4$(s)	−350.2	−323.4	31.6

SELECTED THERMODYNAMIC DATA AT 298.15°K

	ΔH_f°, kcal/mole	ΔG_f°, kcal/mole	S°, cal/mole-deg
Be(s)	0	0	2.28
Be(g)	77.9	68.9	32.55
BeO(s)	−143.1	−136.1	3.37
BeCl$_2$(s)	−122.4		
Bi(s)	0	0	13.6
Bi(g)	47.5	38.2	44.67
Bi$_2$(g)	55.3	43.9	65.40
Bi$_2$O$_3$(s)	−137.9	−118.7	36.2
BiCl$_3$(g)	−64.7	−62.2	85.3
Br$_2$(l)	0	0	36.4
Br$_2$(g)	7.34	0.75	58.64
Br(g)	26.71	19.69	41.81
HBr(g)	−8.66	−12.72	47.44
BrF(g)	−11.0	−14.7	54.8
BrF$_3$(g)	−75	−69	69.9
BrF$_5$(g)	−120		76.4
BrCl(g)	3.51	−0.21	57.34
C(graphite)	0	0	1.36
C(diamond)	0.45	0.69	0.58
C(g)	170.89	160.04	37.76
CO(g)	−26.42	−32.81	47.30
CO$_2$(g)	−94.05	−94.26	51.06
CH$_4$(g)	−17.89	−12.14	44.50
H$_2$CO(g)	−27.7	−26.2	52.26
HCOOH(g)	−90.39	−83.96	60.0
CH$_3$OH(g)	−48.08	−38.69	56.8
CF$_4$(g)	−218.3	−207.6	62.7
CCl$_4$(g)	−25.5	−15.3	73.95
CBr$_4$(g)	12.0	8.6	85.6
COF$_2$(g)	−142		
COCl$_2$(g)	−52.47	−49.48	69.13
CH$_3$Cl(g)	−19.6	−14.0	55.97
CH$_2$Cl$_2$(g)	−22	−14.0	64.68
CHCl$_3$(g)	−24	−16	70.86
CS$_2$(g)	27.55	15.55	56.84
COS(g)	−33	−39	55.34
HCN(g)	31.2		
C$_2$H$_2$(g)	54.19	50.00	48.00
C$_2$H$_4$(g)	12.50	16.28	52.45
C$_2$H$_6$(g)	−20.24	−7.86	54.85

SELECTED THERMODYNAMIC DATA AT 298.15°K

	ΔH_f°, kcal/mole	ΔG_f°, kcal/mole	S°, cal/mole-deg
$C_2H_5OH(g)$	−56.63	−40.69	67.4
$C_3H_6(g)$	4.88	14.99	63.80
$C_3H_8(g)$	−24.82	−5.61	64.51
$C_4H_8\text{-}1(g)$	−0.03	17.09	73.04
cis-$C_4H_8(g)$	−1.67	15.74	71.90
trans-$C_4H_8(g)$	−2.67	15.05	70.86
$C_6H_6(g)$	19.82	30.99	64.34
$Ca(s)$	0	0	9.95
$Ca(g)$	42.2	34.1	36.99
$CaO(s)$	−151.9	−144.4	9.5
$CaF_2(s)$	−290.3	−277.7	16.46
$CaCl_2(s)$	−190.0	−179.3	27.2
$CaSO_4(s)$	−342.4	−315.6	25.5
$CaC_2(s)$	−15.0	−16.2	16.8
$Cd(s)$	0	0	12.37
$Cd(g)$	26.75	18.50	40.07
$CdO(s)$	−60.86	−53.79	13.1
$CdCl_2(s)$	−93.00	−81.88	28.3
$CdS(s)$	−34.6		
$Cl_2(g)$	0	0	53.29
$Cl(g)$	29.01	25.19	39.46
$ClO_2(g)$	25.0	29.6	60.1
$Cl_2O(g)$	18.20	22.40	63.70
$Cl_2O_7(g)$	−63.4		
$HCl(g)$	−22.06	−22.77	44.62
$ClF(g)$	−13.3	−13.6	52.05
$ClF_3(g)$	−38.8	−29.0	67.4
$Co(s)$	0	0	7.18
$Co(g)$	101.6	91.0	42.88
$CoO(s)$	−57.2	−51.5	12.66
$Cr(s)$	0	0	5.70
$Cr(g)$	95.0	84.3	41.64
$CrO_3(s)$	−138.4		
$Cr_2O_3(s)$	−272.7	−253.2	19.4
$CrF_2(s)$	−181		
$CrF_3(s)$	−265	−248	22.44
$Cr(CO)_6(s)$	−257.6		
$Cs(s)$	0	0	20.16
$Cs(g)$	18.67	12.18	41.94

SELECTED THERMODYNAMIC DATA AT 298.15°K

	ΔH_f°, kcal/mole	ΔG_f°, kcal/mole	S°, cal/mole-deg
$Cs_2O(s)$	−76.0		
$CsF(s)$	−126.9		
$CsF(g)$	−78.6		
$CsCl(s)$	−103.5		
$CsCl(g)$	−55.2		
$CsBr(s)$	−94.3		
$CsBr(g)$	−47.7		
$CsI(s)$	−80.5		
$CsI(g)$	−33.8		
$Cu(s)$	0	0	7.97
$Cu(g)$	81.1	71.6	39.74
$CuO(s)$	−37.6	−31.0	10.19
$Cu_2O(s)$	−40.4	−35.0	22.4
$CuCl(s)$	−32.6	−28.5	20.8
$CuCl_2(s)$	−49.2		
$CuBr(s)$	−25.3	−24.4	23.0
$CuBr_2(s)$	−33.2		
$CuI(s)$	−16.4	−16.8	23.1
$CuS(s)$	−11.6	−11.7	15.9
$CuSO_4(s)$	−184.0	−158.2	27.1
$F_2(g)$	0	0	48.45
$F(g)$	18.6	14.5	37.92
$OF_2(g)$	7.6	11.8	58.95
$HF(g)$	−64.2	−64.7	41.47
$Fe(s)$	0	0	6.49
$Fe(g)$	99.83	88.91	43.11
$Fe_{0.947}O(s)$	−63.8	58.7	13.74
$Fe_2O_3(s)$	−196.8	−177.3	20.9
$Fe_3O_4(s)$	−267.8	−243.2	35.0
$FeCl_2(s)$	−81.86	−72.6	28.7
$FeCl_3(s)$	−95.7		
$FeS(s)$	−22.72	−22.81	14.41
$Fe(C_5H_5)_2(g)$	50.6		
$Fe(CO)_5(l)$	−187.8		
$Ge(s)$	0	0	7.43
$Ge(g)$	90	80	40.10
$GeO_2(s)$	−128.3		
$GeCl_4(l)$	−130		
$H_2(g)$	0	0	31.21
$H(g)$	52.09	48.58	27.39

Selected Thermodynamic Data at 298.15°K

	ΔH_f°, kcal/mole	ΔG_f°, kcal/mole	S°, cal/mole-deg
Hg(l)	0	0	18.17
Hg(g)	14.66	7.62	41.80
HgO(s)	−21.68	−13.99	17.2
HgCl$_2$(s)	−53.4	−42.4	34.5
Hg$_2$Cl$_2$(s)	−63.32	−50.35	46.8
HgS(s)	−13.90	−11.67	18.6
I$_2$(s)	0	0	27.76
I$_2$(g)	14.88	4.63	62.28
I(g)	25.48	16.77	43.18
HI(g)	6.20	0.31	49.31
IF(g)	−22.5		56.4
IF$_5$(g)	−195.1	−178.3	78.7
IF$_7$(g)	−224.2	−194.2	82.9
ICl(g)	4.20	−1.32	59.12
IBr(g)	9.75	0.91	61.80
ICl$_3$(s)	−21.1	−5.36	41.1
K(s)	0	0	15.39
K(g)	21.42	14.59	38.30
K$_2$O(s)	−86.4		
KOH(s)	−101.8		
KF(s)	−134.5	−127.4	15.91
KF(g)	−77.2		
KCl(s)	−104.2	−97.59	19.76
KCl(g)	−50.9		
KClO$_4$(s)	−103.7	−72.7	36.1
KBr(s)	−93.73	−90.63	23.05
KBr(g)	−42.7		
KI(s)	−78.31	−77.03	25.2
KI(g)	−29.8		
K$_2$SO$_4$(s)	−342.7	−314.6	42.0
KNO$_3$(s)	−117.8	−93.96	31.77
KMnO$_4$(s)	−194.4	−170.6	41.04
Li(s)	0	0	6.75
Li(g)	38.44	30.57	33.14
Li$_2$O(s)	−142.4	−133.7	8.97
LiF(s)	−145.7	−139.0	8.52
LiF(g)	−80.2		
LiCl(s)	−97.7	−92.0	14.17
LiCl(g)	−46.2		
LiBr(s)	−83.72		

Selected Thermodynamic Data at 298.15°K

	ΔH_f°, kcal/mole	ΔG_f°, kcal/mole	S°, cal/mole-deg
LiBr(g)	−35.0		
LiI(s)	−64.79		
LiI(g)	−20.6		
Mg(s)	0	0	7.81
Mg(g)	35.6	27.3	35.51
MgO(s)	−143.8	−136.1	6.4
MgF$_2$(s)	−268		
MgCl$_2$(s)	−153.4	−141.6	21.40
MgSO$_4$(s)	−305.5	−278.5	21.9
Mn(s)	0	0	7.65
Mn(g)	66.73	56.64	41.49
MnO(s)	−92.0	−86.8	14.4
MnO$_2$(s)	−124.5	−111.7	13.7
MnF$_2$(s)	−190	−180	22.25
MnF$_3$(s)	−261		
MnS(s)	−49.5	−50.5	18.7
N$_2$(g)	0	0	45.77
N(g)	112.98	108.89	36.61
NO(g)	21.60	20.72	50.34
NO$_2$(g)	8.09	12.39	57.47
N$_2$O(g)	19.49	24.76	52.58
N$_2$O$_4$(g)	2.31	23.49	72.73
N$_2$O$_5$(g)	3.1	27.9	85.0
NH$_3$(g)	−11.04	−3.98	46.01
HN$_3$(g)	70.3	78.5	56.74
NF$_3$(g)	−29.3		
NH$_4$Cl(s)	−75.38	−48.73	22.6
NOCl(g)	12.57	15.86	63.0
NOBr(g)	19.56	19.70	65.16
Na(s)	0	0	12.21
Na(g)	25.9	18.6	36.71
Na$_2$(g)	33.80	24.69	54.99
Na$_2$O(s)	−99.4	−90.2	18.2
NaF(s)	−136.3	−129.1	12.26
NaF(g)	−69.2		
NaCl(s)	−98.23	−91.79	17.33
NaCl(g)	−42.7		
NaBr(s)	−86.0		
NaBr(g)	−34.0		
NaI(s)	−68.84		

SELECTED THERMODYNAMIC DATA AT 298.15°K

	ΔH_f°, kcal/mole	ΔG_f°, kcal/mole	S°, cal/mole-deg
NaI(g)	−21.3		
Na₂SO₄(s)	−330.9	−302.7	35.73
NaNO₃(s)	−111.5	−87.5	27.85
Ni(s)	0	0	7.14
Ni(g)	101.3	90.4	43.52
NiO(s)	−58.4	−51.7	9.22
NiS(s)	−17.6		
O₂(g)	0	0	49.00
O(g)	59.16	54.99	38.47
O₃(g)	34.0	39.0	56.8
H₂O(g)	−57.80	−54.64	45.11
H₂O(l)	−68.32	−56.69	16.72
H₂O₂(g)	−32.54	−25.21	55.65
H₂O₂(l)	−44.88		
P(white)	0	0	9.80
P(g)	75.18	66.71	38.98
P₄(g)	13.42	5.18	66.90
P₄O₁₀(s)	−720.0		
PH₃(g)	2.21	4.36	50.2
PCl₃(g)	−66.6	−61.8	74.49
PCl₅(g)	−88.7	−70.9	84.3
POCl₃(g)	−141.5	−130.3	77.59
PBr₃(g)	−35.9	−41.2	83.11
Pb(s)	0	0	15.51
Pb(g)	46.34	38.47	41.89
PbO(s)	−52.07	−45.05	16.6
PbO₂(s)	−66.12	−52.34	18.3
Pb₃O₄(s)	−175.6	−147.6	50.5
PbF₄(s)	−222.4		
PbCl₂(s)	−85.85	−75.04	32.6
PbS(s)	−22.54	−22.15	21.8
Rb(s)	0	0	18.22
Rb(g)	19.6	12.9	40.63
Rb₂O(s)	−79.0		
RbF(s)	−131.3		
RbF(g)	−77.2		
RbCl(s)	−102.9		
RbCl(g)	−51.8		
RbBr(s)	−93.5		
RbBr(g)	−44.1		

Selected Thermodynamic Data at 298.15°K

	ΔH_f°, kcal/mole	ΔG_f°, kcal/mole	S°, cal/mole-deg
RbI(s)	−79.0		
RbI(g)	−31.7		
S(rhombic)	0	0	7.62
S(g)	66.4	56.7	40.09
S_8(g)	24.36	11.88	102.8
SO_2(g)	−70.96	−71.79	59.40
SO_3(g)	−94.45	−88.52	61.24
H_2S(g)	−4.82	−7.89	49.15
SF_6(g)	−289	−264	69.5
SCl_2(l)	−12.0		
SCl_4(l)	−13.6		
S_2Cl_2(g)	−5.70		76.4
Sb(s)	0	0	10.92
Sb(g)	62.7	53.1	43.06
Sb_4(g)	49.0	37.1	83.7
Sb_2O_5(s)	−234	−200	29.9
$SbCl_3$(g)	−75.2	−72.3	80.8
Se(s)	0	0	10.14
Se(g)	49.4	39.8	42.21
Se_2(g)	34.1	22.2	60.23
SeO_2(s)	−56.4		
H_2Se(g)	20.5	17.0	52.9
SeF_6(g)	−246	−222	75.10
$SeCl_2$(g)	−9.7		
$SeCl_4$(s)	−45		
Se_2Cl_2(l)	−20.0		
Si(s)	0	0	4.47
Si(g)	105	94	40.12
SiO_2(quartz)	−209.9	−196.9	10.00
SiH_4(g)	−14.8	−9.4	48.7
SiF_4(g)	−370	−360	68.0
Sn(s)	0	0	12.3
Sn(g)	72	64	40.25
SnO(s)	−68.4	−61.5	13.5
SnO_2(s)	−138.8	−124.2	12.5
$SnCl_2$(s)	−83.6		
$SnCl_4$(g)	−117.9	−108.4	87.2
$SnBr_4$(g)	−78.2	−82.1	98.2
Sr(s)	0	0	12.50

Selected Thermodynamic Data at 298.15°K

	ΔH_f°, kcal/mole	ΔG_f°, kcal/mole	S°, cal/mole-deg
Sr(g)	39.1	31.1	39.32
SrO(s)	−141.1	−133.8	13.0
SrCl$_2$(s)	−198.0	−186.7	28.0
Te(s)	0	0	11.88
Te(g)	46.5	37.0	43.64
H$_2$Te(g)	36.9	33.1	56.0
TeF$_6$(g)	−315.0	−292	80.7
TeCl$_4$(s)	−77.2		
Ti(s)	0	0	7.33
Ti(g)	112.6	101.9	43.07
TiO$_2$(rutile)	−225.75	−212.5	12.04
TiCl$_4$(l)	−191.7		
TiBr$_4$(l)	−148.1		
Tl(s)	0	0	15.35
Tl(g)	43.0	34.7	43.23
Tl$_2$O(s)	−44.0		
TlBr(s)	−41.9		
TlCl(s)	−48.79	−43.90	25.59
TlCl$_3$(s)	−83.9		
V(s)	0	0	7.01
V(g)	122.8	111.9	43.55
V$_2$O$_3$(s)	−296	−277	23.5
VO$_2$(s)	−171	−158	12.25
V$_2$O$_5$(s)	−373	−342	31.3
Zn(s)	0	0	9.95
Zn(g)	31.19	22.69	38.45
ZnO(s)	−83.17	−76.05	10.5
ZnCl$_2$(s)	−99.40	−88.26	25.9
ZnS(s)	−48.5	−47.4	13.8

Formula Index

FORMULA INDEX

List of Symbols

LIST OF SYMBOLS

The following superscripts are used with the thermodynamic, and some other symbols, to provide additional information:

$^{\circ}$ standard state,
$*$ absolute quantity,
$\ddagger$ quantity of activation.

In addition, the temperature in $^{\circ}$K may be included as a subscript.

Symbol	Quantity	Page Defined
a	lattice constant	237
a_X	activity of X	313
a_0	radius of ground state Bohr orbit	65
$\mathbf{a}$	lattice vector	235
b	lattice constant	237
$\mathbf{b}$	lattice vector	235
BM	Bohr magneton	216
c	speed of light	403
c	lattice constant	237
c_X	concentration of X	318
$\mathbf{c}$	lattice vector	235
C_p	specific heat at constant pressure	299
D	Debye	160
$D(X{-}Y)$	dissociation energy of XY	104
e	electronic charge	403
E	electron affinity	104
E	total energy	5
E_{elect}	electronic energy	124
E_{vib}	vibrational energy	124
E_{rot}	rotational energy	124
$\mathbf{E}$	electric field	251
ε	electrostatic potential	28
ε_{cell}	cell potential	357
$\varepsilon(X/Y)$	electrode potential of the X/Y couple	361
F	force	28
$\mathcal{F}$	Faraday constant	403
ΔG	free energy change	310
$\Delta G_f(X)$	free energy of formation of X	310
$\Delta G_{hyd}(X)$	free energy of hydration of X	332
h	Planck's constant	403
ΔH	enthalpy change	97

423

Symbol	Quantity	Page Defined
$\Delta H_{atom}(X)$	enthalpy (heat) of atomization of X	107
$\Delta H_{comb}(X)$	enthalpy (heat) of combustion of X	101
$\Delta H_{cryst}(X)$	enthalpy (heat) of crystallization; (crystal energy) of (X)	32, 252, 265, 277
$\Delta H_{diss}(X{-}Y)$	enthalpy (heat) of dissociation of XY	38
$\Delta H_{diss,\,ion}(X{-}Y)$	enthalpy (heat) of dissociation of XY into ions	38
$\Delta H_f(X)$	enthalpy (heat) of formation of X	98
$\Delta H_{fus}(X)$	enthalpy (heat) of fusion	252
$\Delta H_{hyd}(X)$	enthalpy (heat) of hydration of X	325
$\Delta H_{ion}(X)$	enthalpy (heat) of ionization (ionization energy) of X	104
$\Delta H_{sub}(X)$	enthalpy (heat) of sublimation of X	36
$\Delta H_{vap}(X)$	enthalpy (heat) of vaporization of X	252
i	inversion center	119
I	ionic strength	318
I	ionization energy	104
IP	ionization potential	104
k	Boltzmann's constant	403
k	force constant	54
k	rate constant	374
K	kinetic energy	5
K_a	acid dissociation constant	318
K_b	base dissociation constant	338
K_c	equilibrium constant (concentration units)	289
K_n	stepwise formation constant	348
K_p	equilibrium constant (pressure units)	287
K_{sp}	solubility product	319
K_{th}	thermodynamic equilibrium constant	313
K_w	ion product for water	336
l	azimuthal quantum number	64
LCAO	linear combination of atomic orbitals	139
m	mass of electron	403
m	mass of atom	5
m	mirror plane	118
m_l	magnetic quantum number	73
m_s	spin quantum number	76
M	mass of proton	403
M	molecular weight	303
MO	molecular orbital	137
$\mathfrak{M}$	Madelung constant	29
n	principal quantum number	63
N	Avogadro's number	403
p	pressure	97

Symbol	Quantity	Page Defined
p	steric term	381
p_X	partial pressure of X	287
pK	$-\log K$	337
pX	$-\log (c_X)$	352
P	total pressure	31
P	probability	55
q	heat of reaction	97
q	charge	28
r	spherical polar coordinate	67
$r(X)$	radius of X	20, 134, 245, 261
R	Rydberg constant	46
R	gas constant	403
$s(X{-}Y)$	internuclear separation (bond length) of XY	5
s_e	equilibrium internuclear separation	5
S	solubility	319
S	screening constant	87, 89
S	entropy	300
ΔS	entropy change	297
$\Delta S_f(X)$	entropy of formation of X	301
$\Delta S_{\text{hyd}}(X)$	entropy of hydration of X	328
T	temperature	291
T	term value	48
ΔU	change in internal energy	97
v	velocity	5
v	vibrational quantum number	60
V	volume	31
VB	valence bond	137
W	work	97
z_+, z_-	net ionic charge	29
Z	atomic number (nuclear charge)	49
Z	collision number	381
Z_{eff}	effective nuclear charge	87
α	polarizability	251
α	coefficient of thermal expansion	19
α	interaxial angle	237
β	volume compressibility	19
β	interaxial angle	237
β_n	overall formation constant	348
γ	activity coefficient	313
γ	interaxial angle	237
δ	phase angle	54
Δ	crystal-field splitting	219

Symbol	Quantity	Page Defined
θ	spherical polar coordinate	67
λ	wavelength	46
μ	dipole moment	160
μ	reduced mass	53
μ_0	Bohr magneton	216
μ_{ind}	induced dipole moment	251
ν	wave number	47
ν'	frequency	47
ρ	electron density	18
ρ	repulsion constant	30
ϕ	spherical polar coordinate	67
Φ	potential energy	5
χ_X	mole fraction of X	287
ψ, Ψ	wave function	58

Index

INDEX